Mrs. Florence H. Staniels
145 Gregory Avenue
Passaic, New Jersey.

July 8, 1930.

D0365655

AN INTRODUCTION TO REFLECTIVE THINKING

BY

COLUMBIA ASSOCIATES IN PHILOSOPHY

LAURENCE BUERMEYER, WILLIAM FORBES COOLEY
JOHN J. COSS, HORACE L. FRIESS, JAMES GUTMANN
THOMAS MUNRO, HOUSTON PETERSON
JOHN H. RANDALL, JR., HERBERT W. SCHNEIDER

HOUGHTON MIFFLIN COMPANY

BOSTON   NEW YORK   CHICAGO   SAN FRANCISCO
The Riverside Press Cambridge

153

PRINTED IN THE U.S.A.

PREFACE

In *An Introduction to Reflective Thinking* nine members of the staff of the Department of Philosophy at Columbia University have coöperated in writing a book which is intended to show thinking at work by describing some of the great achievements of thought in the fields of science and morals. They have tried to indicate the characteristics of effective thinking and to clarify some of the methods of experimentation, investigation, and verification apparent in the thoughtful handling of various subject-matters. The book may be used for a first course in philosophy, or in connection with an introduction to science; and it is the hope of the authors that not a few persons who have gone out from college halls, or have never entered them, may find interesting this new survey of the workings of the mind.

The authors have been much helped in their treatment of the different subject-matters by advice from colleagues. Among the many who have advised, especial thanks are due Professors John Dewey, F. J. E. Woodbridge, W. T. Bush, and A. L. Jones, of the Department of Philosophy; Professor Henry Preserved Smith, of Union Theological Seminary; Professor Harold Jacoby, of the Department of Astronomy; Professor W. B. Fite and Dean H. E. Hawkes, of the Department of Mathematics; Professor J. H. McGregor, of the Department of Zoölogy; Professor H. W. Farwell, of the Department of Physics; Dr. B. D. Wood, Assistant to the Dean of Columbia College; and Dean Harlan F. Stone, of the Law School.

Columbia University

CONTENTS

AN INTRODUCTION TO REFLECTIVE THINKING

• •

CHAPTER I

INTRODUCTION — WHAT REFLECTIVE THINKING MEANS

Section 1. What Reflection Is [1]

To speak of reflective thinking seems strange. Is not all thinking reflective? If all thought had to do with reaching a well-founded belief which could be defended from attack and which might be followed in action, it would be possible to say that all thinking is reflective.

But sometimes we think in a rambling sort of way and are not interested in any particular outcome. Man's discovery of valuable hints as to the conduct of his life is of two kinds — rambling and direct. As dogs, when companions on a walk, range the fields, sniff about in all directions, follow a multitude of paths, and nose about under many fallen branches, thickets and patches of brambles, so human beings, when they idly, playfully think about the common objects of daily life, or about ideas so usual as to be old friends, display in their own way much the same activity as the roving dogs. Such activity is casual or undirected thinking, and it turns

---

[1] For this section, as for the entire text, a knowledge of John Dewey, *How We Think* (Heath & Co., 1910), is important since the ideas of that book have influenced greatly the writers of this one. Irwin Edman, *Human Traits and Their Social Significance* (Houghton Mifflin Company, 1920), will also prove useful.

up, now and then, important new combinations which may be valuable discoveries.

Sometimes, too, our consciousness is fully taken up with the appreciative consideration of beautiful objects. A noble building, a chapel window of old glass, an autumn hillside with blue sky and floating cloud-bank above it, a chorus from Euripides or a simple and lucid mathematical solution may command our admiration. To deny to such appreciative mental experience a place in thought seems to do violence to the common understanding of the term.

On occasion thought may not be roving or primarily appreciative, but concerned only with the spinning of a yarn which makes no pretense to reaching correct belief, but is content, as Dewey says, merely to maintain an emotional congruity. Such thought must tell a story which holds together; it need not be concerned to make its content conform to statements about the actual relations of things.

When thought, however, is bent on solving a problem, on finding out the meaning of a perplexing situation, or reaching a conclusion which is trustworthy, it is to be distinguished from other types of mental activity and should be called reflection. Such thinking may be defined as: "active, persistent and careful consideration of any belief or supposed form of knowledge in the light of the grounds that support it and the further conclusions to which it tends." [1]

Section 2.   Dewey's Analysis of an Act of Thought

a. THE OCCASION OF REFLECTION

The occasion of reflective thought becomes clear when the activities of a day are reviewed.   We rise, dress,

[1] John Dewey, *How We Think*, p. 6.

breakfast, read headlines, go to business, but only when the morning's mail brings up a question requiring a decision does real thought make its appearance. Thought comes when decisions or conclusions are necessary, when the usual succession of acts is interrupted and consideration has to be given to the next step.[1] A doctor thinks when he has to diagnose a new case, a lawyer thinks when he considers the elements of a dispute and their relation to precedent, a student thinks when he applies his knowledge to the solution of an original problem in geometry, a city official thinks when he considers the best method of making a tax levy or improving the school system.

b. THE DEFINITION OF THE DIFFICULTY

In each of these cases a difficulty is faced. The morning's letter asks whether money should be invested in the common stock of an industry or in government bonds. Before any progress can be made in reaching an answer, the conditions of the question must be clarified. A widow of slender means is asking the question, how she may invest her capital most safely and profitably. The reader of the letter, understanding her situation, has cleared his field, and the next step in thinking occurs.

c. THE RISE OF SUGGESTIONS

This next step is the rise of suggestions or possible answers. What advice is to be given — that is the perplexity. Answers flash up — buy bonds, buy stocks,

---

[1] Consideration of thought when its operation is more contemplative than decisive will be found in Chapters IX and XIII. It is the hope of the authors that a later edition may contain a chapter on the place of reflection in æsthetic judgments.

buy neither, but rather buy a farm mortgage. Such suggestions or others would arise. The psychological machinery of their appearance we do not fully understand, but the factors conditioning their excellence may be named. Save by chance, penetrating suggestions come only (a) when the difficulty is clearly defined, (b) when the thinker is thoroughly familiar with the background into which the problem fits and has had a wide range of experience with similar difficulties, (c) when the thinker has a more or less indefinable something called now native ability, now disciplined but daring imagination, now shrewdness, now penetration.

d. THE MENTAL ELABORATION OF SUGGESTIONS

When the suggestions have arisen, they must be tested by reference to foundations and consequences. Suppose the idea of buying stock should be entertained as the solution. In thought the circumstances attending such investment would be reviewed — is the stock safe, what is its cost, what its return, what its likelihood of ready sale. Each item would be considered in reference to the conditions of the purchaser, and if all the factors surveyed in the mental investigation fitted her need, the suggestion to buy stock would be thought to be a good one; if not, other proposed solutions would be tried in the mental examination.

e. EVIDENCE IN FACT AND CONCLUSION

When the suggestion is accepted, after this imaginative grilling, as apparently true, the careful thinker seeks confirming evidence — he may seek to ascertain the opinion of others as to the wisdom of his view, or investigate the class of persons holding the stock. Such investigation may confirm his opinion and leave him ready to accept his judgment and say "buy." Unhappily, before his advice is given he cannot, as he might in other kinds of decisions, experiment with the actual operation of his conclusion before determining finally upon practice. His experimentation for the verification of his belief must be undertaken at the widow's expense, since after she follows his advice the genuine verification will follow when time shows whether the stock bought proves a safe and lucrative investment. The closing of the reflective process incident to his reaching a conclusion comes, however, only after the experimental verification.

The steps in the reflective process have been described in a logical and schematic fashion. In the actual thinking of every day the order is sometimes as clear as the outline, but usually suggestions come to a person before he has analyzed the problem very far, in which case he develops the suggestions or hypotheses immediately. These suggestions, the outcome of a hasty or inadequate impression of the problem, are necessarily superficial and may lead seriously astray the man who accepts them precipitately. They may, on the other hand, guide and check the observation by which the difficulty is more precisely defined, and where the situation is complex and baffling, the final determination of the difficulty is possible only as the climax of such partial and tentative suggestions. Not infrequently in the successful completion of each of the steps practically all are involved. An instance of such an occurrence is given in the treatment of observation in the next chapter. Thus it will be seen that the order given above is seldom the order consistently followed in an actual thinking process; it is rather a diagram of the necessary steps.

Section 3. The Variations in Human Ability[1]

The quality of reflective thinking will vary with the excellence or grade of the thinker. There is a very wide variation in human ability to think. A day's walk through almost any county in this country, undertaken as a kind of exploration into the society of human minds, would be a startling excursion for an acute observer who is at once a good questioner and listener. At the end of the day the inventory of minds would show a range of ability reaching from the near idiot to the near genius; the real genius or the complete idiot would be difficult to find. The stock-taking in the evening would, however, abound in middle grades. Most men are neither geniuses nor idiots.

The thoroughgoing explorer might undertake to work out sharply contrasting classifications for the minds he had encountered. He would find that he had few perfect examples of these sharp distinctions, but many minds that had certain amounts of both contrasting qualities. He would distinguish the educated and the uneducated, but he would find most of his specimens in the partly educated class. He would call some minds resourceful and some helpless, though few would be thoroughly helpless under all circumstances. Some of his discoveries would be classified as impetuous, others deliberate; but almost none would always think things out before conclusions were accepted or actions under-

[1] E. L. Thorndike, *Individuality.* Irwin Edman, *Human Traits and Their Social Significance*, chapters 9, 1, 2, 3; John Dewey, *How We Think*, chapters 1, 2.

taken. A few would be subject to all kinds of superstitions, even the most obviously absurd; while others would be so critical and analytical as to cause the stock-taker to wonder if they would ever accept any statement as above suspicion. Another group would be entered as narrow or closed-minded, and their brothers at the other extreme ultra-liberal, some even faddists. Closely akin to this classification would come the rigid minded, and their contrasting group the flexible minded, or, in slightly varied terms, the traditional or hidebound and the progressive or free-minded folk. Then there might be the imaginative with the literal-minded as opposites. And for a last contrast the far-sighted matched by the short-sighted, or, put differently, the predicting and the surprised.

These classifications are but the faintest beginning of the analysis to which the day's observation of human minds might be subjected. But carried even this little way, one is led to exclaim, "What striking contrasts and varied traits are to be found in the society of minds!"

A question is apt to arise at this point, some interrogation as to the value of these different minds. Before an answer could be given, one would have to know just what kind of value was to be considered. A slow and stolid mind may be good under certain conditions; great imagination useful under others. If, however, those minds were, for the time, considered most valuable that could best find out the "real truth" about things, that would care most keenly to be right, and that could go on to make new discoveries about the world of men and things in which we live, it seems likely that certain of the traits would be found much more desirable than others.

A man suddenly confronted with a new kind of danger, such as swept over the Canadian lines when the first gray-green waves of poison gas were released, would want as his comrade in distress a fellow creature who was something more than a bundle of fixed habits. Such a man might do a well-learned and often-repeated task very well indeed. Habitual ways of doing things are genuinely first-rate, after their fashion. They are good servants, taking over the performance of the thousand and one acts which we all have to do every day. But they are fixed, otherwise they would not be habits. The set, rigid, inflexible, unvarying behavior which characterizes the predominately habitual man cannot successfully meet new situations. The blind man can make his way easily over old ground, but on a new and unlearned path he walks slowly, and is in danger at every step. The habit-man is a blind man, he is not a pathfinder.

This does not mean, of course, that the ideal discoverer is the man who has had no previous knowledge of the ground he surveys. The intellectual explorer in any field should be acquainted with, familiar with, habituated to, the subject in which he works. But this habituation must not mean the easy following of long familiar routes; routination is the greatest enemy of progress.

Another kind of man who cannot help in the sudden danger is the impulsive person. A big bluebottle fly in a sunlit room buzzes about in a most energetic way, but there seems no direction or purpose to its blundering flight. Its activity is "full of sound and fury signifying nothing"; it does n't know what it's about. Neither do some human beings when in a kind of feverish haste they try first this, then that way out, instead of taking stock of the difficult situation first and estimating the varying likelihood of success attending each possible line of action considered.

It seems clear that neither the habitual nor the impulsive man who follows on the instant whichever controlling tendency is present can be called an intellectual leader. Such men cannot be trusted to blaze new and reliable trails in the wilderness of human ignorance. Yet for all that, trails have been blazed, and for many hundreds of centuries they were hacked out, not in a wilderness, but in a veritable jungle. When we look back on the eight or nine thousand years of history, and let our imagination reconstruct the one hundred thousand or more years of human life that went before, and the half million years of pre-human yet man-like existence that separate human beings from their more brute-like ancestors, we ask ourselves how man ever came to be civilized at all. A part of the answer is that happy accidents occurred. They may have helped in getting fires going, in the cooking of flesh, and in the smelting of metals. Another fact is that there were rare individuals who were curious — free and flexible minded — and tried different combinations. They had imagination and after a time could tell in advance what would happen if different things were put together. They were able to predict. Their efforts were short-lived until speech and writing became the transmitters and preservers of knowledge. But after that the store of knowledge increased, and those acquainted with it (the educated, if they also displayed curiosity, imagination, and the ability to predict) were able to find out more and more ways of doing things, of escaping dangers, of producing pleasing and desirable things.

Just here, when the benefits which progressive minds have brought to man have been indicated, one should stop for a moment to consider how sharply two-edged the sword of human intelligence is. Men find out things which are of great use — explosives, steam, electricity, gas, and so on — and yet just these same things unless kept in control turn against their discoverers. Steam and steel made railroads possible, but they also create congested cities, prove sources of high finance and public corruption, and give us an apparently never-ending series of labor troubles. The mind of man seems much more capable of learning how to control nature than of learning how to use the new knowledge to the complete good of human beings.

This melancholy fact does not, however, diminish the brilliance of the pathfinders. It only indicates the supreme importance of men who can work effectively on the many problems of human relationship. We have many good bridge engineers. We need good engineers of social relationships and institutions, of economics, politics, law, and education.

After all, only a small number of men have sufficient originality (a combination, still, of curiosity, imagination, and prediction) to break through habits and avoid the difficulties of impulse. The discoverers are like field marshals or generals. They need great armies, supplied with minor leaders, to be sure, but composed largely of the rank and file. Man might well be proud if each human being could rank as a general by reason of his mental penetration; since, however, in the society of minds few attain the grade of genius, the part of wisdom is to make capital of the discoverers and create a quick and ready understanding of and sympathy with them.

The function of education, in large part, is the mould-ing of minds capable of taking and using the best that the world has given. Such minds must be well stored with information, free from prejudice, critical of new ideas presented, and fitted to understand the kind and quantity of proof required before they may adopt the pronouncements of the generals of the society of minds. To be sure a formal education is probably the first step in the career of these generals, but nature has already given them an endowment far surpassing that of the average man.

To come back to just this average man. He makes up most of the world's population, but he has not begun to use his power in a well-trained and disciplined way. His mind is an instrument for the control of things and of men. The keener, the more penetrating, the more persistent, the more inclusive the operation of this mind is, the greater is the likelihood of the moulding of the world in which we live into an environment satisfying our needs. Not merely in the attainment of the satis-faction of human wants is the mind the instrument, but in the criticism of these wants or needs it is the agent. The kind of life which seems natural, the kind of values which are accepted without hesitation, the plays and pictures, clothes and houses which men admire may be accepted quite uncritically as a nation's, a group's, or a family's inheritance. If accepted critically or rejected with reason or modified consciously, it is because the mind has been at work, the mind as an instrument in the creation of a more excellent human existence.

Section 4. How Thought is Limited

If thought is such a creative and vital element in a

plastic world, one wonders why the world is n't by now a kind of restored Garden of Eden. There are many reasons why it is not. One of the most important of these is to be found in man's own nature which is impetuous, impulsive, and passionate. Thought is slow; the very term "reflection" comes from the Latin words — "back" and "to turn." Thought is deliberate and questioning. Appetite is headlong and compelling. Some one has said that we are ninety-five per cent habit and desire, and five per cent thought. The figures may be wrong, but the idea is right. Take a single instance — that of eating. Thought can determine and regulate a diet, but a hungry boy eats anything in sight and as much of it as he can hold — there is no check to his appetite. The motive power of our natural desires drives us, and thought lags behind, and comes to our rescue only when trouble surprises us.

Habit is another of thought's excluders. When we get into any particular habit, we repeat acts easily and comfortably as a perfectly adjusted and well-oiled engine runs in a power plant. The engine does n't think; neither need we in that part of our life which is so well unified as to run itself. Habits grow into a very real part of us, and we like them. Old ways are pleasant ways, and we love them and hate those things or persons that disturb them. When we are defending our habits — of belief just as well as of act — passion reinforces custom; and criticism or reconsideration has a poor chance to win the day. All this is not at all to say that the drive of desire and the easy continuity of habit are not good things. They are; but they may take over too completely the management of a human life. When they control, we miss discrimination, freedom of action, change, improvement. They make us feel comfortable and pretty contented, and thought implies a real discontent, not complaining, but energetically investigatory.

The defense of habits of thought manifests itself in a multitude of ways. " Prejudice " is derived from roots meaning "a judgment before." When we are prejudiced, we tend to repeat an earlier decision and to object to interference. Under such circumstances we are apt to refuse to consider. Men find themselves swayed by personal preferences, self-advantage, dislike of one of the parties of a controversy; and in this mingling of desire and habit, they are apt to omit unbiased consideration of all of the factors in the case.

Another trouble with thought is that it requires a considerable accumulation of experience and knowledge. Not everybody can think well because not everybody knows enough. And what applies to persons applies to peoples too. Fancy expecting an Eskimo to think out an electric heater! To get such an accumulation of knowledge as thought requires, men must have a stable civilization, books and investigators who bequeath their findings, schools or places to impart knowledge. Thought on a wide range of subjects makes very large demands indeed.

New thinking requires besides old information a human endowment of great imagination, and this we have seen is a rare native gift. It requires also means of experimentation, of checking up the brilliant idea to see how the world of fact corresponds to the hypothesis formed. How could a doctor be sure that he had found in a small organism the cause of malaria unless he could discover this organism microscopically in malarial patients?

The path-finders need instruments, tools to enable them to use their own personal instrument — thought.

Section 5. Mind and the Future

From what has been said already it is clear that man's ability to think is his most powerful weapon in his combat with nature, and in his ascent to the level of genuinely humane existence. It is not at all difficult to see why mind by reason of its presence in the world enhances even the glory of reality. Understanding, appraisal, criticism, appreciation, prediction, verification, control — all these are products of mind.

The utility of mind has already shown itself in the development of well-organized systems of belief — the exact sciences, and in the application of these beliefs, sometimes called truths, to practical problems. The great French scientist Pasteur stated in abstract terms that fermentation could not take place in sterile fluids. Then he proceeded to apply his knowledge to the preservation of export wines. He had an "idea," he tested it by experimentation to his entire satisfaction, and then he had the courage to say, "I can put this idea to work in the practical everyday life of men."

In the future one may expect an indefinite advance in our theoretical understanding of physical phenomena, and in our actual control of natural forces. Old operations will be performed more easily and new ones added. Even the most enthusiastic prophet would probably fall far short of the accomplishment which only a hundred years will see.

It is not too much to expect that in the understanding of man's nature notable advance will be made. We know more now about individual and public health than had been suspected in 1840. The knowledge of bacteriological infections, anæsthetics, and, with these two, practically the whole of modern surgery has come since then. Psychology and human physiology, or the study of man's behavior, are but infant sciences. Their development will probably greatly increase the welfare of men.

An exact and dispassionate study of, and a scientific procedure in, the field of group life is still a goal to be accomplished. In spite of this fact the study of public administration is each year increasing and new ways of obtaining control over group action are being standardized. No one can say of the phenomena of human behavior, individual or group, that they are simple, static, or as yet thoroughly predictable. But many believe that, in spite of their great variety, and their complication by reason of consciousness, we shall some day understand and direct them.

Section 6. The Purpose and Method of the Book

The advantages of a reflective life have been indicated very incompletely in the preceding pages, but enough has been said to make clear the importance of thought in a life which is interested in the selection of the best. This book is written to emphasize the part which thought plays in the formation of beliefs, and to stimulate its readers to a more lively realization of the road to a more congenial world which lies open to those who think. It hopes to point out some of the workings of thought and the habits of mind which those who desire to participate in the enterprise of knowing should cultivate. It does not desire to hide the dangers to which thought is exposed, nor to omit the limitations which thought encounters. It cannot expect to make men think, but it may make them desire to do so and aid them in their effort.

For the accomplishment of its purpose the book follows the method of presenting contrasting solutions of a series of problems. It may be that through the understanding of two beliefs about the same circumstances — such as the relations of the heavenly bodies which both Ptolemy and Copernicus studied — and through the realization of the way in which these beliefs were reached and the reasons why one was discarded and another kept, some appreciation of the character of thought at its best may be reached, and some of its methods laid hold of by the reader.

In the course of the presentation much of the material which logic has treated in a formal way is shown in a setting so concrete and real as to bring it near to the actual thinking of the reader. By watching the thought game of some of the masters perhaps the rules which they used will be better understood and followed by the novices than they could be if the rules were all read together in the "Laws of Thought." The older so-called formal logic seems strangely technical and remote to the student of the present day. Its nice distinctions and mathematical precision may be appreciated and enjoyed, but they do not seem to be carried out of the textbook into everyday thinking. Yet the importance of the end which the traditional logic seeks to accomplish was perhaps never more appreciated than it is to-day. To serve this end, which is the increase of thought and the improvement of its quality, a new approach has been adopted.

A careful reading of the Table of Contents will show

the progress of the text. Through chapters two to six, the stages in an act of thought are illustrated and developed by the examples chosen. In the chapter on "Diagnosis" the meaning of observation, definition, and classification are treated as elements in clearing up a difficulty — the second stage in an act of thought. In chapter three, "The Development of Hypotheses in Astronomy," the suggestions or probable solutions are especially emphasized. The elaboration or verification of hypotheses or tentatively accepted suggestions (the fourth and fifth steps in an act of thought) form the theme of the fourth chapter on "The Methods of Experimental Science," with its treatment of inductive reasoning, and of the fifth chapter on "Deductive Elaboration and the Relation of Implication in Mathematics." Chapter six brings with it a general consideration of the whole problem of explanation. Chapter seven, on "Evolution," gives in broad outline the development of all the steps in thought by the survey of the history of a great inquiry. This chapter, too, presents the part which anthropomorphic influences play in our thinking. Historical investigation and its methods are the subject of chapter eight. This treatment of the contrasting methods of handling an historic document has been included since men are so commonly uninformed and uncritical in their acceptance of traditional views. The last section of the book, including chapters nine to twelve, deals with problems of value, questions of better or worse, and attempts to show in what fashion reflection serves as a guide to right opinion on personal and social problems. A summary chapter brings a review of the principles and methods of thought which have been illustrated and developed throughout the book.

In the early chapters including the treatment of historical method, the illustrations are from fields in which a definite and on the whole an accepted method of verification has been worked out.   In the natural sciences we have found how to reach conclusions to which men will generally assent.   In the later chapters, dealing with conclusions about values, good things and bad, desirable and undesirable, we find a different situation. There is little agreement on findings and there are few objective methods of verification.   One of the chief reasons for increasing the acquaintance with the kind of thinking which has brought certainty in science is to increase the possibility and desire of applying reflection in the so-called social sciences.   We know fairly well the interactions of material forces; we know very poorly the interplay of psychological forces.   Yet our attainment of a more secure and reasonable existence in a world so complicated as our own requires such knowledge.   Reflective thought must win new victories in the empire of man.

QUESTIONS AND EXERCISES

1. Make an outline of *How We Think*, chapter 6.
2.   *a.* Name two fields in which you consider yourself sufficiently acquainted to be fairly sure that good suggestions as to the solution of problems in them would come to you.
    b. State a problem which does arise in one of these and give the suggestions for its solution which you find coming to you.
    c. How do you make such suggestions come faster or better?
3. Tell what you mean by the phrase "a fruitful suggestion," and the adage "The proof of the pudding is in the eating."
4. Explain what "critical acceptance" means.   Distinguish between fault-finding, analysis, and criticism.   Describe a critical spectator at a baseball game.
5. Look up the word "instrument," and the word "tool," and write out their derivation.
6. Look up the words "implies," "implication," "inference," and "meaning."   Write out definitions and derivations.

7. Why is it just to say that reasoned behavior is a greater advantage than instinctive?
8. Make a list of twenty-five persons whom you know well. Draw a line and divide it into five parts. Call the sections very poor, poor, fair, good, very good. Write the names of the twenty-five persons on the line in order of merit for honesty. Do this again for general intelligence. Again for amiability.
9. Make your own list of mental qualities or traits (ten at least) and check those which you would consider most important (a) for an explorer, (b) for a salesman, (c) a mathematical astronomer.
10. Name some invention of great importance for man's conquest of nature which has also brought changes undesirable from the point of view of the best society. Describe the changes, their causes, and suggest remedies.
11. Name several men and women whom you might call human engineers, and state why.
12. Give an example of the way in which a strong party man, who is conscious that his party has just done a foolish thing, reacts to an adverse critic of his party. What is the meaning of "bigot"? Of "a dogmatist"? Of "a reactionary"?
13. Read William James's *Pragmatism*, Chapter II, and write a paragraph on "When may we follow desire in accepting belief?"
14. Show why an habitual or customary judgment of a certain type of conduct is often right.
15. What are some good reasons why men dread change in the laws of a state?
16. Why is real freedom of action dependent on thought? (See John Dewey, *How We Think*, p. 64.)
17. How did the American Indians hand down their knowledge of tribal custom? Of hunting?

BIBLIOGRAPHY

John Dewey, *How We Think*. Heath and Company, 1910.

Francis Bacon, *Novum Organum*, Book I, §§ 39–65, The Idols, § 129. The Clarendon Press, 1889.

Francis Bacon, *The New Atlantis*. World Classics Series, Oxford Press.

Irwin Edman, *Human Traits and Their Social Significance*. Houghton Mifflin Company, 1920.

E. E. Slosson, *Creative Chemistry*. The Century Company, 1921.

E. L. Thorndike, *Education*. The Macmillan Company, 1912.

John Tyndall, *Fragments of Science for Unscientific People* (Scientific Use of the Imagination). Longmans, Green & Co., 1871.

James Harvey Robinson, *The Mind in the Making*. Harper and Brothers, 1921.

William James, *Principles of Psychology*, chap. 22. Henry Holt & Co., 1905.

CHAPTER II

DIAGNOSIS: ANCIENT EGYPT AND THE MASSACHU-SETTS GENERAL HOSPITAL

OBSERVATION — CLASSIFICATION — DEFINITION

Section 1. Two Ways of Treating a Sick Man

ON October 8, 1906, a farmer entered the Massachusetts General Hospital. He was thirty-five years of age. About August 1st he began to have eruptions, swellings in various parts of his body. He had previously been treated for an attack of a disease of the skin characterized by non-inflammatory swellings on various parts of the skin and mucous membranes. In the middle of August he had smothering sensations in his chest, which lasted from one to three hours. On October 3d he began to have headache, which grew rapidly worse. On October 6th he had a chill at 3 P.M., and the next day one at 7 P.M. Since the onset of his headache, he had fever continuously. He had lost much money recently, but said he did not worry about it. A physical examination showed that glands in the neck, armpits, and groins could be felt. An examination of his chest and abdomen revealed no signs of disease.[1]

If this man had lived in Egypt, let us say in the year 400 B.C., what would the doctors have done with him? As far as we can judge from the remaining historical records, he would have been treated by many physicians, each one specializing upon the difficulties presented in

[1] The facts of this case have been described almost verbatim after R. C. Cabot, *Differential Diagnosis*, vol. I, pp. 72–74.

some particular part of the man's body. One physician would have applied some paste or liquid to the swellings in his mouth. A second would have recommended something for the smothering sensations in his chest, a third for his headache, and a fourth for his chill. Still another would have applied himself to the reduction of his fever, and perhaps some one might also have been found to suggest a treatment for the glands. Meanwhile what would have happened to the man receiving all this attention? Perhaps he would feel a little better for it. Some of his aches and pains might in this way be removed. But for several weeks he probably would not feel wholly well. He might get suddenly worse, and die, or he might recover quite completely, and in another month or two forget entirely about his illness. At any rate, during the course of his illness, it is highly probable that he would not avoid contact with other people. When not feeling too miserable, he would probably be up and about, he would see his friends as usual, and his way of life at home would not be changed. In consequence of this, it is very likely that others who lived with him, or even near his dwelling, would soon fall ill, and also be obliged to seek the aid of doctors.[1]

Now what happened to the farmer at the Massachusetts General Hospital in 1906? First, a doctor examined him carefully. This doctor asked himself the question: What is really the matter with this man? What is his trouble fundamentally? What disease has he? What the doctor saw upon a first examination of the patient suggested several diseases as possibilities. Though the man said he did not worry about his money

[1] On Egyptian medicine, see *Herodotus*, Book II, sections 84–88; also F. H. Garrison, *History of Medicine*, pp. 44–51.

losses, perhaps he did, and such anxiety continued over a considerable period of time might possibly account for his symptoms. The chills might indicate malaria. The glandular enlargement suggested the possibility of syphilis, or of leukemia, a condition occasioned by an excess of white corpuscles in the blood. Finally, the swellings which appeared on various mucous membranes, and for which the patient had been previously treated, might themselves explain some of the other symptoms, such as the headache and the fever. And if these swellings were also present in the respiratory tract, they might account for the smothering sensations which the man had experienced in his chest some weeks earlier.

The doctor considered each of these suggestions in turn. The constancy of the patient's fever seemed to eliminate the possibility of his condition being due to financial anxiety alone. A microscopic examination of his blood likewise promptly negatived the suggestion of malaria. Moreover, the blood appeared wholly normal in other respects, the number of white corpuscles and their proportion to the red corpuscles being such as to prevent a diagnosis of the case as leukemia. The glandular enlargement itself, which had suggested leukemia was not at all general. Not general enough to support the thought of syphilis, and there was nothing else in the case to suggest syphilis. Indeed the glandular conditions were such as are frequently found in normal persons, so that there was no need to regard them as pathological at all. Finally, if the headache and fever were due to the swellings, there ought to have been some external eruptions on the skin, since such swellings almost never occur on mucous surfaces and serous membranes alone.

Thus none of the doctor's suggestions seemed to him convincing. He was confronted with a patient having "a continued fever and nothing to show for it." This very inability to associate the fever with any of the other symptoms made the doctor suspect typhoid. For typhoid fever is a disease which presents a great variety of general symptoms, no one of which, however, occurs in all cases, except possibly the fever itself. (And even the fever may sometimes be absent, at least for a time. — "Afebrile" cases) The diagnostic principle which physicians employ in this predicament may be formulated somewhat as follows: In any case of continued fever, where the other symptoms lead to no positive diagnosis, make laboratory tests for typhoid fever.

There are six or seven specific laboratory tests for typhoid fever, and two of them are in very general use. In this case the doctor had a specimen of the patient's blood sent to the laboratory, to see if a typhoid culture could be developed from it. The culture revealed typhoid bacilli. This completed the diagnosis, the patient could now be isolated as a typhoid case, and all our knowledge of that disease applied to his cure, and to the protection of others.

Section 2.   Differences in Observation and Their Causes

The Egyptian and the modern treatments both rested on the observation of a patient suffering from typhoid. The Egyptians looked at the man carefully, no doubt. They saw a number of different ailments. They treated each separately. They did not see the typhoid bacillus at all. It is easy to say, then, that the observation attendant on the location of the difficulties (the cause of the man's illness) was the reason for the difference in treatment. But to understand why that difference in observation existed, is not so easy as the saying.

The location of the difficulty by the modern physician depended on his knowing what to look for, what to disregard, how to check his findings. These items in turn depended upon the accumulation of a great body of medical knowledge. The first point concerning the excellence of the observation is, therefore, that men observe with the eye of the past. The most searching analysis of the difficulty is possible only when the searcher is acquainted with his field. The modern physician had, as a part of his medical equipment, the constantly functioning knowledge that fever is a key symptom, and that it is sometimes caused by microscopic organisms which can be determined by laboratory tests and which must be the center of medical attack. Until the middle of the nineteenth century men did n't know how to find nor how to interpret these organisms. Men observe with the eye of the past.

But such a statement needs qualification. Although the past furnishes the background of experience and knowledge necessary to the understanding of a problem, not everything in the past is important, and not the past alone will fit for discovery by observation. The past is rich because there have been men of genius who have seen afresh, who, in the words of the analysis of our act of thought, have had new and fruitful suggestions as to the problems at hand and who have diligently checked their findings. Their discoveries remain embedded in the heritage of the past, yet they are perpetually new, for they may be rechecked at will by any new investigator. To see clearly with the eye of the past means to use such signal discoveries as illuminate the present situation and to keep these verified by reinvestigation. But to do this is not enough to secure the best observations. As additions were made in bygone years to the fund of knowledge, so to-day men come at their problem with inquiring minds and searching observation, and, because they have in addition to past knowledge a spark of genius, imagination, deeper insight, they see things which have never been noticed before or thought important. Such men are usually willing to take great pains to be thorough and exhaustive in their investigation, and to follow every implication or suggestion, even the most casual, which appears while the investigation is proceeding. These discoverers are in most instances high in the scale of intelligence. They bring great native endowment to their work. They work thoroughly; they use the past, but they are not blinded by it, for they look with searching attention for new factors which will explain and control the difficulty at hand.

In observing the fever and taking it as a key symptom, the modern physician would not proceed to diagnose without getting all the available qualifying information about his patient. He could not clarify or define his difficulty merely by saying "fever." Had his patient been a young child and the fever slight, he might not have made fever his key. Had his patient had none of the symptoms associated with the onset of typhoid, the fever would not have been so significant for his diagnosis, or at any rate might not so clearly have indicated a specific diagnosis. The observation, then, included the whole case. The diagnosis, furthermore, called for further investigation and further observation of the blood when tested. The observation was comprehensive.

Observation, furthermore, if complete, is not limited to an isolated circumstance, but is progressive. With Hippocrates in Greece (c. 460–359 B.C.) men began to realize that the history and course of a disease had to be known and studied. Our modern examiner would ask for the history of the patient, and our modern hospital would keep a record of daily, sometimes hourly, change. Why? Because the most significant feature for diagnosis may be the relation of the observed facts to one another, rather than each fact taken singly. The great mistake of the Egyptians was their failure to connect their observations sufficiently. Observation is at work all through the thought process and its verification.

Observation depends on something more than seeing or hearing. It is reinforced by suggestions arising in its course. The physician observes characteristic a. This perceived, suggestions arise as to probable additional characteristics b, c, and d usually associated with a. Back he goes in his observing to see if b, c, and d are there; hidden away, perhaps, but there. Observation demands the whole man and not merely his sense organs. This fact throws additional light on the statement that the trained observer is one who knows his field through and through. The young physician in the clinic marvels at the things which his chief sees and looks for. But his chief sees with his mind's eye, and the young physician has not yet freely developed this indispensable organ of acute and searching observation.

Important as is this inner sense organ, the fact must not be neglected that perfect sense organs of the unusual kind are necessary for trustworthy observation. The Egyptian physician might have been handicapped for all his observing by bad vision. So, too, might his modern colleague, but this observer of to-day could correct or offset his physiological handicap by glasses. His failing hearing he might find harder to compensate, and through it he might miss important symptoms in the sounds of the heart or lungs. Were the hearing unusually keen and well trained in detecting the slightest abnormalities the physician would have a corresponding advantage — provided, of course, that his mind's ear knew the significance of these rarely detected sounds. Physiological normality or supernormality are preconditions to correct observation.

Another kind of eye, still, is used in observing to supplement the human organism. The modern diagnostician is greatly handicapped unless he has at hand his laboratory with its equipment of microscopes to increase his vision many fold and give him access to exact observations of the most minute organisms which may be the root cause of the disease. He also creates elaborate apparatus for the experimental or artificial construction of conditions under which he can verify a suggestion which arises as he observes his case. He has instruments of all kinds to use in his examination, merely to get complete observation so that the difficulty may be made so thoroughly clear that the proper solution may arise. The thermometer is one of his most constant assistants. He does not have to rely on flushed cheeks or hot brow, felt by a hand which may itself vary in temperature as it is plunged in hot or cold water before it touches his patient. His little glass instrument with its mercury column, tested by a constant standard, cannot mistake; it has no subjective factor which must be discounted.

Helpful mechanical instruments, keen senses, and a proper mental attitude are, therefore, the three pre-

requisites to correct observation. By a proper mental
attitude is meant having valuable information which
guides your investigation fruitfully, being free of prejudices or prejudgments, and so on. Correct observation
is the very first demand of science, for tested facts are
like stones out of which the solid edifice of knowledge is
built. But how do we know when our observations are
correct? When can we be sure we have the facts? This
is a difficult question which we cannot answer very satisfactorily until we have surveyed the whole process of
reflective thinking. Suffice it to say, at this point that
there are three principal tests of observation. The first
is the agreement of competent investigators; the second
is the agreement and congruity of observations with
each other. And the third is the utility of observations
in helping us to solve our problems.

Section 3. Classification and Implication

The doctors in Egypt and in the Massachusetts General Hospital had both classified their patients. The
difference between the physicians was that their classifications were not equally significant. The Egyptian
had a class "enlarged glands." For this class he had
one treatment. The modern has not one class "enlarged glands," but several, falling under different
causal classifications. Not the superficial appearance of
the glands is the basis of classification, but the underlying and fundamental ailment of which the glands are
but one manifestation. The importance of the way in
which things are grouped varies with the significance or
implication of the basis of classification.

The nature of the instances under consideration, and
the uses to which the knowledge about them will be put,

must both be known before things can be arranged together. One single object may be put in half a dozen different classes, and each time usefully, if it serves the purpose of the classifier. The classification of enlarged glands, as "things to be treated in order to cure the man," was bad, for the more important "thing to be treated" was the bacillus causing the fever, and if the man was to be cured, the right thing had to be put in the class "things to be treated." But the typhoid patient could also be classified by the health authorities as "possible cause of infection," as "patient for Ward D," as "holder of disability insurance," as "interesting typhoid case with new features," or as "Smith, Martin Stone," with perfect propriety and usefulness.

The reason such grouping is useful is that it carries with it implications. Call the man "cause of infection," and that means "keep him from infecting others." It also means "case which came from town X, and town X must be inspected in regard to its milk and water supply." This fact of implication gives further indication of the skill required in making and interpreting classification. Nothing must be put in a class having certain implications unless it, too, has them; and no classification can be understood and made use of unless the user knows its wider meaning. But to the physician who knows what typhoid means, the diagnosis by any expert of a patient, as of the group typhoid cases, is full of significance because this group has associated with it rules for care and cure.

A class may be too large for significance. The typhoid patient is a sick man — true, and in a sense significant, because this means he must have attention. But put him in the class suffering from "bacillus typhosus" and he can be treated specifically. A class is a key to meaning, and the richer in meaning it is for a particular purpose — such as effecting a cure — the better is the classification.

The history of progress in the sciences is in a sense the history of classification. When Copernicus put the earth in the class "body revolving about the sun," he worked a revolution. But before he could make a class of "bodies revolving about the sun," he had to understand the system of heavenly bodies and their relations. Classes, then, are a product of investigation. When significant characteristics are found in a number of bodies, a class may be made, and to include a body in that class means thereafter to give it all the significance of the class. Good observation demands the whole of one's powers; it is not mere looking. Good classification requires the most comprehensive knowledge, not mere ordering in group by any chance resemblance.

In a real sense classification is the basic process in all the steps of thought. A circumstance would not appear difficult if it were recognized at once as falling into a class, and on the other hand, if it resisted ordering under every relationship, it could never be understood; in fact, such utterly unrelated circumstances would probably not stir us, for the thing which perplexes us is the questionably or partly classified, rather than the totally unrelated. When a suggestion arises it is significant only in so far as it associates the perplexing element with a class or classes through union with which it gains clarity. In the final acceptance of the suggestion confidence is felt that an exact classification has really been accomplished. Such an achievement may, furthermore, involve some adjustment in classes already established

if the new difficulty solved presents aspects different
from other members of a class to which it belongs by
reason of exhibiting the more significant characteristics
of that group.

Section 4. Definition as a Formula for Work

When things have been put in classes, men frequently
find it convenient to record the fact in concise form, for
their own convenience in explaining what a thing is, and
as a service to others who may know the name of a thing
but nothing of its relationships.

The malady which we call typhoid fever men studied
for many years, and as they made new discoveries they
recorded them in a brief formula of identification and
implication. In other words, they defined typhoid.
The definition would not be complete until it was such
a compressed classification and identification as would
point out typhoid and no other disease. The definition
might be, "typhoid is a fever usually associated with
such and such symptoms, with such and such a bacillus
determinable through laboratory tests of a specified
character, and responding to treatment of a prescribed
nature." The definition would be good if it were unerr-
ing; that is, if it would give such a class and such sub-
classes as could apply to typhoid and typhoid only. The
definition would then be exact, not so narrow as to exclude any case, nor so broad as to take in any case not
typhoid. A brief definition suitable for dictionary or
encyclopædia purposes rather than a descriptive one
valuable for the physician might be "typhoid is a fever
caused by Bacillus typhosus."[1]

The definition would be a formula for work because it

[1] *Encyclopædia Britannica.*

would carry within itself indications of tests to verify
the identity of the thing defined. If it said, caused by
bacillus typhosus and gave the methods of testing for
this bacillus, it would be as good as to say, "make these
tests and find out if this case you think to be typhoid
really is that." Who had made this definition? Medical men who worked before the physician now using
it. Why had they included these items of information?
Because each was significant for identification or for
subsequent action in handling the disease. The framers
of the definition had had their eyes on practice, and the
doctor who used the definition found in it a guide for his
observation: a fever — yes; a bacillus discovered and
identified by specific tests — yes; the disease responding
to the prescribed treatment — yes. The case is clear,
this sick man belongs to that well-known class of typhoid patients.

It is very clear that classification and definition are
closely related. Classification involves definition, and
definition is possible only by including the thing defined
within a class, and then by identifiable characteristics
separating it from other members of the class. Both
are important in clarifying the situation because of the
implications contained in them; and both in their framing are determined by the purposes which they are
meant to serve.

Section 5. Summary

The discussion of the two cases of diagnosis and the
explanation of some of the processes useful in clearing
up a doubtful situation have emphasized several factors.
In adequate observation a basic idea is important, such
as, "fever is the significant and correlating phenom-

enon." The past may give us such an idea, but the present must always recheck and be alert to discover a still better idea. Personal interest or bias may befog observation or lead it astray. Observation must not miss any circumstances; it must know all about the past and future of the thing to be observed. Observation demands a rich fund of knowledge in order that an "inner eye" may interpret the facts observed and make capital of their implications. The observer must use all his senses, unimpaired, and may supplement them by instruments, apparatus, and experiment.

In valuable classification, groups must be based on genuinely significant similarities. The purpose of the classification will determine its character. The importance of classification resides in the fact that to classify is to give a member of the class a group of implications. Classification cannot be valuable unless there is present a penetrating and comprehensive knowledge of the thing to be classified and of all its relationships.

Definition is compressed classification. The definition must prove the means of identifying the thing defined and no other. The definition is a formula for work because it indicates means of doing or observing things to render sure the identification of the thing defined.

QUESTIONS AND EXERCISES

1. Read John Dewey, *How We Think*, p. 30.
2. Name several instruments which aid observation.
3. Give an instance of mal-observation due to psychological causes.
4. Give an instance in which physiological drawbacks debar men from professions or vocations.
5. Show the parts played by past experience and fresh insight in the good observation of: — a slide under the microscope; the rise and fall of prices; a Beethoven symphony.
6. Read the section on "Classification" in one of the logics in the Bibliography and list the errors which should be avoided in classifying.

7. Indicate several ways of classifying the mosquito and tell the purpose of each.
8. A book was once written on "The Great Henries of History." What objections do you find to such a classification?
9. Read the section on "Definition" in one of the logics in the Bibliography and list the qualities of a good definition and the mistakes to avoid in defining.
10. Make four definitions of "College Spirit" suitable for a younger brother, an enthusiastic classmate, a loyal and serious-minded alumnus, a dictionary.
11. What is a fact?
12. Describe and illustrate with specific examples the three tests of correct observation.

BIBLIOGRAPHY

On diagnosis in medicine:
R. C. Cabot, *Differential Diagnosis.* W. B. Saunders Company, 1920–21.
F. H. Garrison, *An Introduction to the History of Medicine.* W. B. Saunders Company, 1921.
Herodotus, book II, 84–88. A. D. Godley translation. Loeb Classics, Putnam, 1921.
W. Osler, *Modern Medicine.* Appleton, 1920.
On observation, classification, and definition:
J. E. Creighton, *An Introductory Logic.* The Macmillan Company, 1920.
A. L. Jones, *Logic Inductive and Deductive.* Henry Holt & Co., 1909.
W. S. Jevons, *Elementary Lessons in Logic.* The Macmillan Company, 1914.

CHAPTER III

THE DEVELOPMENT OF HYPOTHESES IN ASTRONOMY

Section 1.   The Nature of an Hypothesis

THE last chapter, in dealing with the indispensable processes of the careful observation of all phenomena that may have a bearing on the problem in hand, of their classification in such ways as seem most fruitful, and of thus providing the material for an accurate definition, was really an account of the method by which the trained scientific thinker seizes upon the first step in our analysis of the everyday act of reflective thought and elaborates upon it with all the resources at his command.   Although the type of diagnosis that we encounter in modern medicine, dependent as it is upon the microscope, the culture dish, and all the rest of the apparatus of the laboratory, to say nothing of the carefully tabulated results of the experience of thousands of physicians, may seem enormously different from the kind of analysis which we all bestow upon every problem whose solution demands real thinking, in the fundamental principles upon which it proceeds it is to be distinguished therefrom only by its complexity and thoroughness.   We saw that this analysis was followed by the occurrence of one or more suggested solutions to the difficulty.   In the history of science these suggestions are usually elaborate and complicated explanations of certain observed phenomena, and are known as "hypotheses."   In the present chapter we shall examine two famous scientific hypotheses in the interest of finding out how a theory is formed to account for certain facts, undergoes successive modifications as new facts are gradually brought to bear upon it, and then may have to give way to an entirely different theory if further facts are discovered with which it cannot be reconciled. How is a great hypothesis formulated by the labors of a whole series of investigators? What conditions must such an hypothesis fulfill if it is to be accounted as in all probability the true explanation? Why is one hypothesis, even though it possesses great plausibility, discarded in favor of another? In answering these questions we shall be discovering what the scientist has learned to be the greatest safeguards that can be thrown about the third stage in the typical act of reflective thinking.

To illustrate these principles we have chosen from the field of astronomy the Copernican and Ptolemaic theories of planetary motion. It is appropriate that we make this selection, for astronomy was historically the first of the natural sciences to be developed, and the replacement of the Ptolemaic theory by the Copernican is the intellectual event from which the birth of modern science is usually reckoned. The theory of Ptolemy was marvelously ingenious in the way in which it did explain the observed motions of the heavenly bodies, and the conflict between it and that of Copernicus was not a struggle between a poor and a good hypothesis, but between a good hypothesis and one that proved to be even better. Few tales are more impressive than that of the long line of patient investigators who built stone by stone the vast edifice of modern astronomy.

Section 2. The Observed Facts of Astronomy

So firmly ingrained is our belief in the daily rotation of the earth upon its axis and its yearly revolution about the sun that it is extremely difficult to think ourselves back into the position of men to whom these explanations of the observed phenomena of the heavens had not occurred. But since we are to contrast our interpretation with another and quite different one, it will be well to start first with those facts which observation of the sky can actually establish. It is these facts which every hypothesis must explain; and it is by its accord with these facts that it must be ultimately tested. From the earliest times men have observed the heavenly bodies and have kept some account of their changes in position. These records are the result of careful observations kept and corrected through long years. The Chaldæan and Egyptian priests whose records we possess, however, formulated no theories as to the way in which the sun and the moon and the planets are related to each other and to the earth; they were seemingly content to tabulate and to note certain recurrent sequences of events like eclipses. They furnished a series of more or less unconnected items, usually marked and kept for some practical purpose, such as the fixing of religious festivals or the dating of important political events. Even to-day Easter is fixed by reference to astronomical phenomena, and farmers still talk of planting in the dark of the moon.

Just what are these facts which form the data of astronomy? A little thought will convince us that all that we can really see when we look at the heavens is a number of spots of light, which appear from time to time in different directions from the earth, and which change their position with regard to each other. The varying directions of these light spots form the only immediate facts for the astronomer; his theories are all designed to account for the particular way in which these spots move about. Their size, their distance, their rate of movement — these are all items that cannot be directly observed, and that are based on inferences from the primary data.

From earliest times men have classified these points of light into distinctive groups. They have picked out certain of them and given them the names of the fanciful figures which they seemed to resemble. Thus the Greeks named the constellations of the Great Bear, The Twins, Orion's Belt. But another kind of classification, based not on this resemblance, but upon the kind of motions which they performed, proved far more fruitful. For the sake of city dwellers who have forgotten the sky, let us list a few of the most important types of observable motion.

First, the great body of so-called fixed stars, together with the sun and moon, appears to rotate about the earth once a day, rising in the east and setting in the west. To the unsophisticated observer, these heavenly bodies seem to be fixed upon the inside of a great spherical surface of which the earth is the center, and the vast majority of them appear to possess no motion but this daily rotation about the earth. This apparent spherical surface upon which the spots of light which we call stars are seen is known to astronomy as the celestial sphere. The fixed stars receive their name because they remain always in the same position relative to each other, although of course when viewed from the earth they share in the rising and setting in which all the heavenly bodies participate.

But certain of the light spots are not fixed, and change their positions with relation to the other stars. These are, besides the sun and the moon, those called planets or wanderers; and from the earliest times their courses amongst the fixed stars have been plotted with great care. Since the primary reason for theories of the solar system is to account for the seemingly irregular movements of these points of light, we shall have to note just what these courses appear to be.

The moon, while sharing in the daily rotation of the

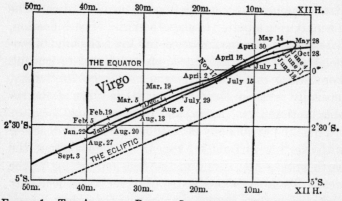

FIGURE 1. THE APPARENT PATH OF JUPITER FROM OCTOBER 28, 1897, TO SEPTEMBER 3, 1898

The dates printed in the diagram show the positions of Jupiter. (From Berry, *A Short History of Astronomy*, Charles Scribner's Sons, 1910.)

celestial sphere, appears to lag behind it somewhat, so that it rises about fifty minutes later every day. In the course of approximately a month, it has traversed a complete circle about the sky, and the celestial sphere has gained upon it one entire rotation. Though it is not so easily observed, the sun also travels in a great circle around the sky, losing four minutes upon the fixed stars each day, so that at the end of a year it has returned once more to the same relative position. These two courses are quite regular, but the planets, while in general per-

forming similar circles from west to east that require
greater or less time, seem to possess a much more erratic
motion.   At times their progress from west to east
gradually slackens and stops, and they then seem to re-
trace their steps for a period from east to west. Soon
they again seem to slow up, stop, and then return once
more upon their normal course from west to east.   The
accompanying diagram shows the apparent course of the
planet Jupiter among the fixed stars on the celestial
sphere during a period of about a year. (See Figure 1.)

These are the chief motions of the heavenly bodies
which the various theories of the relation between the
members of the solar system are designed to explain:
the daily rotation about the earth, the more extended
courses of the sun, moon, and planets around the surface of the celestial sphere, and the backward or retrograde motions of the planets.   There are various minor
movements which the great accuracy of modern tele-
scopes is able to detect, and some of these minute variations in direction shared even by the fixed stars will be
noted later for their importance in deciding between the
theories of Ptolemy and of Copernicus.

Section 3.   Ptolemy's Hypothesis

The first attempt at the systematic ordering of these
observations was made in the second century B.C. by a
Greek named Hipparchus.   Following his lead, in the
second century A.D., Ptolemy at Alexandria wrote a
treatise which has come down to us under the title of
the "Almagest." He took the accumulated teachings
of his predecessors and made from them what he called
"a great" [1] or "a mathematical composition."   He

---

[1] Unless otherwise noted, quotations in this chapter are from J. L. E.
Dreyer, *History of the Planetary Systems*. Cambridge University Press,
1906.

placed the earth as an unmoving sphere at the center
of things. The spherical character of the earth he accepted from his predecessors. Pythagoras, or at least
his followers, had believed it, on what grounds we do not
know. The earth was at the center of the heavens because "heavy bodies descend to the center of the heavens, which is the center of the earth," and because if the
earth were not in the center "one side of the heavens
would appear nearer to us than the other and the stars
would be larger there." The earth was immovable
because there must be "some fixed point to which the
motion of others may be referred," and because, "if
there were motion, it would be proportionate to the
great mass of the earth and would leave behind animals
and objects thrown into the air."

Around the earth there circled the moon, the sun, and
the planets, and outside of all was the sphere in which
were fixed the stars, which was thought of by Ptolemy
as an actual sphere. These circlings were not at quite
the same rate; the stars rotated fastest, then the planets, the sun, and the moon. This slight gain of the stars
upon the other heavenly bodies accounted for their
apparent paths among the stars. Ptolemy explained
the irregular retrograde motions of the planets by a simple and ingenious method. While the sun and moon
circled about the earth directly, the planets really took
part in two circular movements. An imaginary point
on a planet's great circle, called the "deferent," did
travel regularly about the earth, but at the same time
the planet itself was revolving in a smaller circular orbit
about this imaginary point. The center of this smaller
circle traveled west to east at a uniform rate, but the
planet itself was revolving about this center. Its ap-

parent path was thus a combination of the two circular movements. Figure 2 will make this clear. It shows both the large orbit, or *deferent*, and the smaller orbit, or *epicycle*, and the consequent epicycloid path of the planet. By comparing his figure with Figure 1, it will be seen how, if we assume that the epicycle orbit is

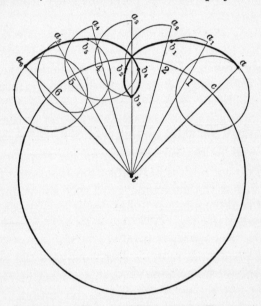

FIGURE 2. A PLANET'S MOTION IN THE EPICYCLE

(From Todd, *New Astronomy*, American Book Company.)

The center, *c*, of the small circle, called the "epicycle," moves round the center *t* of the large circle, called the "deferent"; and at the end of each 24th part of a revolution, it occupies successively the points 1, 2, 3, 4, 5, and so on. But while *c* is moving to 1, the point *a* is traversing an arc of the deferent equal to a_1, b_1. By combination of the two motions, therefore, the point *a* will traverse the heavy curve, reaching the points indicated by b_1, b_2, b_3, b_4, b_5, when *c* arrives at corresponding points 1, 2, 3, 4, 5. In passing from b_2 to b_4 the planet will turn backward, or seem to describe its retrograde arc among the stars. By combining different rates of motion with circles of different sizes, it was found that all the apparent movements of the planets could be almost perfectly explained.

slightly tilted from the plane of the deferent orbit, the apparent path viewed from the earth would correspond to the observed course of Mercury. It should be noted that Figure 1 represents what can be seen when looking along the plane of the orbits, while Figure 2 represents the orbits looked at perpendicularly from above. (See Figure 2.)

In taking this position, Ptolemy apparently did not assert that he was picturing a real system. His interest seemingly was in calculating and predicting the positions of the planets on the celestial sphere, rather than in portraying an actual relationship among heavenly bodies. He generally begins the theory of a particular fact of a planet's motion by saying, "Let us imagine a circle," and in the introduction to his *Hypotheses* he says: "I do not profess to be able thus to account for all the motions at the same time; but I shall show that each by itself is well explained by its proper hypothesis." It is interesting to know that, though it is now held to be quite false, if considered an objective picture of things, it is still possible to base exact calculations and predictions verifiable by experience on this system, elaborated in accord with its own fundamental conceptions. Ptolemy's system was thoroughly scientific, in that it started from observed facts and assumed nothing that could not be tested by comparison with those facts. It forms a great contrast, for example, with the somewhat similar system propounded by Aristotle and elaborated during the late Middle Ages, which regarded each of the seven bodies, moon, Mercury, Venus, sun, Mars, Jupiter, and Saturn, as fixed in a great actual sphere of crystal, the whole series being included in an outer opaque sphere to which were attached the stars, and by whose movements the whole eight concentric spheres were kept rotating. Such a fanciful conception had obviously little but superficial similarity to the scientific theory of Ptolemy.

Why do we admire this system and call Ptolemy a great scientist? He taught a theory long since discarded and fixed human opinion in incorrect views for thirteen hundred years!

1. He was great because he looked for natural explanations. All of the movements were accomplished by reference to orderly and well-known types of physical behavior, which were subject to study at will. No mysterious and arbitrary power came into his system at any point to help him out of some unmastered difficulty — he did not assume the existence of anything whose operation could not be observed and verified.

2. He was great because he could understand and hold an enormous number of items of information and beliefs and compose them into an harmonious system. As a work of the scientific imagination his creation is superb. Such achievements bring with them a sense of mastery and security in a world where before no order seemed to rule. Such systems may, indeed, give a false sense of finality by reason of their seductive completeness. They may stifle further inquiry. In spite of all this, they do not fail to call forth admiration from those who comprehend them.

3. He was great because he could construct hypotheses conforming to a single type, to meet his phenomena, and clearly recognize them as working formulas. His hypotheses were assumptions made to aid in solving problems. They served their purpose if they were of use in this way. Ptolemy did not demand that, in addition,

they should be hypothetical constructions of natural conditions. In his one-sided adoption of hypotheses he illustrates one of the enduring uses of scientific suppositions, but he also shows his limitations.

4. He possessed remarkable mathematical ability and ingenuity in several particular solutions, which for the sake of simplicity are not given here.

Ptolemy lacked instruments of exact observation, and, as noted above, he seems not to have been troubled by the question: "Is this system actually a real picture of the universe?" Such a question is vital when the belief is concerned with physical objects. In addition, Ptolemy did not seem to be offended by the need of complicating his explanations.

Section 4.   The Conflict of Authoritarian and Scientific Explanations

In contrast to Ptolemy's close hold on observation and theory conforming to nature, there may be cited the position of one of his critics, who started not from nature, but from an uncritical acceptance of a dogma — an inflexible and unexamined belief.

A Syrian bishop of the fifth century, in attacking the theories of the heathen, wrote that "the heaven is not a sphere, but a tent or tabernacle; 'it is He ... that stretcheth out the heavens as a curtain and spreadeth them out as a tent to dwell in'; the Scripture says that it has a top, which a sphere has not, and it is also written: 'The sun was risen upon the earth when Lot came unto Zoar.' The earth is flat, and the sun does not pass under it in a night, but travels through the northern parts 'as if hidden by a wall,'" and he quotes: "The sun goeth down and hasteth to his place where he ariseth."

Such a reliance upon the Scripture accepted literally as determining the details of all beliefs, we think of as an improper use of authority in determining opinion. It seizes upon a generalization that is, to be sure, based upon a certain number of observed facts, and applies that provisionally acceptable theory uncritically, without recognizing the modifications which new facts must introduce. It is a characteristic prejudice of the human mind to cling thus tenaciously to an old view even in the face of broader knowledge. Thus it is interesting to note that when finally the Ptolemaic theory was accepted by the Church, it too became an unquestioned criterion for all other doctrines, and its authority was called in to confound the new system of Copernicus.

Section 5.   The Hypothesis of Copernicus

The system of Ptolemy was not subject to serious dispute until Copernicus (1473–1543) issued his *De revolutionibus orbium cœlestium*.   Copernicus was a Pole, educated in mathematics and in astronomy at Cracow and in Italy.   In his writing he tells how he was first induced to seek for a new theory of the heavenly bodies by finding that mathematicians differed greatly among themselves about the earth's motion.   He therefore took the trouble to read the writings of the ancients.   He found a statement that Hiketas had believed the earth to be in motion.   " 'Occasioned thus,' he wrote, 'I also began to think of a motion of the earth, and although the idea seemed absurd, still, as those before me had been permitted to assume certain circles in order to explain the motions of the stars, I believed it would readily be permitted me to try whether, on the assumption of the motion of the earth, better explanation of the revolutions

of the heavenly spheres might not be found.   And thus
I have, assuming the motions which I in the following
work attribute to the earth, after long and careful investigation, finally found that when the motions of the
other planets are referred to the circulation of the earth,
and are computed for the revolution of each star, not only
do the phenomena necessarily follow therefrom, but the
order and magnitude of the stars and all their orbs and
the heaven itself are so connected that in no part can
anything be transposed without confusion to the rest
and to the whole universe.' ''

His work had indeed been long — it began in 1506
and was written out only in 1531 or 1532.   He states
that " ' the world has the form of a sphere, the most perfect as well as the most roomy figure, which everything
tends to assume as we may see in drops of water and
other fluids.' 'The motion of the heavenly bodies is
circular or a composition of circular motions, since only
a circle can bring a body back to its original position.
The question of the rest or movement of the earth cannot be considered settled since any change observed
may be caused either by a motion of the object observed
or by that of the observer, or by a different motion of
both; so that if the earth had a motion it would produce
an apparent motion of everything outside it in the opposite direction.' '' ''To Ptolemy's argument that a rotation in twenty-four hours would be so violent a motion
that the loose earth would long ago have been scattered
over the heavens while falling bodies would never reach
the place intended, as the latter would have been torn
away from under them, and clouds and other bodies in
the air would always be moving toward the west, Copernicus remarks that Ptolemy ought to be more afraid

that the immense heavenly sphere would fly asunder; and as to the clouds we have only to assume that not only the earth and water, but also a considerable portion of the air rotate, whether the reason be that the lower layers, mixed with earthy and watery matter, are of the same nature as the earth, or that the friction with the earth makes the air partake of the earth's rotation."

Copernicus next asserts that the earth is not the center of all circular motions, since the planets vary in their distance from the earth. The planets do, in fact, move around the sun, and so, too, the earth. The irregularities of the movements of the planets are not real but apparent phenomena, caused by the fact that the earth itself is in motion.

Copernicus in the course of his writing proceeds to work out the revolutions of the planets on these assumptions, and rests his case on the possibility of this procedure. He does not, however, avoid the use of epicycles to account for irregularities, though he does decrease the number required for his computations. He is confronted with the difficulty, however, that his system lacks a certain harmony, since he is unable to solve the irregularities found in a single planet by two epicycles both of which can at the same time be thought of as really existent. That is, he is still forced to assume epicycles as hypothetical entities to enable him to account for exceptions in his system.

How, specifically, does the Copernican theory account for the planetary movements? Whereas Ptolemy had to place an extra circular motion or epicycle in the course of each planet, to explain their retrograde movements, Copernicus saw that these movements could be much more easily interpreted by putting a single circular motion in the path of the earth. The retrogression thus becomes an apparent one only, and is easily explained as due to the fact that the earth is at that time moving more rapidly than the planet and overtaking it.

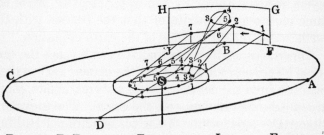

FIGURE 3. TO EXPLAIN THE FORMATION OF A LOOP IN AN EXTERIOR PLANET'S PATH

(From Todd, *New Astronomy*. American Book Company.)

Refer to the figure. The largest ellipse, ABCD, is the ecliptic. Intermediate ellipse is orbit of an exterior planet; and smallest ellipse is the path of earth itself. A planet when advancing always moves in direction GH. The sun is at S. When earth is successively at points marked 1, 2, 3, 4, 5, 6, 7, on its orbit, the outer planet is at the points marked 1, 2, 3, 4, 5, 6, 7, on the middle ellipse; so that the planet is seen projected upon the sky in the directions of the several straight lines. These intersect the zone F, G, H, J, of the celestial sphere in the points also marked upon it 1, 2, 3, 4, 5, 6, 7, and among the stars of the zodiac. Following them in order of number, it is evident that the planet advances from 1 to 3, retrogrades from 3 to 5, and advances again from 5 to 7. Also its backward motion is most rapid from 3 to 4, when the planet is near opposition, and its distance from earth is the least possible. In general, the nearer the planet to earth, the more extensive its loop.

The teachings of this sixteenth-century astronomer are often referred to as the Copernican revolution, and from them we date the birth of the modern intellectual spirit. Tremendous as was the genius involved in finding a new path through the perplexities of heavenly motions, Copernicus did not prove by any physical experiments that the earth did revolve on its axis and around the sun. His system was a brilliant hypothesis, simpler than Ptolemy's, and equally comprehensive. In this greater simplicity consists one of the chief claims of this system to scientific praise, for the scientist is constantly seeking for that explanation which will meet all the facts with the least expenditure of assumption. Besides this, his theory was confirmed by the work of his successors, Galileo, Kepler, and Newton, each of whom added new observations, and new major theories which gave greater sweep to his creation, and eliminated the exceptions which he had been unable to master. He himself had doubted, been perplexed by contradictory theories, had started to try out a new initial assumption, and had found that the superstructure reared upon it corresponded closely — though he knew that it was not exactly — to the phenomena to be explained. It was a trial of a seemingly possible shift in basic principle and an example of tireless scrutiny of the consequences. In his ability to use the great tool of astronomical theory — mathematics — he equaled, but probably did not surpass Ptolemy; but he built a new system. Ptolemy organized an old one. His main conceptions, furthermore, did, in years to come, fit into new discoveries when the assumptions of Ptolemy proved useless.

Section 6.   Why Men accept the Heliocentric Hypothesis

Although Copernicus had set up an alternative theory to the time-honored Ptolemaic description of the
solar system, and had succeeded in the main in making
it fit the observed facts about the successive positions
occupied by the heavenly bodies, he had not offered any
direct *proof* that his hypothesis was true while that of
Ptolemy was false.   Nevertheless, he was firmly convinced of its truth himself, and despite the fact that
no experimental proof was immediately forthcoming,
within the next century the Copernican theory had been
adopted by all the greatest astronomers.   Why did
these men throw overboard a firmly established theory
and adhere to a new and daring hypothesis, seemingly
utterly subversive of all that had been established in
thought, when there was actually no decisive proof that
the old theory was false or that the new theory was true?
Unless we can understand their action, and the reasons
for it, we shall not be able to understand much of that
fabric of theories and hypotheses which goes to make up
modern science.   Nearly all of the marvelous advance
we have made in solving the secrets of nature has been
due precisely to this, that scientists have preferred one
hypothesis to another, and by that preference, however
unable it may have been to justify itself immediately on
grounds of strict proof, have been led to many new discoveries of fact.

Indeed, it is not usually recognized by the layman
that even to-day it cannot be said that the Copernican
theory has, strictly speaking, been proved true.   It is
still quite possible to explain all of the observed *facts* of
astronomy by means of the Ptolemaic theory, although,

of course, that theory would have to be made much more complex by the introduction of new epicycles for each newly discovered celestial phenomenon. Nevertheless, probably no other scientific hypothesis is so universally accepted as the Copernican, and the astronomer who seriously upheld the Ptolemaic theory to-day would be regarded as an amusing crank. If this belief rests upon no conclusive proof, why do all scientists maintain it as almost axiomatic? In answering this question, we shall discover some extremely important things about the way in which the scientifically trained mind tests hypotheses.

Although Copernicus did not attempt to disprove the Ptolemaic theory, he did work long and hard to show that his new hypothesis would explain all the observable facts. Had there been any planetary motions which it could not explain, while his predecessor's theory could, obviously his theory would have been worthless. This is the first requisite of a good hypothesis, that it must be consistent with all the known facts; at least, with more of them than any rival theory. And when he had proved this of his heliocentric hypothesis, Copernicus was content to leave to others the disproof of the old theory.

Astronomers now had before them two hypotheses, both of which seemed able to account for all the observed motions of the stars. Obviously only one could be true. Either the earth, together with the other planets, went around the sun, or the sun and planets went around the earth — the motion being, of course, measured in comparison with the fixed stars. Hence astronomers, in the absence of direct proof, were forced to choose one or the other, and they chose the simpler hypothesis. The greater simplicity of the Copernican system, which in its completed form got rid of all the

epicycles built upon epicycles, made calculated predictions somewhat easier to work out; though, as a
matter of fact, the actual reckoning is carried out by
means of the same equations under either hypothesis.
But, besides the practical advantage of facilitating computation, the human mind, and perhaps especially the
mind of the scientist, feels that a simple explanation
without undue complexities, one great formula that will
comprehend an infinite series of phenomena, is more at-
tractive, more beautiful, and, other things being equal,
more apt to be true than one that is extremely involved.
Perhaps this simplicity is inherent in the nature of
things, and in seeking for it men are looking for what is a
great truth about our universe.   Many of the foremost
thinkers would agree with Sir Isaac Newton when he
says: "Nature does nothing in vain, and more is in vain
when less will serve; for Nature is pleased with simplicity, and affects not the pomp of superfluous causes." [1]
Perhaps this desire for simplicity is rather a characteristic trait of the mind of man than the result of the experience of nature; certainly with increased facilities for observation we are often forced to recognize that facts are
much more complex than we had hoped.   Whatsoever
its foundation, however, this craving for the simple is of
the utmost importance in scientific thinking.   It is generally known as the "Law of Parsimony," and can be
formulated, If two hypotheses each account equally for
all the observed facts, the simpler one — that is, the one
which makes the fewer assumptions — is to be preferred
to the more complex.   And it was largely because of
the principle so expressed that the Copernican system
gained such rapid and complete dominance.

[1] Newton, *Principia*, Book III.

Naturally, however, astronomers were eager to find some more conclusive demonstration of the correctness of the Copernican theory. Did both hypotheses explain equally all the observed facts? The apparent motions of all the members of the solar system could be calculated and predicted with almost equal facility under both theories. Could men discover certain motions in the fixed stars that would furnish a final proof? Two courses were open. One could proceed to elaborate each theory, to see what further consequences each would imply if it were true, and then to investigate whether these further consequences actually did take place. Or one could observe some new fact that could not be satisfactorily accounted for by one of the theories, and which would thus disprove it. These are the two ways in which all scientific hypotheses are subjected to scrutiny and testing. Whenever a new theory is propounded, there is carried on this double process of elaboration and development to discover its utmost possible bearings, and of constant reference to the observable facts. If it be true, then such and such things must follow. Do they? Such and such phenomena are observed. Does our theory explain them? In the natural sciences this first development is made possible largely by means of mathematical calculation. If such and such a theory is true, then these equations hold, and from them we can deduce other equations which lead to the following conclusion. If that conclusion prove correct in experiment, the original theory has been verified. In astronomy, the positions all the heavenly bodies would have to assume on the basis of the theory are calculated with great precision, and then the telescope is pointed to those spots in the sky to observe their presence or absence.

Men at once saw that if the Copernican hypothesis were correct, and the earth did revolve about the sun, the stars would have to appear in different positions when viewed from different points in the earth's orbit, just as when one walks around his dinner table the pictures upon the walls appear in different relation to each other. But no telescope in the sixteenth or seventeenth century could reveal any change in the apparent positions of the fixed stars. This objection seemed to even the great Tycho Brahe (1546–1601) irreconcilable with the heliocentric hypothesis, and he formulated a system in which, although the planets went about the sun, the sun in turn, together with the starry sphere, rotated about the earth. The upholders of Copernicus replied that the stars were so exceedingly distant that the change in position of the earth in its orbit could make no discoverable difference in their apparent positions. But the fact that if the earth did revolve the stars should change their position, however slightly, and the fact that there was no discernible change, led men to investigate with the utmost precision in the hope of establishing this conclusive proof of the heliocentric hypothesis.

It was not until 1838 that astronomical instruments became accurate enough to detect the extremely small variation in the apparent position of a star attributable to the earth's motion. In that year Bessel measured the minute orbit which the star 61 Cygni seems to describe, and since then some fifty other stars have been found near enough to the earth to be affected by her movement. In explanation of the inability of the early investigators to detect these tiny orbits, it can be said that that of 61 Cygni is as difficult to measure as a penny would be at a distance of three miles.

What had Bessel done? He had observed a fact which could be beautifully explained on the assumption that the earth moved. But could not the geocentric theory also explain such facts? Strictly speaking, it could take account of them; that is, one could still assume that the earth was immobile, but one would have to assume also that all of the stars whose displacement had been observed had an annual motion of their own, and revolved in epicycles. Why should these motions be completed in just a year if they had no connection with the earth? On the Ptolemaic theory, these facts would have been accepted as unrelated; on the Copernican, they could be explained.

Moreover, the English astronomer Bradley discovered an apparent motion in which each star participates that is attributed to the effect of the earth's motion upon the light rays. This is too complicated to explain here, but suffice it to say that these millions of movements can all be beautifully understood on Copernicus' theory, while on Ptolemy's they are only to be accepted as brute and unintelligible facts.

Had, then, the heliocentric theory been proved? In the sense in which astronomers can prove anything, yes. No one who by admitting the revolution of the earth could at one stroke understand and predict millions of other movements would refuse to admit it. Bessel's and Bradley's accomplishments were an example of the Law of Parsimony at its highest development, the summing up of innumerable hitherto unrelated phenomena in one simple formula of explanation. And since that time various other movements of the heavenly bodies have been discovered which, though theoretically admitting of explanation and calculation by the invention of millions of additional epicycles, can with infinitely greater ease and simplicity be shown to follow from the earth's revolution.   As our instruments have become more and more accurate, we have found more and more ways in which the motion of our earth affects the apparent positions of other bodies.

Can we hope to receive confirmation of the Copernican theory in any more decisive way?   Can we hope that we shall some day discover some new celestial motion that no conceivable complexity of epicycles could explain?   The mathematician tells us that we cannot, for in calculating astronomical positions we use only the algebraic functions of sine and cosine, and it can be proved mathematically that everything that can be calculated algebraically by the use of these terms can also be calculated geometrically by means of epicycles. Hence, so far as the computation of mere positions goes, Ptolemy could still, in theory, hold his own.   It is possible that some other phenomenon may be discovered that will add independent confirmation, and that we may be able to demonstrate the revolution of the earth as certainly as we can its rotation, which now is definitely established as depending upon the laws of motion, and as being false only if they are false.   Yet we must not forget that so far at least the theory of the revolution of the earth about the sun is not a fact, but an hypothesis, an inference, and that in the last analysis it rests solely upon the Law of Parsimony.

Section 7.   The Fruitful Hypothesis

There is still another most important reason for accepting the heliocentric hypothesis.   Where the geocentric theory was utterly barren, the other proved enormously fruitful. Ptolemy could always manage by inventing new epicycles to explain whatever new celestial motion might be discovered, but he could never predict beforehand that with more accurate observations men would find those irregularities. His wisdom was the wisdom that is wise after the event. He could absorb the new knowledge into his scheme, but he proved quite unable to discover any new knowledge himself. His theory gave rise to no new suggestions and hypotheses.

The Copernican theory, on the other hand, has suggested many possibilities which later have been experimentally verified. It tells us what we may expect, instead of being profoundly surprised at each new observation. It leads us on to the discovery of further knowledge. It is a signpost pointing out the road ahead, instead of a mere milestone to mark the distance already traversed. A single noteworthy example will suffice to make this difference clear.

In 1781 the planet Uranus was discovered, and after some observation its orbit was plotted and calculations as to its future position made, based upon the heliocentric theory and the gravitational theory of Newton. By 1820 there were noted discrepancies between its calculated and its observed position; by 1840 these had become intolerable. Some other element not included in the computation was affecting Uranus' motion. What would the Ptolemaic system have done in such a case? It would have recognized the fact, and added another epicycle as the explanation. What did the astronomers who adhered to the Copernican theory do? Assuming that Uranus was one of a number of planets revolving about the sun, they further assumed that the discrepan-

cies were due to the attraction of another and unknown
planet. Still working upon the heliocentric theory and
the Newtonian laws of motion, Adams and Leverrier
computed the probable course of the unknown planet if
it were to exert such force upon Uranus. When their
figuring was finished, Galle turned his telescope upon
that particular spot in the heavens, and there he beheld
a new planet, since named Neptune. There had been
made one of the most dramatic discoveries in the history
of science. What would the Ptolemaic system have
.said to the new planet? It could have proceeded to fit
it out with the requisite epicycles, when once it had been
discovered, but it could in no wise have contributed
to that discovery. It would have remained unfruitful
while its rival added directly to our knowledge.

Section 8.   The Marks of a Good Hypothesis

In the Copernican theory we thus have a scientific belief which, though not a fact, in the sense that it can be
directly ascertained by simple observation, as though
from a distant star we could actually watch the earth going round the sun, is yet as firmly established as any
scientific inference can well be. Any hypothesis in the
field of science which is distinguished from a rival hypothesis as the Copernican is marked off from the Ptolemaic theory would be regarded as equally certain and
true. Let us recapitulate those marks.

In the first place, the heliocentric theory enables us to
predict what will occur in the future with the utmost
nicety. Astronomers are able to formulate beliefs about
the movements of the heavenly bodies which are verified as completely as any in the physical sciences. Their
planetary hypothesis thus performs the essential work
of prediction for which it was devised.

Secondly, the heliocentric theory *explains* the move-ments observed among the stars as the geocentric theory does not.   It explains every cyclic motion that is com-pleted in a year as dependent upon a single simple factor, the movement of the earth.   A theory which requires a new explanation for each motion can hardly be said to explain anything at all, for it does not succeed in reduc-ing what is complex to what is more simple.   Hence, while Ptolemy could perhaps enable us to *predict* the small variations in the positions of the stars, he could never enable us to *understand* them as all following from some other occurrence.   Moreover, the simplicity re-sulting from this economy of assumption facilitates our calculations.   It also appeals to the human mind as a precious quality of intellectual beauty; were astronomy still Ptolemaic, it would probably have long since ceased to occupy the place of the most elevating of all the sci-ences.   As it is, its marvelous simplicity furnishes many with an æsthetic enjoyment unequaled in human ex-perience.

Thirdly, the heliocentric theory has proved to be highly suggestive, an opportunity rather than a com-pleted achievement.   It has proved easily congruous with other scientific discoveries, notably the whole of Newtonian mechanics.   It seems to give us a real insight into the essential structure of our planetary system, and to be, as no other system is, the key to unlock its further secrets.   If nature be the great riddle, Copernicus seems to have come very close to part of the answer.   He has found a successful key, and we cannot help but think it must be the true one.

These are the marks of a good scientific hypothesis. We have traced the way in which such theories rise and are elaborated and modified as the discovery of new facts, made possible by improved means of observations, reveals the insufficiency of the old notions. In the next chapter we shall examine more in detail the actual processes by which the scientist formulates an hypothesis, and the careful tests he has devised for guarding against the possibility of error.

QUESTIONS AND EXERCISES

1. In the last analysis by what sort of observations must any theory of planetary motion be tested?
2. Why has the classification of stars into constellations not proved fruitful? What purpose has it served?
3. Make a list of the movements of the heavenly bodies mentioned in this chapter. Indicate which are now attributed to the daily rotation of the earth, and which to the annual revolution of the earth about the sun.
4. Upon what grounds did Ptolemy believe in the immobility of the earth? Were these reasons scientific or merely fanciful?
5. Precisely what questions was Ptolemy trying to answer by his system? Did he regard astronomy as primarily a branch of mathematics or of physics?
6. Why was Aristotle's system fanciful while Ptolemy's was scientific?
7. Why did the Syrian bishop make an improper use of authority, when we consider ourselves justified in accepting the Copernican theory from the astronomers without being able to prove it ourselves?
8. Outline the stages in the thought of Copernicus in deciding for his heliocentric hypothesis.
9. What is the basic principle of the geocentric theory by means of which it can be elaborated to account for all the celestial motions? Contrast this with the basic principle of the heliocentric system.
10. What tests did Copernicus' theory have to meet before it could be regarded as definitely established?
11. In just what way is Copernicus' theory simpler than Ptolemy's?
12. Of what value is simplicity as a criterion of a good hypothesis? Under what conditions may it be employed? Can you suggest any dangers in its use? Give an example.
13. In verifying the heliocentric theory, what use was made of the tool of mathematics? What part did the invention of more accurate instruments of observation play?
14. Make a list of the several superiorities of the Copernican and the Ptolemaic hypothesis. Take some other scientific hypothesis and show how it fulfills all these conditions.

15. Outline the stages of the process of thinking by which Adams and Leverrier discovered Neptune. Why could Neptune not have been so discovered had they worked on the Ptolemaic hypothesis? What further knowledge was necessary?
16. In what sense has the Ptolemaic hypothesis never been absolutely disproved? What would be necessary to do so?

BIBLIOGRAPHY

Historical:
J. L. E. Dreyer, *Planetary Systems*.   Cambridge University Press, 1906.
A. Berry, *Short History of Astronomy*.   Charles Scribner's Sons, 1910.
R. F. Moulton, *Introduction to Astronomy*.   The Macmillan Company, 1906.
D. P. Todd, *New Astronomy*.   American Book Company, 1897.
H. Jacoby, *Astronomy*.   The Macmillan Company, 1915.
For general position taken, see Mach, *Science of Mechanics*, page 232. Open Court, 1892.
On Hypothesis: See logic textbooks mentioned in Bibliography to Chapter II.

CHAPTER IV

THE METHODS OF EXPERIMENTAL SCIENCE: THE DISCOVERY OF CAUSAL RELATIONS IN BIOLOGY

Section 1. The Significance of Causal Relations

"Happy is the man who knows the causes of things," says the poet, and it is precisely this understanding which has seemed to many to be the fulfillment of all intellectual endeavor. To know the causes of things and their effects is to gain a sense of security in the fuller comprehension of past events, and the power of envisaging and perhaps guiding them in the future.

We have seen how the scientist in the field of medicine gains an understanding of his subject by observing certain fundamental similarities in the cases which he is called upon to treat, and how the astronomer advances by considering the relation of numerous celestial changes to some significant occurrence in the heavens. But it was clear that the purpose of the physician and the astronomer is not merely to observe symptoms and events, or even to relate them to other happenings by pointing out resemblances or temporal sequences.

For when we speak of diagnosis and of the construction of an hypothesis, we are really concerned with what caused the appearance of certain symptoms and what effect a definite remedy will have, or we inquire into the cause of a comet's path and the effects of the sun's position. If we know the answers to questions such as these, we have truly penetrated deep into the mysteries of nature. When we realize what is meant by these

terms "cause" and "effect," we shall see why the discovery of causal relationships in different fields of knowledge is so important a step in scientific progress.

The usefulness of this discovery is apparent in the process of verification which we noted as being an important
step in our analysis of a typical act of reflective thinking. It is in this connection especially that we shall
study the meaning of scientific experimentation. We
shall have occasion to notice that experimentation is
not, what it so frequently seems to the uninitiated to be—
fooling in a more or less haphazard way with a variety
of materials; but that it is, commonly, the method by
which the scientist tests the validity of an hypothesis
formulated in accordance with the principles studied in
the last chapter. Having been led by observation and
analysis to the tentative opinion that certain facts or
events are the results of other facts or events, he sets to
work to test this opinion. In doing this he relies, as has
been said, chiefly on the above-mentioned conceptions
of "cause" and "effect."

Though these conceptions are useful in all fields, it is
perhaps evident that they are more readily applied in
some than in others. You can more easily explain the
cause of a severe headache than the cause of your affection for a dear friend. It is simpler to discover the
cause of the failure of your vegetable garden to yield all
that you had hoped for than to find the cause of widespread business depression. Just what we mean when
we say that the cause of the headache was that extra cup
of coffee, or that the garden's failure was the effect of insufficient rain, we shall have an opportunity to inquire
later on. For the present, however, let us note that the
establishment of causal relationships is easier in some

cases than in others. Superficially it may appear, and it has often been said, that it depends to a great extent on the degree of complexity of the objects whose relationship we happen to be studying. There is some basis for this explanation, however partial it be; though one may question whether to some extent those things which we understand do not therefore seem simple, whereas those which we fail to comprehend seem complex. In any case we are forced to realize that we do know more about the causes of electricity than about the causes of life, that the effects of sulphuric acid on zinc are better understood than are the effects of fright on an immature mind.

However complex or simple these several relationships may be, our greater knowledge of some than of others undoubtedly depends to a very large extent on our ability to demonstrate and test out our judgments about these relationships. When we can provide for the repetition of an event, such as the reaction of zinc to an acid, under controlled conditions, we can gain a greater understanding of what is taking place than when our powers of observation are restricted as in the case of psychological influences. By means of experimental investigation, our preliminary observations, even in very complex fields, are improved and corrected, and, as we perfect our methods of studying these subjects, we may reasonably hope to learn more about them, even about such complex subjects as the nature of life and the factors in mental development. The advance in various sciences has depended largely on the discovery of more applicable methods of experimentation whereby various theories might be tested and further facts secured for their subsequent elaboration.

In the following sections we shall trace the history of the biologist's efforts to understand certain events; namely, the processes by which the individuals of various species are generated. Are they all brought into the world by well-definable methods of reproduction, as the offspring of creatures similar to themselves? Or are they the unaccountable, spontaneous products of a form of nature fundamentally different from themselves? Questions such as these long puzzled the biologist. How were they to be answered?

Section 2.   "Spontaneous Generation" as the Origin of Life

The natural scientist has always recognized that in most instances organisms are propagated by parents similar to the offspring. Another mode of generation, however, was formerly widely believed in. "Heterogenesis," the creation of a living organism out of inorganic matter, was generally accepted as another method. Animals as high in the scale of life as the frog were thought of as being in some cases the product of spontaneous generation. Eels were said to have come into being suddenly from the slimy ooze of the river Nile, and caterpillars and many insects were supposed to be the spontaneous product of the leaves on which they fed. A formula for creating mice was even suggested; and it was shown that they could be procured by putting grains of wheat with some dirty linen in a receptacle, whereupon the mice would presently appear. Decaying meat was regarded especially as a source of spontaneous generation of living matter. Worms and maggots were supposed to find their origin in putrefying flesh.

An Italian, Francesco Redi, in the seventeenth cen-

heterogenesis = creation of a living organism out of inorganic matter

spontaneous generation = something from nothing

tury, disproved the truth of this last example. He placed the meat in a receptacle over which he fastened a paper cover. The meat yielded no products. Changing the cover, he put gauze over the meat through which the odor of the flesh could rise. Flies were attracted to it, laid their eggs on the gauze, and these developed upon it instead of on the meat. By such simple experiments as this the theory of spontaneous generation gradually lost ground and might well have been vanquished altogether but for the invention of the microscope.

It is a curious fact, not without parallel in other cases, that the development of this instrument led temporarily to the revival of an erroneous theory. The microscope, which has in so many directions advanced our understanding of the world of nature, was the immediate cause of the revival of the theory of heterogenesis, for by its aid there were discovered innumerable tiny organisms invisible to the naked eye, but which lived and had their being and could now be observed. These microorganisms, it was said, came spontaneously into being in any liquid, however free it had been from these infusions previously. For this reason these organisms were given the name of "Infusoria." The liquids in which these animalculæ were generated were spoken of as "putrescible."

Many experiments were performed by the defenders of the theory of spontaneous generation to show that previously sterile water generated life in this way and possessed "vegetative force." The question was the subject of endless debate and much abstract speculation. The doctrine of spontaneous generation, mysterious though it was, appealed to simplicity-loving minds, and the opposing views found it well-nigh impossible to substitute a convincing explanation. Moreover, the heterogenists pointed with assurance to innumerable "men of genius" from Aristotle down who had accepted their opinion. They regarded as ridiculous and fantastic any effort to discover how the swarm of minute creatures disclosed by the microscope could have entered the medium in which they were found. And they spoke with such assurance and conviction, and with such an array of erudition, that they seemed to carry the day by sheer enthusiasm. An earlier defender of the theory had written that "to question this view is to question reason, sense and experience"; and the new converts to the doctrine failed to realize that that is precisely what wisdom demands that we should do. Many ingenious systems, such as that of Buffon, were set forth, and new and elaborate terminologies were invented to describe the phenomena: a frequent but a poor way to explain things.

What was most needful was a mind which would frankly face the problem, locate the difficulty, and suggest some natural hypothesis susceptible of proof or disproof. What conditions are necessary before these living beings can appear? That question had to be answered. But the opposing theorists failed to suggest any method of testing their conclusions. Indeed, every one seemed to secure the very results which he had anticipated and desired. And when an opponent offered contrary testimony, his "error" could readily be assigned to special causes of which he had failed to take account.

Section 3. Pasteur's Investigations into the Origin of Living Beings

It remained for a patient and open-minded investigator to make a fresh start, to state his problem as simply as possible, to consider the implications of his statement, and to examine each of these in order to see which were relevant to the question and which were not. It was the great French biologist, Louis Pasteur, who in 1860 set about this laborious task. Not neglecting the testimony of the past, but refusing to accept without scrutiny the opinions even of "men of genius," he was not afraid to consider any theory, however "ridiculous or fantastic" it might at first appear. Above all he conscientiously avoided jumping to conclusions; for whereas, as he himself stated, it was impossible not to lean to some theory, he endeavored to hold it in suspended judgment and, "while marching forward to establish some new facts, sought arguments against himself and turned back to strengthen points which seemed yet weak."[1]

"Can matter organize itself? Can living beings come into the world without having been preceded by beings similar to them?" Thus he stated his problem. Locating the question more definitely, he asked himself whence the minute organisms which the microscope disclosed in previously sterile liquids had come. Can these have come in from the air, and if so can they be there discovered? If such germs exist in the atmosphere, it should be possible to gather them from it, and to this attempt Pasteur first addressed himself. By drawing a current of air through a cotton filter, he found deposited on the latter germs and spores like those under consid-

[1] Vallery-Radot, *Life of Pasteur*, p. 99.

eration. Had he then proved his point?   No, for the cotton was itself an organic substance, and might therefore have given rise to these organic particles. Pasteur substituted a mineral filter, asbestos, for the cotton, and again an air current left its deposit!

But the heterogenists were ready with another objection. If these germs exist in the air, they asked, why is the atmosphere not clouded with them, or are they, perchance, unevenly distributed, being thick at one point and rare at another?   Such an arrangement seemed utterly ridiculous.   But while they laughed, Pasteur set about his investigations, using specimens of air in different places to discover whether their effects were indeed uniform or different. In the streets of Paris, in his cellar laboratory, in country fields, and on Alpine glaciers Pasteur performed his tests.   The results varied greatly, and upon completing these investigations he was led to formulate his belief that "the dusts suspended in atmospheric air are the exclusive origin, the necessary condition of life in infusions."

How could Pasteur justify so daring an hypothesis? Up to this point he had, as we have seen, merely discovered that the germs which he was studying could be found in the atmosphere, and this in varying degree. But, granting that the air contained germs, could it be shown that these invariably came from the air?   Predecessors of Pasteur had attempted to boil "putrescible" liquids in closed tubes, and had thus succeeded in destroying the living organisms which they contained. But their opponents insisted that the excessive heat had also changed the "vegetative force" of the fluids.   How could Pasteur demonstrate that the air was the cause of the appearance of life in previously sterilized water without apparently impairing the liquid and thus introducing a new and perplexing problem?

He did it by taking liquids sterilized in each case by the same method and showing that organic life appeared in certain flasks and not in others. Here is his own description of the experiment:

I place a portion of the infusion into a flask with a long neck. . . . Suppose I boil the liquid and leave it to cool. After a few days mouldiness or animalculæ will develop in the liquid. By boiling I destroyed any germs in the liquid or against the glass; but that infusion being again in contact with air, it becomes altered as all infusions do. Now suppose I repeat this experiment, but that before boiling the liquid I draw the neck of the flask into a point, leaving, however, its extremity open. . . . Now the liquid of this second flask will remain pure. . . . What difference is there between these two vases? . . . The only difference between them is this: in the first case the dusts suspended in air and their germs can fall into the neck of the flask and come into contact with the liquid, where they find appropriate food and develop. Thence microscopic beings. In the second flask, on the contrary, it is impossible, or at least extremely difficult, unless air is violently shaken, that dusts suspended in air should enter the vase. They fall on its curved neck.

This experiment is full of instruction. For this must be noticed, that everything in air save its dusts can easily enter the vase and come in contact with the liquid. . . . Only one thing cannot enter easily, and that is dusts suspended in air. And the proof of this is, that if I shake the vase violently two or three times in a few days it contains animalculæ or mouldiness. Why? Because air has come in violently enough to carry dust with it.

Could the heterogenists maintain that some of this liquid had "vegetative force" which had been destroyed in the other flasks? Clearly not, for the liquid was identical in all cases. The only varying factor was the dust-

laden air which was introduced in some and kept out of
others, the former of which produced organic beings,
while the latter remained sterile.

We have here the secret of Pasteur's method.   He
carefully controlled his conditions so that each factor
could be considered.   If the only changed condition
was the change of atmosphere, then that change was, beyond peradventure, to be regarded as the cause of the
varying results.   Moreover, as this precondition varied,
the consequences varied similarly.   The clear light of
analysis had been thrown on the situation, and had revealed the origin of the living organisms.

It may be noted that this discovery of Pasteur's
yielded far-reaching and significant results.   His own
work was to apply his new knowledge to the study of
ferments, and these also he showed to be living beings,
not yielded spontaneously as a matter of accident, but
the product of entirely natural and controllable processes.   The tremendous progress in the investigation of
disease which the last half-century has witnessed followed this work, with the isolation of specific germs and
the consequent discovery of remedies.   In two instances,
anthrax and smallpox, Pasteur himself was the pathfinder, but other scientists of all nations followed his
lead.   The marvelous advance in surgery and in methods of sterilization associated with the name of Lord
Lister, all owe their inspiration to this beginning.

What had Pasteur proved?   Before we go on to review in greater detail the processes by which he reached
his conclusions, it is important to stop and consider precisely what the results of his tests were.   All too frequently at the conclusion of an argument it is by no
means clear what has been proven.   All too often the re-

sults of even a valid proof are vitiated by attempting to make it signify more than it really does. You prove that a man is thoroughly honest, which fact, if his good name has been questioned, may be a very important thing to do, and you thereupon jump to the conclusion that he would make an excellent club treasurer, which requires other qualifications in addition to honesty. Or you insist that you have symptoms of typhoid fever, which should, of course, require careful treatment and examination, and you argue that it is therefore quite proper for you to be with your favorite brother who has the disease, since exposure will no longer endanger you.

It is therefore desirable for us to ask: What had Pasteur proved? Had he proved that all life is the effect of previous life, that "biogenesis" is universal and always has been? This view is held by numerous scientists, who either take an agnostic position as to the ultimate origin of life on earth, or hold that living organisms were "created" at the same time as the inorganic world, or suggest that living cells drifted to the earth on "solar dust" from some other world where life existed previously. But whichever of these views be valid or false, Pasteur's investigations do not prove their truth or their falsity. Nor did he prove that life was always the result of earlier life — though he did show that this was the case in those many instances where his opponents had advanced the occult explanation of "spontaneous generation." He did not even demonstrate that organisms could not be produced synthetically from inorganic substances, or that this process was not taking place continually on this planet under favorable conditions. These questions remain to be answered. But Pasteur did prove beyond peradventure that the living micro-organisms which he was studying, like other organisms with which we are familiar, had definite life histories, specific modes of generation; that their presence was not due to unforeseeable, uncontrollable, mysterious processes, but that they were the offspring of parents similar to themselves which floated on the dusts of the air and were thus introduced into previously sterile liquids. We have seen how this discovery made possible an understanding of the processes on which the appearance of these bacteria and similar organisms depend, and their increased control and uses. But, of course, though we speak of Pasteur's proof of the nature and activity of these creatures, he had really only demonstrated certain facts concerning particular individual representatives of this type. What justified him in assuming that they were truly representative, and in proceeding from the facts which he had observed to the generalized statement which made these facts significant?

Section 4. The Experimental Methods

It is this process whereby the investigator is enabled to go from the restricted individual case which he has studied to a generalized conclusion concerning all such cases, which we must now consider in detail.   This transition from particular facts to a general knowledge about these facts is known as the "process of induction."   It is, of course, involved in other stages of reflection which we have studied in earlier chapters.   It assists the diagnostician in determining what facts it is important for him to observe and in classifying those facts.   The tremendous advance from collected data to an hypothesis about these facts has itself sometimes been referred to as the "inductive leap," and it is indeed

an enormous "jump."   And again, as we have seen in
the case of Pasteur, the experimental scientist endeavors to perform certain tests which will lead him to verify
his hypothesis by linking it close to the facts which
he wishes to comprehend.   Thus the whole system of
reflective thinking is an almost continuous process forward and back from the facts to be explained to the hypothesis or theory which embraces them.   In this way
the mind of an intelligent man is forever turning from
the things which he observes to a fuller understanding
of these things, from his theory back to the facts which
are illuminated and clarified thereby.   In studying
these processes of reciprocal reference from hypothesis
to experience and from experience to a more adequately
established theory, we will consider the widely used
methods of experimental science.

What, then, is the significance of those methods so
fruitfully employed by the experimental scientist?
How can he safely go from his observations to his generalizations?   How could Pasteur, on the basis of a few
selected experiments, say that these proved that micro-
organisms did not appear in "putrescible" liquids as an
effect of the "vegetative force" of these liquids, but that
their appearance was caused by the introduction and
propagation of germs carried as floating matter in the
air?

Let us see first what determines the selection of certain experiments as being crucial and convincing.   A
plausible hypothesis has arisen in the mind of the investigator: what experiments shall he perform to test it?
Clearly he will not manipulate his materials at random,
he will not use the primitive, "monkeying," method of
trial and error.   He will rather consider just what will

prove or disprove his hypothesis. "If I am right," Pasteur in effect said to himself, "then, whenever the germ-bearing atmospheric dusts are present, micro-organisms will propagate in these liquids; whenever they are not present, the liquids will remain sterile. I must try it out to see if this is the case."

What is needed in all such cases is a full analysis of the circumstances under consideration. The investigator requires an exhaustive list of all the factors which may possibly be determining the processes which he is study-ing. How inclusive this list must be in order to be re-garded as genuinely exhaustive of all the possibilities, it is difficult to say. Much will inevitably depend on the skill of the investigator and on the obscurity of the events which he is analyzing. The hope held forth by Bacon in his *Novum Organum* of a "fool-proof" method which would "leave little to the acuteness and strength of wit" of the investigator seems to overlook the fact that in the enumeration of factors to be considered the training and insight of the scientist are of the greatest importance. It is evident that a really complete enu-meration of all the circumstances involved would be beyond attainment. Indeed when we stop to consider that the purpose of such an enumeration is to make pos-sible the testing of these various factors and the elim-ination of those which are definitely not operative, we see that a list, unnecessarily long, would by no means be desirable. The methods which we are about to study serve to suggest what factors may be regarded as espe-cially significant, and, when the situation has been sub-jected to this analysis, to make possible the elimination of those which in all probability are not the cause or causes sought.

This analysis is the basis of all experimentation: if this fact a is really the cause of this event b, then we must try to see if whenever a occurs b inevitably also occurs, and if whenever a is absent b fails to occur. It must be borne in mind that, whereas a and b are simple symbols, the events which they signify are complex and involved. Thus it is by no means an easy thing to discern the cause a. What we see is rather a total situation a, of which some aspect or part, a_1, a_2, a_3, . . . may be the significant factor. It is therefore essential that our enumeration of these parts be adequate so as to include the relevant factor a in the total situation. The methods which are to be discussed aim to identify this factor. An extended analysis of this basis of the methodology of experiment has been made by the British philosopher, John Stuart Mill, and we shall follow his classic discussion.[1] He distinguishes five methods which he found in actual use among men of science, and summarizes them in five famous "Canons." [2]

[1] J. S. Mill, *System of Logic*, Book 3.

[2] A familiar device by which to illustrate symbolically the use of the various experimental methods is seen in the following scheme:

If a set of circumstances a, b, c, d is followed by the result R, and another set of circumstances a, x, y, z is followed by the result R, then the circumstance a is causally related to the result R. This represents the Method of Agreement.

Similarly, if a, b, c, d, e, ... R
and a, c, d, e, ...
then the circumstance b is causally related to the result R.

                                     (Method of Difference.)

Likewise, if a, b, c, d, ... R
and a, m, n, d, ... R
                   a, p, q, d, ... R
                   a, x, y, d, ... R
then both a and d seem to be related to R.

But if a, e, f, g, ...
                   h, i, j, k, ...
                   a, r, s, t, ...
then not a but d is causally related to R.   (Joint Method.)

1. The Canon of the Method of Agreement is stated by Mill in this way: *If two or more instances of the phenomenon under investigation have only one circumstance in common, the circumstance in which alone all the instances agree is the cause of the given phenomenon*. This has been more simply, though negatively, stated by a recent writer,[1] who says that "Nothing is the cause of a phenomenon in the absence of which it nevertheless occurs." Let us, in order to understand the uses and implications of this method, see how it was applied in Pasteur's work.

When his opponents objected that the filter used by Pasteur was itself an "organic" substance, and might therefore produce the micro-organisms, he simply changed the nature of filter substance, using the mineral asbestos. The point of this change was, of course, that the material used for the filter was irrelevant and was not the cause of the germs which appeared on it, but that the atmospheric dusts which were caught by either filter were the cause. Again, in the subsequent experiments Pasteur held that if the germs were produced when the dust-laden air was brought in contact with the liquids, and if no other factors were common to all cases, the air or some factor connected with the air would be shown to be the cause of the appearance of the living beings.

We must recognize that the strict requirements of this method were not, and really could not be, observed in either of these instances. Many other factors were common to all tests in addition to the condition of the air. In a sense it may, indeed, be questioned whether this method can ever be employed with absolute precision.

[1] H. W. B. Joseph, *Introduction to Logic*, p. 403.

For will not some feature remain common to any test, some feature which just because it is so common escapes attention and is nevertheless of great importance? For example, the effects of gravitation are constantly present, and the success of numerous investigations has been seriously impaired by the failure to take this into account as a common factor in the several instances. However, though we must remember these deficiencies in the application of the method of agreement, its practical usefulness in suggesting a solution when the common factor is somewhat unusual and in the elimination of supposed "causes" (the cotton filter, for instance) is very great. Whereas it cannot prove what is the cause of a phenomenon, it can be used to show that certain assumed "causes" are not genuinely so. Other difficulties which the method of agreement shares, more or less, with the other experimental methods will be noted below.

2. The second method, called by Mill the "Method of Difference," is rather more readily applicable to the laboratory conditions of experimental investigation. Mill phrased the canon of this method thus: *If an instance in which the phenomenon under investigation occurs and an instance in which it does not occur, have every circumstance in common save one, that one occurring only in the former; the circumstance in which alone the two instances differ is the effect, or the cause, or an indispensable part of the cause of the phenomenon.* Again, to cite a simpler expression of this method phrased negatively, it may be said that "nothing is the cause of a phenomenon in whose presence the phenomenon fails to occur."

It is this test which the experimenter uses when, carefully controlling the conditions of his investigation, he seeks to eliminate some supposedly significant factor in order to see precisely what influence this will have on the whole procedure.   In the case of Pasteur's researches, we saw how he prepared a series of vessels under identical conditions filled with the same sterilized liquid, but constructed so that the air could enter some, but not the others.   The fact that the bacteria subsequently appeared in the former and not in the latter (or in the latter only after air had been forcibly injected by shaking) justified the conclusion that the circumstance in which alone the two sets differed — i.e., the entry of the air — was the cause of the varying result.

It might, of course, be objected that the two sets of flasks were not, and could not possibly be, absolutely alike in all circumstances save the one referred to.   No two things can be identical in this sense; the flasks stood in slightly different positions; they were not filled at precisely the same moment nor in just the same manner; they were not originally manufactured in exactly the same way, and so forth.   Of course we would be inclined to dismiss all of these "differences" as unimportant and inessential, and in the case at hand this would undoubtedly be justified.   Nevertheless, it is important to note that, just as in the case of the method of agreement it was seen to be well-nigh impossible to secure instances which had only one factor in common, so in the use of this second method it is exceedingly difficult to obtain cases differing in only a single circumstance.   Very often these minor differences may be disregarded as irrelevant, but in this, as in other matters, what at one time seemed irrelevant has sometimes been shown later to be really significant, and the cautious scientist will bear this in mind.

3. In order to eliminate as far as possible these practical difficulties, Mill combined these two methods so that the logical conclusiveness of the Method of Difference might be combined with the practical availability of the Method of Agreement. The canon of the Joint Method seems somewhat alarmingly involved, but to those who understand the Methods of Agreement and Difference, the advantage to be gained by their joint use will become apparent. *If two or more instances in which the phenomenon occurs have only one circumstance in common, while two or more instances in which it does not occur have nothing in common save the absence of that circumstance, the circumstance in which alone the two sets differ is the effect, or the cause, or an indispensable part of the cause of the phenomenon.*

The obvious difficulties of this rule are not confined to its involved phraseology. As the above-mentioned critic points out,[1] "it would be better if for 'the circumstance in which alone the two sets of instances differ' we read 'the circumstance in which alone the second set of instances agrees to differ from the first set.'" As may be seen by reference to the symbolic representation cited above,[2] as well as to the illustrations given below, the method is useful in those cases where several factors are common to a set of instances in which the same result occurs. The elimination of certain of these factors is made possible by the discovery of cases in which they are present without bringing about this result.

Take the instance cited in applying the Method of Agreement. We there saw that, by changing the nature of the filter from cotton to asbestos, Pasteur had indicated that the nature of the filter did not matter. We

---

[1] Joseph, *op. cit.*, p. 399, footnote.　　[2] Cf. footnote, page 77 above.

realized, however, that this introduction of the air was
not the only factor common to the two cases; that many
circumstances, such as the presence of the same investigator, of the force of gravitation, of a specific temperature, atmospheric moisture, and the like, were shared by
the two tests.   Could any of them be the cause of the
appearance of the germs?   We shall have occasion later
on to ask ourselves this question in a somewhat different
context.   For the present let us note how, by supple-
menting the use of the Method of Agreement by the introduction of the Method of Difference, it could easily
be shown that none of the above-mentioned factors was
the cause.   It was simply necessary to show that in
many instances where these factors were present, even
if others in addition to the dust-carrying air were not,
the germs did not appear.

   To clarify further the use of the Joint Method, as well
as because it is frequently employed in investigations
such as this, it is desirable to present another illustration,
this time one not taken from the laboratory.   Preven-
tive medicine finds it necessary not only to cure the sick
and to prevent contagion, but also if possible to protect
the healthy from the exposure which caused the original
cases.   It is therefore important to discover how the
sick persons were infected.   In a given town, let us say,
several cases of anthrax have occurred.   What was the
cause?   The health department will inquire about the
habits and recent activities of the various patients.   All
are women and almost all are employed in the same location.   But so are many others who were not infected.
Several are in a brush factory, but then others who also
have the disease are not.   What we must find, if that be
possible, is some circumstance common to all the cases,

which distinguishes them from all persons not infected. This factor is finally found to be that they all purchased a certain cheap grade of fur which they have been wearing and which has infected them; whereas the other women of the town had nothing in common which might have been connected with the disease, save the fact that none of them had worn the furs. Of course, in actual experience the lines may never be so sharply drawn. Some women may have bought fur pieces and avoided infection by reason of greater resistance, or other modifying conditions may have entered. However, the method is effectively employed, though complete precision is impossible. It depends on discovering all the cases united by some common circumstances, and then eliminating other factors also common to them, by discovering that these latter are not actually productive of the results in other cases where they are present.

4. It may not always be possible to find instances in which a phenomenon is totally absent. To cover cases of this kind Mill distinguished a fourth method, the Method of Concomitant Variations, depending on the fact that *Whatever phenomenon varies in any manner whenever another phenomenon varies in some particular manner, is either a cause or an effect of that phenomenon, or is connected with it through some fact of causation.* It will be recalled that Pasteur, in considering the effects of the dusts of the air, took specimens in various places, in the city, in rural districts, even on remote Alpine glaciers. Certain of these specimens, he found, were purer than others in respect to their micro-organic contents. Moreover, the degree of concentration of these germs corresponded to the relative purity of the air in the dif-

ferent localities. Inasmuch as this variation of the atmospheric dust was the only "significant" circumstance which was changed in the different tests, the Method of Concomitant Variations is really a refined use of the Method of Difference. Where the corresponding variations can be quantitatively measured, this method gives striking results.[1] Where such a factor as a specific change in temperature gives rise to corresponding changes, let us say, in the degree of vitality of the organisms affected by these altered conditions, the relationship becomes all the more apparent. This relationship is not necessarily uniform throughout the scale of temperature; there may be no effect apparent for a wide range, but below a certain degree and above another temperature, definite effects will be noticeable and therefore assignable to these heat conditions. Clearly it is not necessary that, as one circumstance increases in quantity or intensity, the other should do the same. Where the one increases while the other diminishes, or whenever there is any proportionate variation between two or more phenomena, especially if a quantitative ratio is discoverable, one is justified in concluding that this relationship is not accidental, but is due to a causal connection.

5. The fifth and last method defined by Mill was called by him the Method of Residues: *Subduct from any phenomenon such part as is known by previous inductions to be the effect of certain antecedents, and the residue of the phenomenon is the effect of the remaining antecedents.* The number of instances in which one can assign to their precise causes all the conditions of a case except the one under investigation, and thereby isolate

[1] Cf. Joule's experiments described in chap. vi, and also section 4, chap. x.

the previously unknown cause of this particular condition, seems exceedingly rare. But such approximate omniscience is not really required for the useful application of the Method of Residues. In practice it is the method which we continually employ when some new and unusual circumstance arises in an otherwise familiar situation. You come into your room and find your desk in total disorder; you hear the sound of a gun in a usually quiet forest — and in either instance you associate these events not with any normal circumstances, but with some happening which you had not previously attended to — say, the stranger who passed you in the hallway or the new campers who pitched their tents recently by the lakeside. Just so the scientist, who in pursuing his investigations discovers some unexpected circumstance, reconsiders and re-analyzes the conditions under which they arose to find the neglected factor which had caused them. It may be seen that this method is rather of service in improving the observation of a case, and its complete diagnosis, than in actually verifying an hypothesis. In this sense the Method of Residues is to be regarded as being comparable to a total consideration and analysis of the problem under investigation, rather than as a testing of those factors which have been enumerated as being relevant to the situation. Such a testing, by means of one or more of the methods previously considered, must follow an application of this analysis. Nevertheless, its usefulness and significance must not be underestimated. Indeed, some of the most magnificent discoveries in the history of scientific research depended on investigations guided by this type of reasoning, as, for example, the dramatic discovery of the planet Neptune. Such a discovery is then tested out by one of the previously mentioned inductive methods; that is, having been led by the Method of Residues to ask whether the desk was rifled by a burglar, the shot fired by a camper, or the planet Uranus diverted from its course by the influence of the planet Neptune, we seek to verify these judgments by employing one of the other methods of proof.

Having considered these methods which the investigator uses in his attempts to validate some general hypothesis concerning a phenomenon, by reference to the precise conditions involved in any such case, indicating how he shall control the factors of his experiment, and what tests will be significant and convincing, it is now necessary to mention briefly the difficulties attending these steps. These difficulties are not restricted to any one or another of the particular methods, but are involved in any effort to discover the causal relationship between objects or events, and in the very concept of what a cause is.

Let us start by considering a practical difficulty which might actually arise if some student were to attempt to reproduce Pasteur's experiments. He would expose his flasks to the air, set them aside for a while to allow the germs to multiply, and then study the infusion under his microscope. His results, we feel confident, should conform to those of Pasteur. But supposing that he had neglected to consider with sufficient care the nature of the liquid in his flasks. If this liquid contained even a comparatively small amount of alcohol, or a strong salt solution, his results would be very different from those expected. To be sure, the bacteria would have presumably entered the exposed flasks, but the germicide present in the liquid would have killed them and prevented their reproduction in sufficient numbers to be readily observable.

Shall we, then, be forced to conclude that, to some extent at least, Pasteur's opponents were right in claiming that the liquids employed were the causes of the life which arose in them? And if that is true, is it not equally proper to claim that decaying meat is the cause of the appearance of worms and maggots, and linen and corn the cause of mice? Are we justified in merely replying to these questions that we can now easily show, by the use of our inductive methodology, that none of these are the true causes of the life which arises in them since the organisms can arise even in their absence? The one thing necessary, we would say, is that the parent organism should be given an opportunity to generate its offspring, and it therefore is the real cause of the resulting life.

If, however, certain other favorable conditions in addition to the mere presence of the parent organisms are necessary, are they not also causally related to the effects which are produced? Moreover, we must go on to consider other factors which have determined the possibility of these events. All the environmental conditions which made it possible for the creature to thrive and to develop seem to enter into the field of consideration, all the long history of the individual and of its species; indeed, it is difficult to decide where to stop. All these innumerable factors and circumstances, it would appear, had their share in shaping the course of events in such a way that this particular object which we are studying could appear in precisely the manner in which it does appear. Are all of these contributing conditions to be viewed as the causes of the phenomenon? Surely that depends on precisely what we mean by "a cause."

Section 5.   What is a Cause?

If a boulder is rolled down a hill, it may crush flowers, break down a fence, and kill a snail. Though we speak of the destruction done as being caused by the boulder, yet we recognize that the presence of the flowers, of the fence, and of the snail were also causes, and the absence of a man may have been the cause of his not being killed. To this we may add as causes, in other senses, the slope of the hillside and the youngster who pushed the stone, gravity, and probably a variety of other influences.

Indeed, in common language we not infrequently use the word "cause" to designate any particular type of explanation. If we hear cries in an adjoining room, we might say, "What is the cause of the disturbance?" Various answers might be given to such a question. Since what is really desired is an explanation, we might say that a child had been the cause of the noise, or we might specify the physiological organs which had been instrumental in producing the outcry. Or we might say that neglect had been the cause, meaning thereby that the child's distress could have been prevented through adequate care. Or we might say that milk had been the cause, meaning that it was the object, conscious or unconscious, which was being demanded.

The philosopher Aristotle presented a classification of possible uses of the term "cause." Taking as an example a wooden statue, he showed that a sculptor might be the cause of a figure, or that the idea in the sculptor's mind might be the cause, or that the wood might be the cause, or else the desire of the artist to honor Hermes. From one point of view none of these factors may be regarded as genuinely being the cause of the artistic product, since any one of them might be present without actually producing the particular effect. And that, as we have seen, is precisely what is demanded of a *bona fide* cause, using it in the strict sense. The whole situation, then, would be the cause, or that aspect of it which inevitably yielded the effect. But can we speak of a total situation in precisely that way, and, if so, where shall we stop? Shall we not be obliged to consider the muscles of the sculptor's arm, the descent of the artist, the forest in which the tree was cut, etc.? And will this not take us to the consideration of some First Cause which accounts for all of that? Very often interesting questions of very different types draw us into the same predicament. So the child questions its parent, asking, "Who made the flowers?" "Who made the mountains and the valleys?" Thus Napoleon sought to refute an atheistic general by pointing to the starry heavens asking him, "Who created the spacious firmament?"

Astronomy offers no reply to this last question, and, indeed, science has no answer to any of these queries when phrased in this way. The botanist explains the flower by pointing to the seed; the geologist finds in meteorological changes the explanation which he seeks for the contour of the land. If we ask who made an automobile or a clock, we may discover the manufacturer of either. But science offers no analogy to disclose the origin of the natural product as was disclosed in the origin of the human product by the man who made it. Though the idea of cause leads us to consider a total situation and all that lies back of it, science is satisfied in finding not a Cause, but many causes.

To claim that any of the above suggested uses of the word "cause" are improper or incorrect would be unjustifiable, but at the same time we must clearly recognize that for scientific purposes the term has a restricted and specific implication. What the scientist seeks are the proximate, not the ultimate, preconditions of the event which he is studying. He is searching for certain natural patterns or ways in which things hang together which will increase his understanding of the event. But before we ask more definitely what the function and characteristics of this understanding are, it will be well to note again the outstanding features of these patterns, these causal sequences which lead to it.

The general scheme of causal relationship has been phrased: "Whenever things occur in certain relations to each other, then a thing having a fixed relation to these things will occur at a date fixed relatively to their dates." [1] You hit one billiard ball with your cue and, if your aim is good, it will presently move another in a definite path. You expose a liquid to the dusts of the air and, unless some other counteracting cause interferes, micro-organisms will shortly be discernible in it. Moreover, we feel certain that, other things being equal, this always has been and always will be possible.

What does this mean? The great skeptic, David Hume, claimed that, when two events are causally related, all that we really know about them is "that they are contiguous in time and space and that the object we call cause precedes what we call effect," or at least comes along with it. Is a causal relationship, then, nothing more than invariable succession? The spokes of a wheel succeed one another and always in the same order, so that if the process continued without end, an observer might be led to believe that Spoke A caused

[1] Bertrand Russell, *Scientific Method in Philosophy*, p. 210.

Spoke B to follow it. If, however, the wheel were to stop turning, he would find that no such causation actually took place; although the movement of the spokes is causally connected, that connection consists in a common relation to a third factor of which their movements are both effects. So also a common cause produces the phenomena which we call winter and spring, or day and night, and provides the basis of their sequence. Wherever such an invariable sequence is discovered, the scientist feels certain that he has discovered a real pattern, a real causal relation in nature. In a complex situation, however, he is always trying to single out particular patterns, to analyze the complex relations into simpler ones. How could he discover whether it was really Spoke B or the common motion of the axle that caused Spoke A to revolve? By removing B; that is, by applying the Method of Difference. Many situations, however, are in practice not susceptible of such simple treatment. It is extremely important not to assume that, just because some event came after another, it was due to its influence; even when the succession is constantly repeated, this may be the result of some common cause rather than the result of either one or the other. In other cases experimental control is entirely out of the range of possibility. We can hardly start pushing the earth over to see whether we cannot pass directly from winter to summer. We cannot experiment with the past, and discover whether Louis XVI's weakness was the real cause of the French Revolution. How, then, do we analyze such situations? When we cannot apply the inductive methods in actual experiment, we apply them in imagination. We can imagine what would have occurred had Archimedes found his fulcrum and succeeded

in moving the earth, and we can in imagination observe
summer succeeding immediately upon winter. We can
in imagination kill Louis XVI at the age of ten, and observe that events are not appreciably altered. Such
are the uses of reflection!

What basis have we for assuming that there is uniformity of this kind in nature, that a given situation will
yield definite consequences, and that for every set of
circumstances there are antecedents which account for
them? This question leads at once to one of the fundamental aspects of the universe in which we find ourselves. We discover, as we look about in nature, that
events do not just happen without any relation to preceding or succeeding events, but that certain sequences
in events take place over and over again. We see lightning, and we hear thunder. We are assured that every
time we hear thunder, lightning has previously been observed. When we swat flies, they cease to buzz. No
matter how many we swat, provided we swat vigorously
and accurately enough, the same result will occur.
These two examples are but typical of the myriads that
occur in nature. Our life is one long course of discovery
of these invariable sequences, these fixed patterns in
events, that form so essential a part of our experience.
They are, in fact, precisely that feature of our universe that makes it an ordered cosmos rather than a
mere chaos, in which lightning might be followed now by
thunder, now by cream cheese, and now by purple-
bearded tigers. These patterns which force themselves
upon our attention, and to the analysis of which the
scientist devotes his life, are causal relations, uniform
correlations between causes and effects, such that, unless some other cause has prevented it, when one part of
the pattern is discovered the rest is sure to follow.

How do we know that these patterns exist in nature? Because we have discovered them in our experience, and have found that they repeat themselves again and again. Sometimes, to be sure, exceptions seem to occur, but we have hitherto been able to explain these exceptions as cases in which one pattern entered into and was altered by another pattern. Most bodies, we have found, fall to the earth; but balloons rise. This anomaly is explained by reference to the more general laws of mechanics, which furnish patterns into which we can satisfactorily fit bodies lighter than air. How do we know that these sequences will continue to repeat themselves in the future? Strictly speaking, of course, we don't; it is possible that to-morrow the trump of doom will sound, that the dead will arise, and that all things will be made new — with, it is to be supposed, quite new millennial patterns for events to follow. Yet no man can really believe that such an overthrow will take place; the uniformity of nature, the conviction that things will continue to occur in the same manner as they have hitherto, is undoubtedly the best-founded generalization in the whole range of human experience.

It is this very generalization which provides the basis for scientific understanding and gives to it its outstanding characteristics. If these patterns are discoverable, then they can be traced out in detail. Prediction, as well as historical reconstruction, with all the innumerable advantages which it entails, then becomes possible. When we see clouds gathering, we learn to seek shelter from the approaching storm. And closely allied to this possibility of prediction come the occasions to control some at least of the events involved in any sequence. Not only do we learn to seek shelter in houses, we also attach lightning rods to our homes in order to protect them from the effects of electric bolts — we modify the particular series of events, alter the pattern of nature. Of course, the particular pattern which we select in the interests of prediction and control will depend on the purposes which we aim to accomplish. If we wish to photograph the flashes, we will concern ourselves with a somewhat different set of causal relations and arrange our actions accordingly. Sometimes the fact that microbes multiply in certain liquids will guide us; at other times the fact that they may be killed by other media will be more significant for our purposes. It was this same consideration which led us to remark, in an earlier chapter, that any phenomenon could be classified and defined in different ways for different contingencies.

The very fact that it is possible to achieve knowledge by observation and experiment rests on the existence of uniform and invariable causal sequences in nature and on the fact that events do not occur detached from sequences. If we can find one of these sequences or patterns, we are as sure as we can be of anything in experience that it will follow its stereotyped routine. Hence a single crucial set of experiments can prove to us a universal causal law. By the use of the experimental methods we can verify an hypothesis. We can proceed from particular instances to general law; that is an ultimate fact of our experience. It cannot be explained by anything else; but it throws a flood of light upon the very nature of our universe. For knowledge to be possible, our universe must, to that extent, be an ordered cosmos; which is but another way of saying that the existence of scientific understanding, prediction, and control depends on the intelligibility of our

universe and the possibility of framing universal laws.
How these laws may be developed we shall see in the
next chapter.

QUESTIONS AND EXERCISES

1. Precise observation is the necessary preliminary to the discovery of causal relationships. How may the recognition of causal connections lead to further important observations? Illustrate.

2. Does the same mutual relationship, referred to in question 1, exist between the formulation of a general hypothesis and the testing of causal sequences? Give reasons.

3. What is the relation between the discovery of the cause of an event and the ability to bring about that event? What does this suggest regarding the development of chemistry? Of astronomy? Of the social sciences?

4. What is heterogenesis? How does it differ from abiogenesis? From biogenesis? Define "spontaneous generation."

5. What did Redi's experiments prove?

6. What definite questions did Pasteur propose? What characteristics of his method facilitated the answering of his questions? Compare his observations with those of the diagnostician mentioned in Chapter II.

7. What requirements of a good hypothesis (as developed in Chapter III) did Pasteur's hypothesis fulfill?

8. *a.* Why is it easier to discover the causes for the failure of a wheat crop than to discover the reasons why a successful crop yielded an inadequate financial return to the farmer?

   b. What factors would be especially significant in answering the first question?

   c. If you were led to believe that an excess of rain caused the crop failure, how would you proceed to test your hypothesis?

   d. If the opinion were advanced that the farmer's loss was due to his failure to attend church regularly, how would you test this view? If you disproved its truth, what would this indicate as to the advisability of attending church regularly?

   e. If the excess of rain were causally connected with the crop failure, how could you account for a large wheat harvest on a neighboring farm?

   f. If the wheat fields of the district yielded a poor return, while the potato crop was unusually good, what might this indicate? Would you regard your answer as wrong if one farmer had a poor wheat and a poor potato crop?

9. Indicate briefly the use of the five experimental methods in (*a*) the symbol system suggested in the note on page 77; (*b*) in Pasteur's work; (*c*) in any other problem.

10. Why, despite its apparent simplicity, is the Method of Agreement difficult to employ?　Give illustrations.
11. Why is mere temporal succession insufficient proof of causal connections?　Why does it suggest the presence of some "cause"?
12. How does the discovery of causal sequences effect the possibility of prediction?　Of greater control?　Of increased understanding?

BIBLIOGRAPHY

On the Field of Biology:
　Sedgwick and Wilson, *General Biology*.　Henry Holt & Co., 1907.
　W. A. Locy, *Biology and its Makers*.　Henry Holt & Co., 1908.
　Jordan, Kellogg, and Heath, *Animals*.　D. Appleton & Co., 1911.
On the Origin of Life:
　H. F. Osborn, *Origin and Evolution of Life*.　Charles Scribner's Sons, 1917.
　B. Moore, *Origin and Nature of Life*, Home University Library.　Henry Holt & Co.
　J. Tyndall, *Floating Matter of the Air*.　D. Appleton & Co., 1902.
　R. Vallery-Radot, *Life of Pasteur*.　Doubleday, Page & Co., 1916.
On the Inductive Methods and the Idea of Cause:
　J. S. Mill, *System of Logic* (especially Book 3).　Harper & Bros., 8th edition, 1900.
　W. S. Jevons, *Principles of Science*.　The Macmillan Company, 1892.
　H. W. B. Joseph, *Introduction to Logic*.　Clarendon Press, 1916.
　B. Russell, *Scientific Method in Philosophy*.　Open Court, 1912.
　Also chapters in any of the Logic texts mentioned in the bibliography to Chapter II.

CHAPTER V

DEDUCTIVE ELABORATION AND THE RELATION OF IMPLICATION IN MATHEMATICS

Section 1. The Nature and Function of Mathematical Reasoning

THE fourth stage in our analysis of the typical act of reflective thinking we found to be the elaboration of the various hypotheses that had been suggested as solutions to the initial difficulty, and the careful ascertaining of all the consequences they might be expected to have if true. Thus, in our example of the Copernican theory, we saw how men reasoned that, if that were a correct explanation of the planetary motions, then there would have to be some apparent displacement, no matter how slight, in the positions of the fixed stars when viewed from opposite sides of the earth's orbit.

It is this process which we purpose to examine in more detail in this chapter. Just how can we ascertain the consequences that will follow from certain other truths? It is obvious that we are here dealing with a kind of reflection that differs markedly from that summing up of great bodies of facts under general laws that has occupied our attention hitherto. We are concerned here with the relations that subsist between two or more propositions, not with those obtaining among facts; and more especially with that type of relation which holds between two propositions when from the truth of the first we can infer the truth of the second. We can express this relation in several ways. We can say that one proposition is "implied" by another, or we can say that the second "follows necessarily" from the first. It is significant that the truth of the *relationship* in no wise depends upon the truth of the first *proposition*. It makes no difference whether John has a sister Helen or not; we know that *if* he has a sister Helen, *then* she has a brother John.

This relation of "if . . . then . . . " is called the relation of *implication*, and the elaboration of hypotheses which constitutes the fourth stage of our analysis consists in the discovery of the various propositions which are *implied* by the original suggestion. This whole process of following the network of relations which bind truths together is called "deduction"; whenever we can deduce one proposition from another, we know that a relation of implication obtains between them. This relation of implication has been defined as that which holds between two propositions when the denial of the second is inconsistent with the truth of the first.

Our example of this deductive elaboration of hypotheses will be drawn from mathematics, whose very definition is "the science of implication." For mathematics is concerned with that structure of things which by its existence makes it possible to proceed from one truth to another deductively. That is why in every completely developed science the part played by mathematics is very large indeed. The relations with which the mathematician deals seem to be a part of the very foundation of the world we live in, so that we have discovered that, if any proposition that holds true of experience is elaborated in accordance with the rules of mathematics, the conclusions thereupon reached will also hold of experience. This fact about our universe, and the additional fact that the quantitative methods of mathematics admit of the utmost accuracy and precision of formulation, explain why in each of the fields we have looked at so far mathematics is so fundamental. It does seem to be true that the more highly developed a science becomes, and the more knowledge we gain about the relations between its objects, the more its beliefs tend to fall into mathematical form, and to admit of treatment by purely mathematical methods. So true is it that a science is successful just in so far as it is able to formulate its beliefs mathematically, that many men have naturally come to think that in mathematics is to be found the exemplar of all true knowledge.

They have been aided in reaching this conclusion by the seeming absolute certainty with which mathematical conclusions are vested. In experimental science, in even so well-established a body of knowledge as modern chemistry, however sure we may be that, tested again and again in the laboratory, our beliefs are true and un- shakable, we can never be quite certain that some new discovery may not upset all our theories and require an entire readjustment. We have just been astounded to learn that astronomy, which we had fancied in all its essential features fixed since the days of Newton, has suddenly been forced by the theory of relativity to reconsider a great many of its fundamental beliefs. Hence it is little wonder that investigators have looked enviously upon mathematics as that science in which truths can be proved with no fear that they will ever be questioned. When a proposition in mathematics has been proved, within the field of its own presuppositions, it is *so*. In no other field of human knowledge can this be said. For this reason, there have even been men who have dreamed of the time when it would be just as easy to determine whether a certain course of action is right or wrong, and when that question would be just as finally settled, as it is now to determine once and for all the product of 674 and 45367. Or they have painted pictures of the replacing of our present costly, cumbersome, and exceedingly inefficient system of popular election as a means of determining the best man to govern us, by a mathematical method that would give us the fittest candidate as infallibly as we can now compute the area of a triangle with given sides.

Are these admirers of mathematical reasoning indeed right? Is the mind that has been trained to think in terms of mathematics, to solve mathematical problems and to reach certainty by rigid and unassailable mathematical proofs, really the best? Though this has been believed by many of the world's greatest thinkers, most men at the present time do not maintain it. While admitting all that is claimed for the certainty of mathematical thought, they hold that the field to which it applies has its limits, and that, although it is an invaluable tool, it is by no means the only one that must be employed.

Mathematics, then, guides us into the world of the relations between truths, and hence helps us incalculably in the interpretation of nature. But the great advantage of mathematical beliefs is that we can know beyond peradventure of doubt when they are right. Since the trained mind is the mind that is right, and knows it is right, we have in mathematics an opportunity to observe the trained mind at work in a field where it has succeeded in testing out its hypotheses rigorously. In fact, mathematics is preëminently an instrument for testing, for proving what has been suggested, and it is only secondarily that it served as a direct means for the discovery of new truth. This holds especially of nearly all of the mathematical reasoning that finds its way into books. Of course, the discovery of new knowledge in geometry or algebra springs out of the imagination that can envisage new suggestions, and is not different from such discovery in any branch of science. But what the ordinary demonstration contains is not the intuitive insight, the creative synthesis which is the mark of the great mathematical pathfinder, but rather the setting forth of the precise proof of relationships in such a form that their validity can be established for all. And one reason at least for the certainty of mathematical knowledge lies in the great ease and simplicity with which it is possible to apply to it the most rigorous tests.

For example, take the simple proposition in geometry, the sum of the angles of a triangle is equal to two right angles. We *know* that this is true.[1] It is thoroughly *tested* knowledge. We know that if there is at any time a triangle anywhere, this *must* be true of its angles. We know it because it has been *proved*, proved in a very simple way. We do not have to measure the angles of any triangle to verify this, say, on the planet Mars, because we have established it once and for all, for every possible triangle.

Section 2. The Pythagorean Theorem — the Empirical Discovery

Let us now take a simple piece of mathematical reasoning with which we are all familiar, and analyze it

---

[1] Provided we know what we mean by all the terms involved, of course. See Section 5.

carefully, both to discover the superiority of good over poor mathematical thought, and to find out if possible the significance such reflective thinking possesses. We shall trace the development of the Pythagorean theorem from its early beginnings in crude experimental surveying to its classic formulation in the 47th proposition of the First Book of Euclid, and we shall then subject that elaborate reasoning to careful scrutiny.

The science of geometry originated, we are told by the earliest historians, in the necessity for finding some means of laying out the boundaries of the Egyptian cornfields after the floods of the Nile had swept away the old marks. Egyptian surveyors were called "rope-stretchers" because they worked with a rope twelve units long, divided by knots into three lengths of three units, four units and five units, respectively. When this rope was stretched into the form of a triangle, they found that they had, between the sides of three and four units, an angle that was sufficiently like a right angle to suit their purposes.

What had these rope-stretchers discovered? They had observed the fact that apparently a rope of a certain length, stretched into a triangle of a certain size, formed a right angle. How had they tested this? By measuring ropes and by comparing the angle formed with right angles formed in other ways. Their test was obviously crude and inexact, and they could never be certain whether they had a right angle or only an approximation of one, or whether if they had more accurate measurements they might not get an angle less rather than more like a right angle.

In Greece there lived men who were more interested in knowing for its own sake than in any practical application of that knowledge, and they studied these curious discoveries of the Egyptians. One of them, as the tradition goes, a somewhat mysterious figure, Pythagoras, observed that in the triangle of the rope-stretchers the sides bore a relation to each other such that 3^2 plus $4^2 = 5^2$; that is, that in a triangle with sides 3, 4, and 5, the squares of the two sides equaled the square of the side opposite what seemed to be a right angle. This set him to thinking. Was it true? It was proved only by measurements of doubtful accuracy. Or, granted that the angle was really a right angle, was this merely an accident, due to the particular lengths of sides chosen? Was there any reason for the fact? Or, was it possible that it was due to the very nature of right triangles? If so, was there any other shaped right triangle of which it could be proved true? Pythagoras was a pathfinder in mathematics, and truths that had remained unfruitful in the minds of others suggested further possible truths to him.

Section 3.   The Pythagorean Theorem — The Proof for the Isosceles Right Triangle

Pythagoras found that there was in truth another shape of right triangle of which he could prove that the sum of the squares upon the legs was equal to the square upon the hypotenuse. In the case of the isosceles right triangle, not only does the same relation appear, but it is possible to demonstrate it by means of a simple figure. Thus, take the isosceles right triangle ABC, with squares erected upon its three sides, and draw the diagonals of the three squares. It is easy to prove that the eight new right triangles formed are equal to each other. Thus, right triangle 1 = right triangle 2, because two sides of the one are equal to two sides of the other, respectively. Similarly, right triangle 2 = right triangle

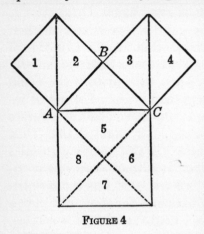

ABC = 3 = 4. Now, the diagonals of a square bisect each other at right angles, and hence, for the same reason, right triangle 5 = 6 = 7 = 8. Right triangle 5 = right triangle ABC, as the side and adjoining angle of the one is equal to the side and adjoining angle of the other. Hence, all nine triangles are proved equal, and 1 + 2 + 3 + 4 = 5 + 6 + 7 + 8. Thus, for the right triangle with equal legs, the Pythagorean theorem has been proved to hold.

Now, just what has been done in this geometrical *proof* of a special case of the right triangle? In the first place, it is now seen that it is not an accident that the sum of the squares on the legs is equal to that on the hypotenuse. We know that it follows from the very nature and structure of the isosceles right triangle, and that it could not be otherwise. We have *proved* it to be so, and we have proved it not for just some particular triangle, like the 3, 4, 5 triangle of the rope-stretchers, but for *every* and *any* right triangle whose legs are equal. Did we have to measure the legs and the angle of the triangle? No, not at all. In fact, were we to try, we should soon discover that we could not do so, for, as we know, the sides of such a triangle are incommensurable. How,

then, are we justified in assuming that every isosceles
right triangle has such a relation between its sides when
we cannot measure those of even one?

Before answering this question, let us ask another.
Of what triangle is the proposition true? Is it true of
the figure on the paper? No, because that is manifestly
inaccurate. Is it true of any right triangle we could
draw or lay out anywhere, with the most exact of instruments? No, because no instruments are accurate
enough to construct one absolutely right angle. Then
of what is it true? We have just said, of every isosceles
right triangle. But just what is the isosceles right triangle of which it is true? Obviously, it is no existent triangular object anywhere in the world, but rather a
geometrical figure we have defined as "a plane surface,
bounded by three straight lines, two of whose sides are
equal and enclose a right angle." We have proved that,
if there should actually exist such a thing, the squares
on its sides would have to equal the square on its hypotenuse; but we have no means of knowing that such a
thing *does* exist, and we are here dealing with an *abstract*
figure, made by selecting certain characteristics of existent things, and by excluding others, such as inac-
curacy, etc., by our definition. Starting with this definition, and assuming that certain other relations are also
true (such as, for example, that the diagonals of a square
bisect each other at right angles), we have shown that if
there is such a thing, and if those other relations are
true, then if we consider the squares on the sides of such
a triangle they must be equal to the square on the hypotenuse. These proportions are related by a chain of
implications.

Let us now ask, what advance has been made in this

strictly mathematical proof over the purely empirical testing of the 3, 4, 5, triangle? First, it is a much more thorough test. We could not be quite sure of the latter; we know, with absolute certainty, that the former is true. Hence we have achieved a belief that has been rigorously tested. Secondly, we are no longer concerned with particular triangles of certain sizes. We have proved that *every* isosceles right triangle has the same relation between its sides. Thus we have achieved both certain proof and universality.

Yet there is a third and a most important distinction. The two propositions have been proved about entirely different kinds of things. In the first case, we were dealing with an actual rope of a certain length. In the second, we are dealing with an abstract figure defined by selecting certain chosen qualities from existent triangular objects. We have proved our proposition to be true in the realm of such abstract figures, that is, in what we call geometrical space, and to be true of any figure conforming to the definition; but how do we know that it will hold true of real triangular objects in the actual world? It will do so only as those real objects possess a structure that is like that of the abstract triangle we have been discussing; that is, only as the inaccuracies and other adventitious qualities characteristic of these real objects are irrelevant to our purposes with them. Now, the whole secret of the enormous success of the mathematical interpretation of nature lies precisely in this fact, that, so far as we can ascertain by means of repeated experiments, for many of our most important purposes these inaccuracies *are* irrelevant, and thus actual triangular objects do possess a structure that does coincide closely enough with the abstract triangles of which we prove things so that our proofs can be counted upon to hold of them also. Were this not the case, our geometry would be a pleasant game and nothing more; as it is, just because it seems to give us an insight into the nature of our world, it has proved immensely illuminating, and has served as one of the most potent tools in man's hands for the understanding and the consequent conquest of nature.

Section 4. The Pythagorean Theorem — the General Proof [1]

But Pythagoras was not satisfied to stop with this proof. He still suspected it was possible to prove the relation for the 3, 4, 5 triangle, and if it held for the two cases, it might also hold for *every* case of right triangle. With this hypothesis in mind, he sought to discover a proof for the general case. In this he eventually succeeded, and this theorem we shall now examine more carefully, for it represents geometrical

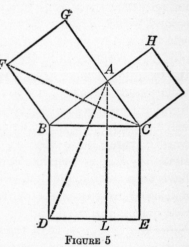

FIGURE 5

thinking at its fullest. However, we shall not take up the proof that Pythagoras worked out, but rather the simpler form that was given to it by Euclid.

Theorem: If a triangle, ABC, be right-angled, the

[1] Euclid, book I, proposition 47.

square constructed upon the side BC subtending the right angle is equal in area to the sum of the squares constructed upon the sides AB and AC which form the right angle.

Construction: On the sides AB, BC, and AC, construct the squares BG, BE, and CH; through A draw AL parallel to BD, and join AD and FC.

For our purposes it will not be necessary to give the entire proof in detail, as an examination of a single part will suffice. It will be remembered that the general method consists in proving first that triangle FBC = triangle ABD; then that triangle FBC is equal in area to one half the area of the square BG, and that triangle ABD is similarly equal to one half the rectangle BL, and that consequently BG is equal in area to BL. In the same way it is proved that the square CH is equal in area to the rectangle CL, and hence BG plus CH = BL plus CL, or the square BE. Let us examine the first part of the proof.

Angle FBA = angle CBD, because both are right angles (definition of a square), and magnitudes which coincide with one another are equal. Add to both the angle ABC, and angle FBC = angle ABD, because if equals be added to equals the results are equal. FB = BA, and BC = BD, by definition of a square. Hence triangle FBC = triangle ABD, because two triangles are equal if two sides and the included angle of one are equal respectively to two sides and the included angle of the other. Because the angles GAB and BAC are both right angles, GA and AC are in the same straight line. Now the square BG is double in area the triangle FBC, because they are on the same base FB and between the same parallels FB and GC, and similarly the rectangle

BL is double the triangle ABD, because they are on the same base BD and between the same parallels BD and AL (the area of a rectangle is equal to the base times the altitude, while that of a triangle is equal to one half the base times the altitude). Because the doubles of equals are equal to one another, the square BG is equal to the rectangle BL. And so on.

What does this theorem prove? Like the proof about the isosceles right triangle, it proves nothing about any real object, but is true only of an abstract triangle. But now, in this more general case, we have proved our theorem, not about a triangle of some particular shape, such as one whose legs are equal, but of *all* right triangles whatsoever, and of the 3, 4, 5 kind incidentally. How did we reach this conclusion? Had we attempted to measure *all* right triangles, following the method of the rope-stretchers, we should have required an infinite time. We might have reached a great probability, but we could never have become certain, as we are now, that no exception would ever be found. Instead, we have now shown the relation to follow from the nature of the right triangle itself, and have discovered that size and shape are quite irrelevant. That is, just as before we selected from our diagram triangularity, right-angled-ness, and equal-leggedness, leaving out of account particular lengths, thickness of line, breadth, inaccurate drawing, etc., just so here we can disregard the equal-leggedness and consider only the two properties of triangularity and right-angledness. We have become more general and more abstract; the truth of our proposition depends upon fewer presuppositions. And, incidentally, we have proved a proposition that not only suggests an infinite number of further propositions, but that also is the basis of all the indirect measurement of geometry, and without which the practical applications of trigonometry to surveying could scarcely exist.

Section 5. Critical Examination of the Proof

This, then, is an example of one type of mathematical reasoning. We have seen how it differs from the crude observation and untested experiment of the rope-stretchers; we have seen how Pythagoras first proved a particular case, and then how that case was made more general. Let us now examine this reasoning more searchingly, that we may ascertain its precise nature and its validity.

What is the general nature of this reasoning? It is a series of "implications" or "necessary truths," each depending on or following from some preceding truth. Each step is true if the preceding step is true. Angle FBC = ABD if it is true that the results of adding equals to equals are equal. Triangle FBC = ABD if it is true that two triangles are equal if two of their sides and the included angles are equal, and that proposition in turn is true if other relations are true. It is obvious that this chain is no stronger than its weakest link, and also that the chain must be attached at its end to something. If the reasoning follows step by step, the whole conclusion depends on the truth of the initial assumptions. The proof is true only if these are true. Now what exactly are the initial assumptions in this case?

First, there are *definitions*. We have defined our triangle in certain arbitrary terms, suggested by, but differing greatly from, any triangular object in the actual world. But here, again, definition is possible only in terms of something further. and so there are some terms with which we must start, leaving them undefined. Our triangle is defined in terms of straight lines. A straight line is defined as "the shortest distance between two points." But it is impossible to define distance without doing so in terms of a straight line, and we have got nowhere.

Secondly, there are *axioms* such as that about equal magnitudes. These are first truths which cannot be proved to follow from any simpler truth. Geometry, like all mathematics, has a certain number of such ultimate beliefs lying at its basis.

Thirdly, there are the fundamental *principles of implication* itself, by which we pass from one step to the next. These principles, sometimes called the "laws of thought," are so ultimate that it is almost impossible to formulate them into words without at the same time employing them. An outstanding example is the so-called "principle of contradiction," that a thing cannot be that which it is not.

Now whence come these axioms, whence come these laws of thought? How do we know that they are true? For upon their validity depends the entire certainty we have found so characteristic of mathematical reasoning. Here we reach a point where great disagreement of opinion has existed since the very beginning of thought and is very widespread to-day. The oldest and most common answer has been, we just *know* that they are so. They are self-evident truths, which cannot be denied without bringing indescribable confusion and contradiction into our thinking. Unfortunately for this point of view, it was discovered and proved in the last century that not only could these axioms be denied without introducing any inconsistency into our think-

ing, but that we could build up other systems of reasoning that seemed in every way as valid as our ordinary
Euclidean geometry. Which of these geometries was
true? Both followed from their premises, and as abstract sciences both were able to pass the test of internal
consistency. But which premises were true? Some
took the position that axioms were merely generalizations from experience, and that we just found our world
to be like that which they describe. Unfortunately for
this point of view, although, of course, a geometry that
is to be useful to us must be able to describe the world in
which we live fairly accurately, so far as means at our
disposal for testing out which set of axioms is true are
concerned, there are a number of different sets, each
giving rise to its own different geometry, and each
equally able to interpret our world. For instance, in
one of them it is quite possible to have more than one
straight line drawn between two points, and unless we
were able to measure distances enormously greater than
we can with anything at our disposal, we should never
be able to tell whether we were living in one kind of a
world or the other.

Hence most mathematicians to-day regard the axioms
at the basis of geometry as neither self-evident nor found
in experience, but rather as conventional assumptions
about our world, very much like our definitions of geometrical objects. These assumptions work on the whole,
but we have no means for testing with extreme accuracy
whether our world really corresponds to one set or the
other. Where we can thus not prove which is true, we
sensibly choose that system which will work and which
is by far the simplest, ordinary Euclidian geometry.

Hence geometry is now regarded as a wholly abstract

or hypothetical science, which treats of the properties, not of anything that actually exists, but of objects which are defined in a certain conventional way, and which therefore must have the properties which we as-sign to them in our definitions. The axioms about space are not truths which we discover to hold of the space in which our universe is set, but rather assumptions about an abstract space whose nature we have agreed shall be such as is described by them. It would be quite possible, the geometrician tells us, to assume that our space had a great many other characteristics, and that other axioms described it better than those of Euclid. Such systems have in fact been constructed by Lobachevsky, by Riemann, and by others, and, for the portions of that actual space in which we live and with which we are our-selves acquainted, they could perhaps be made to apply just as well as the ordinary system. But they are very much more complicated, and hence there is every reason for retaining the traditional system in all of the practical applications of geometry.

It is possible, maintain the upholders of this view of mathematics, that the time may come when, in measur-ing the immensities of interstellar space, we shall dis-cover that some one of these other systems of geometry is more nearly like the nature of our space. It is possi-ble that developments following the discoveries of Ein-stein may lead to the adoption of non-Euclidean geom-etry by astonomers in certain cases. This is, however, doubtful, because in such measurements our only yard-rule is a beam of light, and it seems much easier to as-sume that our yard-rule is not quite straight than to assume that the space that perceptibly deviates from it is different from what we had thought.

In contrast to this effort to free mathematics of all dependence upon the world we actually experience, some mathematicians believe that the axioms of Euclidean geometry are fundamental *abstractions from experience*, rather than conventions arrived at independently of it — abstractions so constantly present, so universal to all mankind, so simply and clearly conceived, and so basic in man's thinking, that all men may and at an early age do understand exactly what aspect of our common experience they refer to. Although these men are in a distinct minority to-day, there seems much to be said for their contention that the axioms and the space of our ordinary geometry are not purely arbitrary conventions, and that while they are undoubted simplifications, they are nevertheless derived from a fundamental aspect of our universe. Support is lent to this view by the fact that although the definitions of geometrical figures, and the axioms concerning the nature of geometrical space, may be regarded as constructions of the mind reached by convention and agreement, the axioms about quantity in general, and especially the so-called laws of thought, seem to us to be more deep-seated. Are they, like the geometrical axioms, conventions? Is it possible to interpret our experience just as well if we assume other and contradictory axioms? So far it can only be said that we do not know. It has not yet been done. No one has been able to think consistently while denying the axiom, that two things equal to the same thing are equal to each other. Yet such axioms can certainly not be proved from anything else. They certainly do coincide with our experience. They seem to be part, not only of the very structure of our minds, but also of the structure of the universe to which thousands of years of biological experience has adapted the mind of man. Mathematics can go no further than to attempt to analyze these fundamental axioms, and to make certain that they are really ultimate and cannot be shown to follow from any simpler notions.

Hence, because in mathematics we have to start with certain terms *undefined*, and because we have to *assume* that certain beliefs are true, Bertrand Russell has defined that study as "the science in which we never know what we are talking about nor whether what we are saying is true." We are dealing with abstractions from our world, not with that world as we actually experience it, and we can never *prove*, as the mathematician proves his propositions that the world in which we live is anything like that described by such abstract thinking.

Hence we find that, while those who have seen in mathematics the ideal of knowledge thoroughly and conclusively tested are right, that certainty is possible only because we first put it into our definitions. It is a certainty within a highly abstracted realm, not a certainty in the world we experience. To ascertain just how valid any mathematical formula will be as an interpretation of the way things are in the world, we have to rely upon the tests that repeated experiment and verification will bring, just as does any other scientist. We have abundant proof that in this sense mathematics is marvelously borne out as describing accurately certain aspects of our experience. And that is why it is the wonderful tool and instrument that it is in the hands of the scientist who knows how to use it. As Descartes said three hundred years ago, nature is like a great cipher to be solved by man. We invent a key to the code, and we find that the interpretation makes excellent sense. No wonder we feel proud of our ingenuity and satisfied with our key.

Section 6. The Essentials of Good Mathematical Thinking

We can now summarize the characteristics we have discovered that good mathematical thinking must possess. Since so much depends on our initial assumptions, we must be exceedingly careful to make them as clear as possible. Our definitions must be absolutely clear-cut, that we may know exactly what kind of things we are talking about. We must know precisely what our assumptions are, and both definitions and assumptions must express the essential nature of the realm in which we are operating; that is, it must be possible to prove from them the entire body of beliefs making up the science. This goal, it must be said, has not yet been fully reached by the mathematician. With these tools at our disposal it will be possible for us to test thoroughly every mathematical belief, and to make certain that it follows from the assumptions with which we started. But to discover whether there is in reality anything like those ideal entities about which we have proved so many things, we must adopt an entirely different kind of reasoning. That is the province of the careful experimentation whose principles we have already examined. All that mathematics can do is to tell us that, if certain things are true, then we can be quite certain of the truth of other things. It remains purely hypothetical. But as such it is an invaluable instrument for the deductive elaboration of the various theories and suggestions that occur as explanations to the scientist. It is with the nature of these explanations themselves that our next chapter will deal.

QUESTIONS AND EXERCISES

1. Give several simple examples of the relation of implication.
2. What part did mathematics play in the reasoning of Copernicus? Of Bessel? Of Adams? In the establishment of the molecular theory? In Pasteur's experiments? What is the significance of the difference?
3. Give several illustrations of the sciences that have become more mathematical as they have become more highly developed.
4. "If two lines intersect one another, the vertical angles formed at their intersection are equal."
   a. How do we know this to be true? By actual measurement?
   b. If it is true, what other presuppositions must be assumed as true?
   c. How do we know that these presuppositions are true?
   d. What sort of thing are we talking about in this proposition? Something that can be seen and touched?
5. Why did the proof of the rope-stretchers fail to satisfy Pythagoras?
6. In the proof given in Section 3, what do we mean when we say that it is not an accident that the sum of the squares upon the legs is equal to the square upon the hypotenuse?
7. Why cannot the isosceles right triangle of which we prove the proposition in Section 3 be regarded as an actually existent triangle?
8. Write out the proof given in Section 4 in its complete form, including every presupposition.
9. Give an example of a similar object in some other realm which could not possibly exist, and which yet follows definite laws of its own.
10. Distinguish carefully between the two very different types of testing in the sciences of biology and of mathematics.
11. Give an example of a chain of implications that follow necessarily, but whose initial assumption is false.
12. What enables us to prove things about every triangle, when we can never experience or even imagine all of them?
13. How do we know that mathematical proofs will everywhere and always be valid? What exactly is it about their nature that guarantees this certainty?
14. Define briefly: axiom; definition; implication.
15. Why have mathematicians given up the explanation of common-sense that axioms are simple self-evident truths?
16. Why have mathematicians abandoned the explanation that we derive our axioms from experience? What can experience teach us about them?
17. What is the prevalent opinion amongst mathematicians as to where our axioms do come from?

18. Explain carefully the two parts in Russell's definition of mathematics in Section 5.   Do you think this is a good definition?

19. What method must we employ to determine the applicability of a mathematical proposition to our physical universe?   Give a simple example.

BIBLIOGRAPHY

On the Proposition:
  Euclid, or any textbook in plane geometry.
On the Contemporary Theory of the Foundations of Geometry:
  H. Poincaré, *Science and Hypothesis.*   Walter Scott, 1905.
          Science and Method.   Scribner's Sons, 1915.
  D. Hilbert, *Foundations of Geometry.*   Open Court, 1902.
  O. Veblen and J. W. Young, *Projective Geometry*, Vol. I.   Ginn & Company, 1910.
On the History of Geometry:
  F. Cajori, *History of Mathematics.*   The Macmillan Company, 1906.

CHAPTER VI

THE FUNCTION OF EXPLANATION IN PHYSICS

Section 1.   Explanation by Analogy

WE have now taken up in turn each of the stages of the typical act of reflective thinking, and have examined the methods by which the scientist guards against the possibility of error at each step and arrives at the truth he is seeking.   We have followed his hypothesis from its birth among the multitude of facts and observations he has made, through its gradual shaping and testing in accordance with the criteria of a good hypothesis and the five inductive canons, and its complex deductive elaboration at the hands of the mathematician.   It now remains to consider a little more closely the nature of the scientist's aim and the extent of his achievement in marshaling hosts of facts under the banner of a scientific law.   The discovery of these causal laws we have assumed to be the chief task of the investigator; now we must ask just what these causal laws really tell us.   Although it is in their ability to serve as instruments of prediction that the practical utility of these laws consists, their essential value to the inquiring mind lies in enabling it to *understand* the world in which it finds itself, and to *explain* its events.

Because this function of explaining our world to us is so fundamental to science, and because so many men have been led astray through not knowing just what scientists were attempting to do in this explaining, we shall select from the great realm over which the physicist holds sway this one problem of the nature and meaning of scientific explanation. Through the consideration of a single phenomenon to be explained, we shall show how physicists have come gradually to adopt certain beliefs about that thing because they feel that they are thus "explaining" it much better than they formerly did.

When a man has beheld something new and strange, and returns to inform his friends, they ask him eagerly, "Tell us all about it. Explain it to us. What is it like?" And in his explanation he does tell them what it is like, for he describes it in terms of the things with which they are already familiar. Nor does the scientist do otherwise. When he seeks to explain a certain phenomenon, he too sets out to tell us what it is like. If it is some newly observed occurrence, he seeks to show that it is really like some other occurrence with which we are already familiar, and whose manner of taking place we already know. Were the average scientist to formulate his ideal, it would probably be that of showing that all the complex occurrences in our world are at bottom not dissimilar and different events, but that fundamentally they are all special cases of some more general type of happening. Did we know the laws describing how this one great type of event takes place, and could we show that everything that comes to pass really falls under these laws, then, so far as most scientists are concerned, we should have explained everything in the world. Thus most psychologists are seeking to "reduce" the mental phenomena with which they deal to the more general laws of physiology, and thus "explain" the unfamiliar mental happenings in terms of familiar physiological principles; most physiologists are seeking to "reduce" their physiological laws to special cases of the more general and better known laws of chemistry and physics; while the chemists and the physicists are busily engaged in the attempt to show that all the phenomena of their sciences ultimately depend solely upon the laws of matter and energy — perhaps of energy alone. For that is what they mean by "explaining."

Of course, the scientists have not yet been successful in their attempt to "explain" all phenomena as essentially happenings in the domain of the science of mechanics; many, in fact, feel that this is probably an impossible task, while some few even question its desirability. Yet it remains the ideal of what the average scientist would like to do if he could, for he feels that he can "understand" any type of occurrence only when he has shown that, instead of being something very complex and unique, it is really the combination of things that are very simple and universal. Thus the astronomer, when confronted with the millions of quite unrelated tiny orbits of the stars, even though he might be able to work out on the epicycle theory the positions where they could be depended upon to be at any particular time, could never on that theory feel that he *understood why* the stars had such curious habits. He could take account of the observed facts, but he would be able to *explain* them only when he realized that those habits depended upon the simple orbital motion of the earth about the sun. All those complexly varying motions would then be seen to be merely the result of the simple path of the earth and the direction whence the light came.

Now in the world with which the physicist deals, the profusion of different kinds of occurrence is far greater.

There is an almost infinite number of different sorts of
physical objects, water, air, earth, trees, houses, trains,
animals, cats, granite hills, snow, mosquitoes. Each of
these things differs from all the rest in fundamental qualities. Some are cold, some are hot, some are brown, some
are slimy, some are loud, some are heavy, some are brit-
tle, some are magnetic. All these things are constantly
changing their colors, their sounds, their temperatures,
their shapes, their weights, their positions. Amidst all
this multiplicity of differences, how are we to find anything that we can count upon? How are we to explain
anything, to understand anything in all this welter?

To the physicist, this hurly-burly does not seem to be
a confusion. Rather it seems the soul of orderliness and
regularity. He has discovered so much of order in this
seeming disorder that he can calmly assure us that there
is none of these things that he does not in some measure
understand. For nearly every change that we observe
he is ready with an explanation showing just why that
change took place, and just what change will occur next.
Does a hunter elevate his gun and bring down a duck?
Then our physicist can tell us exactly the path of the shot,
the fall of the bird.   Does the sixteen-inch gun discharge
a shell at an invisible target? He can tell us just where
it will land, how long it will take, how hot it will be, how
great a force drove it, and almost any other question
we may choose to ask. Does something go wrong with
the storage battery in our car? He can tell us what
has been happening in that little black box, and what
the trouble is. Most of the events of nature find him
unsurprised, for he knows what to expect. For nearly
every one he can give some kind of reason and explanation. He has found that things happen in certain fixed

and invariable ways, and that when he has discovered what those ways are, he has the key to every phenomenon that belongs in that class.   For after all the complexities of nature do seem intelligible in terms of a comparatively few simple elementary processes, and the physical laws which explain many of her aspects and enable us to calculate them with uncanny accuracy, could readily be formulated in the compass of a small manual.   And every new discovery is a further simplification, until it seems almost possible that the ideal of the physicist, some all-comprehensive formula from which could be predicted every possible event in the world of nature, may not be absolutely unattainable.

Whether he reach such a goal or not, it is in achieving such explanations that he has won his greatest triumphs. One by one he has been reducing complex happenings to simpler ones, and involved laws and formulas to simpler and more general forms.   We shall take a single example to show the kind of thing that he has aimed at, and the wonderful success that has crowned his efforts. Then we shall examine more closely into just how the new scientific explanation "explains" the events with which it deals, and what that "explanation" really means.

Section 2.   The Scholastic Theory of the Nature of Physical Objects

It is hardly too much to say that during the Middle Ages the world had no scientific explanations of those happenings with which the modern physicist deals.   To the greatest minds as well as to the average man the world of natural objects was just what it seemed to be and nothing more.   Every object in the physical world was just an object of a certain character, quite distinct from all the other objects. Each was a real substance; that is, in the technical definition, each was able to exist by itself. Each substance possessed certain qualities. It was green, it was flexible, it was damp, it was of a certain size, it weighed so many pounds. If any of these qualities changed, the object was no longer the same substance. Substances frequently disappeared altogether, as when one applied a flame to a piece of wood. The wood vanished, leaving only a little of a new substance, ashes, in its place. Or again substances frequently just happened, as when one found dew where a few moments before there had been none. These qualitative differences were real. Ice was one substance, water another, steam a third. If you heated water, it would be transformed into steam, an entirely new kind of substance. If you mixed copper and zinc, you got a new substance, brass, that was gold in so far as its color went. If you could thus transform copper into gold in color, why not in its other qualities also? Nothing was more common than the everyday transmutation of wood into ashes, or of water into steam through the addition of two other substances, flame or fire, and heat, respectively.

This glorification of common sense served the Middle Ages well enough, because they were not very much concerned with either understanding or predicting physical phenomena. But so soon as men came to feel an interest in doing this latter thing, the method that the scholastics had developed for handling objects broke down, because it *explained* nothing. For the scholastic, nothing was *just like* anything else. Each kind of object possessed its own character and individuality, each was qualitatively different from its fellows. This way of looking at objects had been developed primarily for dealing with human beings, where character and individuality are obviously the most important things to be considered. But unfortunately for the physical science of the Middle Ages, methods admirable in dealing with human relations bear little fruit when applied to material objects, and the heavy hand of Aristotle's ethical physics lay for fifteen hundred years upon natural science, and drove out other hypotheses that would have been much more successful. One could make no statements about more than one class of objects, because between classes there were no relations of similarity that would lend themselves to generalization. Cold water was one kind of thing, hot water another, and the difference was due to the presence in the case of the latter of a new substance or thing, heat. Why did heat make things hot? Because heat possessed very strong calorific qualities. Why, in the classic instance, did opium put one to sleep? Because of its well-known dormitive qualities. The operation of any particular substance was always explained as due to something in that substance which was unique to it, and which made it do exactly what it did.

Modern scientists are accustomed to laugh at these pseudo- "explanations" as mere attempts to cover ignorance. That is because they do not realize what the scholastics were doing. They were pointing to and recording observed facts, and the various qualities with which they saddled unoffending materials were scientific labels indicating the presence of those facts. This observation of facts is the indispensable prerequisite to any scientific explanation of them. Until you know *that* heat makes an object hot, you can never hope to explain *why* it performs that function. Without knowing what the case is, you can scarcely show what else it is like. These observed facts, as we saw in astronomy, heap up for centuries before men can explain and account for them. Every new science has multitudes of just such facts, neatly labeled and awaiting the pathfinder who will embrace them all in one great hypothesis. Such labeling is dangerous only if we forget that it is merely labeling, and assume that the label itself is a real explanation. Thus, for example, many psychologists to-day, when asked to explain why human beings like to be in each other's company, and dislike solitude, answer readily, "Oh, that is due to the gregarious instinct." If they imagine that they have given a real explanation, that they have clarified a complex phenomenon by reducing it to one simpler, they are in the position of those who explain the heat-giving nature of heat as due to its calorific qualities. But if they say, "We don't know why human beings behave in that particular way, but we know that they do, and we think that fact so important that we will call it the gregarious instinct," then they are paving the way for the pathfinder who is to overcome their ignorance.

Section 3. The Kinetic Theory of Matter

In striking contrast to the theory of the scholastics, that each physical object is qualitatively different from all the other kinds, and observes its own particular habits in accordance with its own individual nature, is the view known as the kinetic theory. It assumes that all objects are composed of a great number of tiny particles or molecules, of a certain small and definite number of kinds, and that the marvelous qualitative diversity we find in our world is due to the different ways in which these particles are combined, or are behaving. Thus, if this hypothesis be true, we have a really scientific explanation of multitudes of the phenomena we observe, because we can interpret them as consequences of certain simple relations obtaining between these particles. The laws describing the actions of these particles we already know, for they are the same as those governing the motions of the heavenly bodies. We are familiar with what happens when two billiard balls strike each other. If we can show that all the complex phenomena of gases and liquids and solids and pressure and heat, and many others, can be treated as if they were cases of a certain number of billiard balls of a certain size striking each other at a certain velocity and with a certain frequency, we have achieved a marvelous result in showing that all these varied events are really like the mechanical action and reaction with which we are already familiar. We can apply mathematical formulæ to mechanical motions, and predict with the utmost exactitude exactly what will occur in a given case. And just in so far as we can show that different temperatures, different pressures, different forms of matter, different phenomena of all sorts, are really dependent upon the different velocities with which our tiny billiard balls are traveling, we can make similar predictions about them. We have attained a real explanation, because we have succeeded in reducing happenings that we did not understand, and that were qualitatively different, and hence not susceptible of mathematical or quantitative handling, to happenings the laws of which we do know, and which, since they depend upon quantitative differences in velocity, we can handle by means of mathematical formulæ. Thus, if we know that water is composed of certain molecules, and that, when these are vibrating at certain rates, it remains a liquid, but that, when, in general, the rate of vibration falls below a certain level, it becomes a solid, ice, and when the rate rises above a certain level, it becomes a gas, steam, we have really explained these changes as we never could have had we assumed the difference to be due to the addition or subtraction of a substance, heat, and the changes to be real transmutations.

The aim, then, of the kinetic theory is to give a mathematical account in terms of the mechanical action of the molecules of which matter is composed, of all the non-chemical and non-electrical properties of things. It endeavors to reduce all objects to the fundamental elements of matter and energy, and to interpret the various changes that they undergo in terms of the laws of motion, or mechanics, of geometry, and of arithmetic. Hence it is the attempt to find one simple explanation for all those properties which are not chemical or electrical. The reason for this exception of the two latter kinds of properties is that the molecule, which is the ultimate element with which the physicist is dealing, is itself complex, made up of atoms which are in turn composed of electrons, and that while in most cases we can disregard the particular chemical *kind* of molecule, and treat of "matter" indiscriminately, in certain cases we must take into consideration the particular sort of molecule with which we are working. Thus the chemical properties of objects are dependent upon the internal nature and structure of the molecules, whereas the electrical properties seem to depend rather upon the structure of the atom and its component electrons. Just in so far as the scientist has not succeeded in eliminating all qualitative differences, and hence just in so far as he must know with which chemical element or combination of elements he is dealing in order to explain his results, he has not succeeded in his aim of finding one simple principle of explanation for all phenomena. It is, however, very significant that most chemists at the present time feel sure that the atoms themselves, which we used to think were qualitatively distinct elements, of some eighty odd varieties, are really combinations of a simpler thing, the electron, and that these differences of kind are explicable as merely differences of quantitative structure. The ultimate constituent of matter, so far as we are able to discover at present, is the electron — or perhaps the positive nucleus of the atom, the "proton" — and here at last scientists seem to have discovered a thing that is all of one sort. It is already the dream of many scientists that, when we have once discovered the laws describing the nature and behavior of the electron, we shall have a principle of explanation that will enable us to understand every possible occurrence in the world of nature.

However, it would take us too far afield to enter into this question of the component parts of molecules, and hence we shall restrict ourselves in our example to a phenomenon which the kinetic hypothesis, without drawing on any further theories about atoms or electrons, enables us to explain beautifully.

Section 4. The Nature of Heat

The fact that some bodies are hotter than others, and that the same body can vary greatly in temperature, was one of the first observations that men made. They also soon found that, if heat is applied to most bodies, those bodies expand, and that, if you add enough heat, solids will be changed into liquids and liquids into gases. Why is this so? How can we explain these events? Just what is this thing "heat"? From the earliest times, men sought an explanation of these happenings. And quite naturally they assumed that "heat" was a thing, a substance, a fluid like other fluids, that possessed the qualities we associate with "hotness" and that caused certain changes in bodies to which it was added. It could penetrate, expand, dissolve into fluids, and dissipate into gases. This heat fluid was by early physicists given the name of "caloric." Now this theory is a real explanation of the various phenomena connected with heat, because it does interpret them in accordance with certain other types of event with which we are already familiar. Adding caloric to a body will naturally increase its size, just as adding any fluid to another increases the total volume. It will turn solids into new liquids, just as water will turn salt into brine. With these latter occurrences we are familiar, and, when heat is explained as working *like* them, we can *understand* them better.

This was as far as men were able to go so long as they had no means of measuring quantitatively differences in temperature. It is a testimony to the complete dependence of science upon mathematical measurement that no science of heat could develop until the thermometer was invented, about 1612. Strictly speaking, of course, we cannot measure "hotness," any more than we can measure any other *quality*. We cannot tell *how much* hotter we feel to-day than we did yesterday. We can only measure the results of heat in expanding mercury, alcohol, or some other fluid. But once we have invented a thermometer, and can take exact measurements of these results, we can proceed to establish definite quantitative relations; and so soon as the physicists did do this, they found a number of phenomena that the caloric or fluid theory of heat had great difficulty in solving.

Most important were the heat of compression, and the heat of friction. When you compress a gas it becomes much hotter than before, as any one who has ever pumped up a tire knows. Where does this heat come from? Not from outside, as in most other cases of a rise in temperature, because the surroundings do not become cooler, as they would if some caloric passed into the gas. It must come from inside the gas itself, and hence, if caloric is a fluid, it must have been there all along without our knowing it. Similarly, where does the heat that appears when two bodies are rubbed together come from? It also must have been hidden in the bodies. If caloric is fluid, it must be able to lie latent or hidden within bodies on occasion. The explanation which the calorists offered of the appearance of heat on friction or compression was that some of this "latent" caloric was squeezed or ground out of the bodies concerned and became "sensible" or apparent. Obviously, if such was the case, if you rubbed long enough you would eventually reach a limit to the caloric you could rub out, because the supply could hardly be infinite. In a work published in 1798 Benjamin Thompson, Count Rumford, described how he endeavored to find how much he could extract. He placed a metal cannon in a box containing water, and, by the friction of a blunt revolving borer driven by horse-power, the water was heated to boiling in two and a half hours. There seemed no limit to the caloric he could produce. He exclaimed, "What is heat?   Is there any such thing as a caloric fluid? . . . Anything which any insulated body, or system of bodies, can continue to furnish without limitation, cannot possibly be a material substance; and it appears to me to be extremely difficult, if not quite impossible, to form any distinct idea of anything, capable of being excited, and communicated, in the manner the heat was excited and communicated in these experiments, except it be MOTION."

The next year Sir Humphry Davy performed an even more conclusive experiment. A considerable amount of heat must be applied to ice in order to melt it, so that on the caloric theory water contains a much greater quantity of caloric fluid than does ice: that is, ice in itself does not contain enough caloric to melt it.   Davy rubbed two blocks of ice together by clock-work in a vacuum, and succeeded in melting them easily.   On the fluid theory the caloric could only have come from the ice, and it was an observed fact that ice did not contain enough heat to melt itself.   Both of these experiments, it may be noted, were applications of the Method of Difference.

Just what had these two experiments proved? They pointed out two observed facts about heat that the caloric fluid hypothesis was unable to account for. When dealing with them, it made matters more difficult rather than easier to understand for one to assume that the action of heat was like the ordinary action of a fluid added to a body. Hence they conclusively disproved that hypothesis.   But, of course, they could not establish of themselves any alternative hypothesis. So far as the theory of heat as due to molecular activity could explain these two observed facts, as well as all the other phenomena of heat, it was a better hypothesis than its rival; but perhaps still another was even better. The establishment of the kinetic theory depended upon further experiments, and, significantly enough, these were impossible until physicists had learned enough about the behavior of gases to formulate the kinetic hypothesis in definite quantitative terms capable of exact verification. Thus again does physics depend upon mathematics.

The honor of placing the kinetic theory of heat upon a sound experimental basis belongs almost exclusively to the Englishman J. P. Joule. He elaborated the consequences of that theory, and then actually discovered by physical measurements in his laboratory that those consequences did take place. If heat is not a fluid, but is rather the energy of molecular motion within a body, and if those molecular movements take place in accordance with the ordinary mechanical laws of motion, then, when mechanical energy is expended upon a body, say through pressure upon a gas, and is transformed into heat, or the increased motion of the molecules within that body, the energy which disappeared in the act of compression should exactly equal the energy which appears in the increased motion of the molecules, or heat. Conversely, the energy of molecular motion which disappears when a gas expands again (or the heat which it loses on expansion) should reappear as mechanical work done by that expansion. For on the molecular theory we are dealing not with two different kinds of energy, mechanical energy, or the ability to perform work, and an energy of a different sort entirely, heat, but rather with mechanical energy on two different scales, the motion of large bodies, and the motion of very small bodies, or molecules. In other words, the theory could not be regarded as complete until it had been shown that, in the production of work from heat, a certain quantity of heat disappeared, and ceased to exist as heat; and that this quantity was the same as that which could be generated by the expenditure of the work produced.

This actual quantitative determination of what is called the "mechanical equivalent" of heat was the task of Joule, and in experimentally verifying that equivalence he conclusively demonstrated the whole kinetic theory of heat. For he succeeded in showing that heat could be regarded as mechanical motion on a small scale, and that it obeyed the laws of all motion. To this end he instituted a number of different experiments. He measured the heat produced by the expenditure of a certain amount of electrical energy, and found that it was constant. He measured the heat produced by the expenditure of a certain amount of mechanical energy in compressing a gas, and found that it was exactly equal to the heat produced by the same amount of electrical energy. He found also that that same amount of heat, when converted back into mechanical energy, produced the amount that had originally been expended in creating it. He found that the results so obtained tallied exactly with results when he produced heat by friction. He tried also a number of other experiments, varying his methods greatly each time, and in every case he established the same definite ratio between the amount of heat and the amount of work performed. The great value of Joule's work lay in the variety and the completeness of the experimental evidence he brought forth. It was not, of course, sufficient to find the relation between heat and mechanical work in one particular case. He had to show, to fulfill the requirements of the Method of Agreement, that the same relation held in all cases that could be experimentally examined, and that the "ratio of equivalence" of the different forms of energy, measured in very different ways, was independent of the manner in which the conversion was effected and of the material used. Since Joule's day many more experiments have been devised, and in every case the same result has been secured.

Why, then, did physicists adopt the kinetic theory of heat? Because they found that they could thus reduce all the different phenomena of heat to a single simple basis, the energy of motion of the molecules composing bodies, and because that motion was itself of precisely the same nature, and obeyed precisely the same laws as does any motion in the universe. It is a marvelous achievement in scientific *explanation* when we can confidently assert that the tremendous movements of the heavenly bodies and the qualitative differences in temperature of the tiniest objects are both alike, and that they are together like the simple and easily understood and predicted movements of two billiard balls striking each other. One formula will describe all three. Surely few achievements of the human mind are worthy to rank with such a feat!

Of course, the kinetic theory of matter, though it was originally developed as an explanation of heat, does not stop with that phenomenon. There are probably few other hypotheses in the history of science that have proved so extremely fruitful. Men, assuming its truth, have made detailed calculations about what must then occur, and on experimental verification have made multitudes of new discoveries as to the nature of events. Nothing has as yet been observed that has not already been predicted on this basis with uncanny accuracy. Men have proceeded to measure the weight of the molecules, their volume, their size, their speed, the distance they travel, the number of collisions a second, and the number actually within a given space. Almost the only thing the physicist cannot tell us is the precise shape of the molecules. The physicist can well-nigh point under the microscope to actual molecular motions themselves, and enable us almost to see the molecules in their vibration; for he can show us in the so-called "Brownian Movement," the irregular and jerky motions of tiny particles that are the direct result of the terrific bombardment to which they are submitted on the part of the molecules. And all of these things which the physicist, basing his calculations on the kinetic theory, has been able to predict, have been borne out exactly by experiment and observation. It is this remarkable correlation between the results of the kinetic theory and the experimentally determined facts of nature that constitutes the real "proof" of the theory.

This, then, is an admirable example of what the scientist means by "explanation," this reduction of things so qualitatively different as the varying temperatures and states of bodies to the simple terms of matter and the energy of motion. But just what has he done in this "explanation"? What has he, after all, proved about heat? What have we the right to expect from scientific explanation, anyway? In how far and in what way is it "valid"? Is it the only possible kind of "explanation"?

All of these questions are so extremely important that we shall devote our concluding section to a consideration of the problems they suggest.

Section 5.   The Nature of "Explanation"

Just what has the physicist accomplished when he has "explained" heat as a form of molecular energy?   This question may perhaps appear somewhat unnecessary, for most of us would feel that the answer was obvious. Yet upon precisely this point there have arisen so many misconceptions and misunderstandings, and so many men, both laymen and scientists, have felt firmly convinced that they have accomplished much more than they actually have, that it is extremely important that we determine clearly the exact nature of the scientist's achievement.   Nothing unfortunately is more common than for a man to attempt a detailed and elaborate proof of some hypothesis, and to establish that hypothesis successfully, and then suddenly to lose entirely all of his critical faculties when it comes to interpreting the meaning and significance of that successfully tested and verified theory.   This latter task seems, in fact, usually much more difficult than the former, and perhaps there are many more men who can place an hypothesis upon a firm foundation than there are those who can use that achieved knowledge correctly for the attainment of further knowledge.   It is a frequent experience for two men to argue very hotly over a certain contention that one of them has made, and then, when that contention has been finally grudgingly admitted, for the other to cut the ground from under the feet of his adversary by pointing out that really this special contention has little bearing on the main question at issue.

The greatest scientists have at times given the results they have actually discovered significance and further implications which those results will not bear. For example, take the case of the theory of biological evolution with which we shall be concerned in the next chapter. When that hypothesis was first generally received a generation ago, many men felt that if the present species had originated through the long process of natural selection, that fact conclusively disproved their creation by God. It should be obvious that, whatever the indirect effect of the Darwinian theory may have been, a description of the various steps in the process of creation can neither confirm nor invalidate that process itself.

Perhaps, then, it is best to clear away some of these misconceptions as to the real nature of "explanation" at the outset, and to preface our account of what "explanation" does with a list of the things that it does not do.

In the first place, it ought to be obvious that, although we have explained heat as a form of molecular energy, and have found means of measuring that energy accurately, we have in no wise altered the fact that some bodies are hot and some are cold. The scientist uses in this connection a phrase that is very apt to lead to misunderstanding, and that has caused incalculable confusion in interpreting the significance of his results. He tells us that he has succeeded in "reducing" the qualitative and unmeasurable differences between more and less hot to purely quantitative differences that can be accurately measured, and that hence lend themselves readily to mathematical calculation and prediction. He tells us that he has succeeded in "reducing" all the varied colors that meet our eye in a sunset to tiny electro-magnetic vibrations of various determinable lengths. He may even claim to have "reduced" the highest manifestations of ethical activity in man, such as the sacrifice of one's life for an idea, to a process that can be described in these terms: "It might be possible that under the influence of certain ideas chemical changes, for instance, internal secretions within the body, are produced which increase the sensitiveness to certain stimuli to such an unusual degree that such people become slaves to certain stimuli just as the copepods [tiny little crawfish-like creatures] become slaves to the light when carbon dioxide is added to the water." [1]   Now, in so far as this process of "reduction" means the getting rid of something with which we started, and in so far as the scientist in using the phrase means to imply that as a result of his discoveries we now know that hot objects are not really hot, but only vibrating rapidly, or that the sunset is not really a blaze of color, but only complex wave-motions, or that the man is not really manifesting the highest ethical activity, but only responding to chemical stimuli — in so far as he allows this notion to creep into his mind, he is very obviously talking nonsense. The term "reduction" is a technical one that originates in mathematics, and means the transformation of one equation into another, usually, though not always, simpler, by means of the ordinary algebraic processes. This mathematical "reduction" is usually performed for the purpose of greater convenience in handling, and that very fact suggests the reason why the physicist does a somewhat analogous thing in dealing with his complexities. But one outstanding difference between the world of the actually existent in which the physicist works, and the non-exist-

[1] Loeb, *Mechanistic Conception of Life*, p. 62.

ent or hypothetical world in which the mathematician is at home, lies in just this fact, that in the latter one equation is as good as another, and can be substituted for the other, whereas in the former, though for purposes of convenience we must perform this "reduction," we can never take away a single iota from the actual world with which we commenced. The geometer starts with assumptions which he can change at will; the physical scientist starts from facts which nothing can ever change. It is so easy to forget this simple truth that it cannot be insisted upon too strongly.

What the scientist has really done is to establish a certain definite relation between certain changes in molecular motion and corresponding changes in the degree of heat. We know that when the mercury column is of one length, we can experience a certain degree of hotness; and that when it becomes shorter we shall get cooler. But no one would say that the mercury column *is* the hotness, or that the rapid movement of molecules *is* that phenomenon we call heat. When we say that water is hot, we may know perfectly the mass, volume, velocity, and path of the component molecules, but that is not what we mean by that statement. We mean by that hotness something that both the upholders of the calorific and the molecular *explanations* of heat, or any child with no explanation at all, would all recognize as a fundamental fact of experience. Nor are all the king's horses and all the king's men able to alter the fact that hot things are hot, and sunsets colored, and men laying down their lives for an idea truly moral. The scientist, in his explaining of these phenomena, has not taken away from them a jot or a tittle; he has merely *added* a great many things. He has discovered that bodies which are hot are not only hot, but that they are *in addition* composed of rapidly moving particles. He has added new facts, and has not, as he may fondly think, robbed us of any we possessed before. He has correlated molecular velocities with degrees of heat, and this established relation has proved, as we have seen, immensely fruitful. He can measure those velocities, where he could not measure heat directly. He can calculate with them, he can predict with them, he can bring a whole series of phenomena within the scope of a few simple formulæ. But the fact that we have found out just how much hotter it is to-day than it was yesterday can never alter the fact that it is hotter.

Moreover, the molecular explanation, in introducing the same underlying notion of motion into a number of different physical happenings, and in showing that all these happenings can be grouped together because of the fact that all possess this motion, does not alter the great differences that do exist between them. Steam is still a vastly different kind of thing from ice, even if we have learned that the molecules of both are composed of one atom of oxygen and two of hydrogen. The fact that they are both forms of water does not make it a question of indifference which we shall use if we want to make ice cream or a steamed pudding. Ice and steam are just as distinct and act in ways just as different as we ever found them to, but we have learned that, *in addition*, for certain chemical purposes they can be used indifferently. The fact that heat is discovered to be a form of motion does not prejudice its being a very particular and special kind. And the fact that human beings dying for ideas and copepods moving toward the light may have certain characteristics in common is, for most purposes, of infinitesimal importance compared with the enormous gulf that will always remain between them.

Explanation, then, robs us of no facts; on the contrary, it adds greatly to our possessions. Closely allied to this first common misconception, from which even scientific pathfinders have by no means been free, is the notion that those simple and ultimate things, in terms of which every other event is explained, are in some sense *real*, while the complex events and things so explained are not real. The analysis of compounds into their elements does seem to the human mind to make those elements the important things and the compounds fade away into the background. That is the reason why a good many men have felt called upon to do battle vigorously against the whole method of explanation by analysis which is the mainstay of the scientist's success. To them, and also to a great number of scientists, it must be confessed, explaining something really does seem to mean explaining it away. To explain heat seems to explain heat away and leave nothing but molecules. To explain the sacred religious experience of a man who has walked with God seems to be explaining his religion away. Deep down in the processes of men's minds there seems to lurk the feeling, never perhaps put into words, that only those things which are simple and cannot be further broken up into parts, and which remain the same in all the manifold changes of natural events, can be in any significant sense "real." Things susceptible of change, things which come into being and decay, which suffer the mutability of temporal existence, do seem less real, less cosmically important, than those things which are able to preserve their own integrity against the encroachments of time, and to enjoy the blessings of eternal life.   Hence it is perhaps natural that scientists should speak of "the gross world of matter in bulk, which is all that our unaided senses can perceive," and turn with admiration to "the real world, the world of molecules."

"The One remains, the many change and pass,"

and for that reason the many are flitting shadows and the One alone is real.   That men instinctively feel this, it is impossible to deny, and hence it is probably just to say, "It would ill become science to deny the reality of things with which it has no concern.   But it has most definitely, but at the same time unconsciously, limited itself now to the recognition of only those existences which appear to obey the law of conservation, and for which, therefore, there is this much of proof of reality." [1]

Deep as this feeling may be with many, it would be difficult to give any rational argument in its favor. To say that the only real things in the world are the units of matter, energy, and electricity, is to place an unusual interpretation on "real."   Certainly it would seem that everything in our experience has a *prima facie* right to be considered real until proved not to be, and it seems difficult to maintain the contention that only the ultimate simples into which compounds are analyzed are real.   For obviously, on this criterion, the world of molecules could not be the "real world," nor could the world of atoms, nor, it appears highly probable, the world of electrons and "protons."   For all of these it seems are themselves compounds, and in time break up into something else.   If immutability and eternal existence are

---

[1] The quotations are taken from the otherwise excellent little book of Frederick Soddy, *Matter and Energy*.

the sole criteria of reality, then no thing at all, but only the laws describing the behavior of the various things, seem to be able to pass the test, and even their position would be in constant jeopardy. And if nothing we know about is at all "real," the distinction between "real" and "unreal" becomes meaningless to us. But such a distinction obviously exists, and if we try to give it up we shall find ourselves making it again with other terms.

It is, then, safe to assert that explaining a thing can in no sense explain it away. The thing explained remains as "real" as it ever was, and scientists who feel otherwise are merely thinking confusedly. Heat may be molecular energy, but that does not prevent to-day from being a really roasting day. The scientist analyzes and explains for the sake of understanding better the thing he is explaining, not for the sake of arriving somewhere else. Of this error psychology, here as elsewhere, since it is our newest science, furnishes us perhaps with our most glaring examples. No mental phenomenon is so real as that we call "will." Yet the psychologist is prone to analyze that complex thing into its constituent elements, and then calmly to announce that, of course, there really is n't any such thing as willpower; there are only a great number of habits and tendencies! Nor is it any less clear that it is our "conscience" that keeps us from doing wrong. Yet the psychologist, after completing his analysis of that mental phenomenon, is apt to laugh at those who "still believe there is such a thing"!

It is, to be sure, of the utmost importance to point out that there is something permanent in change, and to discover what those elements are; but when the scientist claims that his explanation in any sense lessens the reality of that which he is explaining, he is merely giving way to a deeply rooted misconception of the human mind.

Thirdly, the fact that our explanation has not altered the *facts* nor taken anything from them nor made them any less real, but has rather left them just as they were with the addition of certain new knowledge, is extremely important in the bearing it has upon the limitations of explanation. For it makes it quite possible to have more than one explanation of the same happening, to suit different purposes. No one explanation can possibly exhaust a given occurrence, because it adds to rather than subtracts from it. Thus a man who sees small boys making off with his fruit gets red in the face and there is a marked rise in his temperature. The explanation of the physicist is that the molecules in his blood have increased their velocity. That of the physiologist is that the heart has started to pump the blood through the lungs much more rapidly, and that oxidation has greatly increased. That of the psychologist is that in response to a certain stimulus the instinct of self-defense has been evoked with its accompanying emotions; while the common man would say that the real explanation was that the gentleman had become exceedingly angry at the mischievous boys. Which of the four is right? Obviously all are, for each one is explaining the event in the terms that he finds most convenient to work with, and each one finds that it is like something quite different from that which occurs to his fellows. Moreover, in this case it is apparent that for the great majority of men it is the last explanation and not the first that is really the simplest and most illuminating. But the others, and perhaps still more, are also explanations, perfectly correct and valid in their way, and none conflicts with the rest. Each rather adds to our knowledge of the situation, because each new thing which it is shown to resemble brings into prominence and makes really significant a new aspect of the case.

This is especially important because scientists have again and again claimed more for their explanations than they really do tell us. They have felt that any one explanation, in "reducing" the event to simpler terms, has got at its real or essential elements and that no other explanation could be equally valid. The reasons why this position is erroneous ought now to be apparent. And, in particular, the reasons why the explanation that the physicist gives of events by no means exhausts those events nor makes it impossible for another type of explanation to be applied, should be plain. To the physicist, explaining a natural phenomenon means showing that it is like the behavior of certain ultimate units of matter and energy. This type of analysis he chooses because it is the only way in which he can obtain elements that will lend themselves to quantitative and mathematical handling, that he can measure and weigh and accurately determine in advance. But there are many other purposes in life besides this one of the physicist, and hence there are many other types of explanation quite as applicable. Scientific explanation is of a definite kind determined by the aims of science; it answers the question, "What is this like?" in terms of certain specific things like objects in motion. It explains wholes by analyzing them into their component parts. It explains houses as being built out of such and such bricks. But it is equally important on occasion to explain a brick as the kind of thing houses are made out of, even though that explanation be not the kind the physicist would give. It is certainly as valid to interpret the "Why?" of inquiry as meaning "What is it for?" as it is to interpret it as meaning "What is it like?" When men ask "Why?" they are apt to have a confused notion of both types of answer in their minds. When they wish an event explained to them, they wish to know both what it is like, in what great group of phenomena and under what laws it falls, and also for what purpose it takes place. The first of these questions the physicist attempts to answer; the second lies beyond his province, but it is none the less important.

As an illustration of these different kinds of explanation, take the case of a man at the automobile show who is examining a new engine and wishes the demonstrator to explain to him the new valve which he finds in a strange place. The demonstrator would answer him in several ways. He could show how it opened and closed as the cam shaft revolved, and how it was so made that it closed very rapidly indeed. This would be describing its operation. Or he could tell the inquirer how it was made, and describe the various elements that went into it. He could go into the matter of its origin, and trace how it had come to be there in its place. This would be a causal explanation. But he would probably do neither of these things. He would rather tell the man *why* it had been put there — what good it did there, what function it performed in the working of the engine as a whole. And this latter explanation would not be of the type of the explanation of the physicist, because it would be in terms of *purpose*, in terms of the engine as a whole, of which it, was but a part. Yet it is obviously the most important kind of explanation for the man who wants to run the engine. But it does not conflict at all with the other explanations.

This point has been emphasized because historically many of the greatest pathfinders have felt that these two kinds of explanation really excluded each other. They have felt that men must cleave to the one and forsake the other; that men could not serve two masters, explanation in terms of simple component elements, and explanation in terms of purpose. They have not been able to see how the universe could be a great mechanical system, capable of mechanical explanation, and at the same time be a great whole whose parts could be conceived to be fulfilling certain purposes, to be for the sake of something. They have failed to see how man's actions could be explained both in terms of the purposes for which he performs certain acts and the mechanical way in which his body acts. If the foregoing discussion has made anything clear, it should have served to show us that these two kinds of explanation, different as they are, are quite compatible.

A quotation from the great philosopher Plato's description of the death of his teacher Socrates will illustrate this clearly. Socrates is in prison awaiting execution, talking to his friends, and he is finding fault with the type of explanation given by a scientist of his actions:[1]

I might compare him to a person who began by maintaining generally that mind is the cause of the actions of Socrates, but who, when he endeavored to explain the causes of my several actions in detail, went to show that I sit here because my

---

[1] *Phædo*, paragraph 99, Jowett translation.

body is made up of bones and of muscles; and the bones, as he
would say, are hard and have ligaments which divide them,
and the muscles are elastic, and they cover the bones, which
have also a covering or environment of flesh and skin which
contains them; and as the bones are lifted at the joints by the
contraction or relaxation of the muscles, I am able to bend
my limbs, and this is why I am sitting here in a curved pos-
ture: that is what he would say, and he would have a similar
explanation of my talking to you, which he would attribute to
sound, and air, and hearing, and he would assign ten thousand other causes of the same sort, forgetting to mention the
true cause, which is that the Athenians have thought fit to
condemn me, and accordingly I have thought it better and
more right to remain here and undergo my sentence; for I am
inclined to think these muscles and bones of mine would have
gone off to Megara or Bœotia — by the dog of Egypt they
would, if they had been guided only by their own idea of what
was best, and if I had not chosen as the better and nobler
part, instead of playing truant and running away, to undergo
my punishment which the state inflicts.   There is surely a
strange confusion of causes and conditions in all this.   It
may be said, indeed, that without bones and muscles and the
other parts of the body I cannot execute my purposes.   But
to say that I do as I do because of them, and that this is the
way in which mind acts, and not from the choice of the best,
is a very careless and idle mode of speaking.

In calling his own explanation the true one, Socrates
is, of course, falling into the same error of exclusiveness
that he is reproaching in his adversary; yet it is obvious
that, as an explanation of the conduct of the man in remaining for his death, the scientist's attempt is futile.
For ethics differs greatly from a natural science like
physiology, as we shall see later.   Scientific explanation, then, does not alter or "reduce" an event, but adds
to our knowledge of what that event is like instead of
robbing us.   It does not explain it away; and it in no

wise precludes the possibility of a number of other
equally valid explanations. The importance of these
considerations will become increasingly obvious as we
come to those fields in which the physicist's type of explanation does not seem to produce especially happy results. There we shall see that, because men have failed
to realize what the physicist was trying to do in his explanations, and what was the limitation of that particular type, they have tried to apply methods quite un-
suited to those fields, and have succeeded in involving
themselves in well-nigh inextricable confusion. Perhaps
these men are themselves chiefly to blame for their
own failures, but a good many natural scientists have
great responsibility for their own inability to realize
the nature and the significance of their own methods.

In the course of telling what scientific explanation is
not, we have arrived at a fairly definite idea of what it
is. It will be necessary only to summarize it briefly here.
Scientific explanation is telling what a thing or an event
is like; that is, it is describing it in terms of some other
type of thing or event with whose ways of happening we
are already acquainted. If we can discover some simple type of happening in whose terms we can describe
all other manifold events and phenomena, we shall have
achieved the ideal of such explanation. This the physicist has almost accomplished when he can understand
all non-chemical and non-electrical properties of bodies
in terms of the varying energy of motion of the molecules of which they are composed. In so far as all physical occurrences can be correlated with these molecular
motions, the physicist is in a position to calculate and
predict with extreme accuracy and success, and as a
matter of fact he has found this molecular hypothesis

marvelously fruitful. In particular, it has proved superior to the old caloric theory of heat in enabling us to explain a much greater number of observed phenomena in terms of the one simple type of motion, and to predict other phenomena which later experiments verified. But we must not forget that the scientific type of explanation by analogy is but one among many possible and, depending upon the specific purpose we have in view, equally valid kinds. We can explain the electric light either by expounding the electro-magnetic theory of electricity and light, or by describing the production of bulbs in the Mazda factory, or by considering the need of man for artificial illumination; and our explanation will be analogical, genetic, or purposive according as our interest is predominantly that of the physicist, the manufacturer, or the interior decorator.

QUESTIONS AND EXERCISES

1. Why do we understand events better if we are shown that they resemble something with which we are familiar? How does such a resemblance help us to control them?
2. Does the scientist always choose elements that are familiar by which to explain phenomena? Are we more familiar with molecules or with heat? Give further illustrations.
3. What were the aims of the mediæval scientists in their classification of natural objects? Why does such a classification seem unfruitful to the modern physicist? What basis of classification does he employ?
4. Give examples of the mediæval type of explanation prevalent today.
5. In how far was the caloric theory of heat a scientific explanation?
6. Why do physicists take mechanical action as the most elementary form? Is it more familiar or more simple than the other types?
7. Why do physicists feel and hope that it may be possible to explain every type of event in terms of the behaviour of electrons?
8. If this were possible, how could the electron itself be explained and understood?
9. How does explaining heat on the analogy of mechanical action rather than on that of a fluid enable us to understand it better? To

predict better? To control it better? Which is the more familiar? Which is the simpler?

10. Show how the progress of the science of heat (thermodynamics) was dependent at every stage on methods of exact observation.

11. Why was Rumford so sure motion must be the cause of heat? What had he disproved? What had he proved?

12. Explain how the experiments of Rumford and Davy were applications of the method of difference.

13. Just what did Davy prove? What did he disprove? Joule?

14. Show how the molecular theory of heat fulfills all the requirements of a good hypothesis developed in Chapter III.

15. Give further examples of explanation that have denied the existence of that which they set out to explain.

16. Why do modern scientists tend to emphasize similarities between phenomena at the expense of differences?

17. Can you account for man's instinctive feeling that a complex phenomenon, like the soul, when explained has become less real?

18. Make a list of all the different types of explanation you can think of, illustrating each, and indicating the particular purposes they serve.

BIBLIOGRAPHY

On Heat and the Molecular Theory:
   Encyclopædia Britannica, 11th Edition, Articles "Molecule," "Heat."
   F. A. Soddy, *Matter and Energy.* Home University Library. Henry Holt & Co., 1912.
   J. Tyndall, *Heat as a Mode of Motion.* D. Appleton & Co., 1902.
   Comstock and Troland, *Nature of Matter and Electricity.* Van Nostrand, 1917.
On the Function of Explanation:
   W. James, *Principles of Psychology,* vol. II, chapter "Reasoning." Henry Holt & Co., 1905.

CHAPTER VII

EVOLUTION AS A PRINCIPLE OF EXPLANATION

Section 1. The Variety of Living Things

ONE does not have to look closely in order to see that earthworms, lobsters, spiders, clams, sharks, frogs and monkeys all differ more or less widely from each other. Buried in the earth, there are found the remains of strange plants and animals, unlike any in existence. Thousands upon thousands of species have been minutely described and distinguished by the botanist and zoölogist. In what manner have these extinct and living forms come into being? This question is to be distinguished from that raised in a previous chapter, regarding spontaneous generation. We are not now concerned with the processes by which the individuals of various species are generated; nor shall we inquire about the ultimate origin of life. What we shall consider is *the nature of the relationship* between the great variety of living things.

Two general types of answer have been given to this problem: (1) The forms of life which now or ever have existed have been introduced by separate, distinct, and unconnected creative acts; each species is fixed and genetically unrelated (special creation). (2) All forms of life have descended from a common ancestry; species merge one into another, often by almost indistinguishable differences (evolution).

As historical accounts of the organic realm, the two answers have been, and are, in competition. After formulating them in more detail, therefore, we shall proceed to test them in accordance with the criteria of a good hypothesis. During this analysis, we shall have occasion to refer, in a brief way, to most of the methodological principles thus far examined, as we trace a great inquiry from its beginning in a puzzling situation to its culmination in an hypothesis cumulatively verified from many different fields.

Section 2.   Special Creation: A Fixed World

On the analogy of the jeweler making a watch, or the potter making a vessel of clay, this view asserts that the various kinds of living things were manufactured, produced, fashioned, by some great Artificer whose attributes are essentially human. Appearing very early in the history of the race, the explanation was carried down through oral tradition, popular mythology, and general literature. Numerous expressions of it might be cited, from ancient Babylonian narratives to the pronouncements of present-day literal interpreters of Genesis. But as a more familiar presentation, we may select a number of verses from the seventh book of *Paradise Lost*.

It is the beginning of the fifth day of Creation:

> "And God said, Let the waters generate
> Reptile with spawn abundant, living soul:
> And let fowl fly above the earth, with wings
> Display'd on the open firmament of heav'n.
> And God created the great whales, and each
> Soul living, each that crept, which plenteously
> The waters generated by their kinds,
> And every bird of wing after his kind;
>
>   .   .   .   .
>
> "The sixth, and of creation last, arose
> With ev'ning harps and matin; when God said,

Let the earth bring forth soul living in her kind,
Cattle, and creeping things, and beast of the earth
Each in their kind. The earth obey'd, and straight
Op'ning her fertile womb, teem'd at a birth
Innumerous living creatures, perfect forms,
Limb'd and full grown.

> . . . .

"There wanted yet the master-work, the end
Of all yet done; a creature, who, not prone
And brute as other creatures, but indued
With sanctity of reason, might erect
His stature, and upright with front serene
Govern the rest, self-knowing;

> . . . .

"Let us make now man in our image, man
In our similitude, and let them rule
Over the fish and fowl of sea and air,
Beast of the field, and over all the earth,
And every creeping thing that creeps the ground.
    This said, He form'd thee, Adam, thee, O man,
Dust of the ground, and in thy nostrils breathed
The breath of life: in his own image he
Created thee, in the image of God
Express, and thou becam'st a living soul."

This modern retelling of very ancient stories has well
been called "the Miltonic hypothesis," for in its fundamental characteristics it was the prevailing explanation
of natural science until sixty years ago. Linnæus (1707–
78), for example, the leading botanist of his time, accepted, without question or qualification, the traditional
notion of species, as specially created and unchangeable.
To this effect he wrote: "Reason teaches that, at the beginning of things, a pair of each particular species was
created." And again: "We reckon as many species as
the Infinite Being created in the beginning." Originally
they all appeared at a single spot, resembling the Garden of Eden, and from there spread about the earth. "I
believe that I am not straying far from the truth if I

affirm that in the infancy of the world all the mainland was submerged and covered by an enormous ocean, save one single island in this immeasurable sea, on which all animals dwelt and plants grew luxuriously." [1]

In this connection it would be possible to examine the more or less similar opinions of other distinguished scientists such as Cuvier, Agassiz, and Richard Owen, but our historical interest in this question is only incidental.   Let a summary paragraph from A. D. White suffice.   After surveying widely the growth of the special creation hypothesis, he writes:

Thus down to a period almost within living memory, it was held virtually "always, everywhere, and by all," that the universe as we now see it was created literally and directly by the voice or hands of the Almighty, or by both — out of nothing — in an instant or in six days, or in both — about four thousand years before the Christian era — and for the convenience of the dwellers upon earth, which was at the basis and the foundation of the whole structure. [2]

THE ARGUMENT FOR SPECIAL CREATION

The special creation theory, accepted for many centuries on the basis of an analogy to the making of things by men (see section 5) came to be supported in later years by a number of observations which at the time represented the best opinion of eminent scientists. Palæontology and geology both seemed to substantiate it.

For an extended period there were controversies as to the nature of those peculiar figures that were found imbedded in the rock strata at so many different levels. They were explained by a great variety of conflicting opinions: (a) as mineral concretions, or chance forma-

[1] Quoted by O. Schmidt: *The Doctrine of Descent and Darwinism.*
[2] *A History of the Warfare of Science and Theology.*

tions of mineral matter; (b) as models employed by the Creator; (c) as divine mysteries; (d) as products of the germs of animals and plants which had lost their way. In the eighteenth century, however, palæontology became an important science, and we arrive at Lamarck's modern accepted definition of fossils as "the still recognizable remains of organic bodies." With this conviction, the scientist now proceeded to a more detailed examination of the fossil record, and soon discovered the remains of many extinct plants and animals. He found, further, that there was often no suggestion of relationship between the various levels of fossils, that gradual gradations are not present — in short, that there are wide gaps in the fossil series which would seem to contradict any idea of common ancestry and slow evolution. These observations, which apparently confirm the doctrine of special creation, were the main source of the prevailing assumption in the allied field of geology, while they in their turn were supported by it.

Combining the above conclusion regarding fossil deposits with a belief in the special creation of fixed species and the second important belief that the earth is less than six thousand years old, and we are almost compelled to draw a particular inference regarding the origin of fossils. The inference is that the past history of the earth was marked by a series of tremendous catastrophes unlike any now observable as a result of which all living organisms were destroyed. After each one of these catastrophes, there was no life in the world until the Creator had introduced a new generation of plants and animals. Although the examination of the successive layers of fossils might reveal an ascending order pointing toward the human race, we could only conclude that this order displayed a series of separate creative acts, based, no doubt, on some plan culminating in man, *but furnished no* evidence of genetic relationships. According to this view, then, the present inhabitants of the globe are the lineal descendants of the last creation.

From these views of a broken series of fossils and a short and catastrophic geological history the inference was drawn that special creation was the only hypothesis meeting all conditions. It was an inference only, since no one had ever witnessed the creation of a species. The evidence was consequently indirect.

In examining the evidence we should ask: Does the inference supporting the hypothesis rest on facts correctly presented? Let us examine critically the beliefs regarding fossil groups, and the short space of the earth's history.

It was maintained that the fossil record was broken because a number of past cataclysms brought about the extinction of all life, thereby making necessary innumerable new acts of special creation. When this view was most popular at the opening of the nineteenth century the science of palæontology was at its infancy. But in the interim many gaps in the record have been filled and various series have been made more or less complete, as thousands upon thousands of specimens have been collected and arranged. As early as 1853, Lyell insisted that "There are no signs of an abrupt termination of one fauna and flora, and the starting into life of new and wholly distinct forms."

When there are still gaps in our fossil record there are reasons of seeming adequacy to explain them. "The imperfection of the geological record" is not difficult to understand. Climatic cycles of thousands of years bring about extensive migrations of animals. Driven by the changes from its original habitat, a particular species may return at the end of a very long period. In the interim the remains of that species would not become entombed in the strata then forming. The locations of fossil deposits would be altered by the redistribution of currents and upheavals or subsidences of shores or sea-bottoms., An ocean floor raised to the level of a continent would soon accumulate fossils wholly different from the deeply underlying strata. Vast quantities of fossil remains must have been destroyed by the intense heat in the interior of the earth. But simpler than such geological detail is the fact that many frail organisms not composed of some firm substance such as shell or bone could not possibly be preserved.

The gaps in the fossil series seem susceptible of an explanation other than that of cataclysm, and separate fixed species; and, as these gaps are constantly being filled, the fact of their existence becomes less significant and the thesis of evolution, the rival of special creation, seems better substantiated.

The short duration of the earth's history, a second supposed fact, began under expert geologic investigation to expand itself until the period since life began grew from a few thousand to hundreds of thousands or millions of years — a period of time so vast as to be quite outside the thought of those who had conceived the first account of the origin of living things and had thought in terms of time-spans easily within man's imagination.

The catastrophic theory had, moreover, included a belief in the operation of forces of which we know nothing. These had brought about the great periods of destruction.   In its place a new theory gradually gained followers — the theory of uniformitarianism; that is, the theory which holds that all through the period of the formation of the earth the same uniform forces with which we are acquainted have been at work.   Whenever possible, the scientist prefers to entertain an hypothesis that is susceptible of verification by further investigation.   The catastrophic geology presented a series of incomprehensible revolutions in the past; the uniformitarian explanation made it possible to observe and test in the present those forces to which the past changes were attributed.   The catastrophic theory, furthermore, proved to be an unnecessary assumption in violation of the Law of Parsimony.

In criticism of an hypothesis, in addition to asking concerning the facts from which it is an inference, we ask, Does it bring simplicity into our world view?   In the theory of special creation there is no tendency to derive the simple from the complex; if anything, the problem becomes more complicated.   We are compelled to think of countless species coming into existence, independently of one another.   On estimating the living and extinct species of plants and animals as approximately ten million, we are compelled by this view to think of ten million acts of special creation.

The theory of special creation seems, furthermore, quite unable to throw light on other fields, while its rival, the theory of evolution, does assist in the understanding of the facts of comparative anatomy, embryology, palæontology and geographical distribution.

In a good suggestion we expect to find implications. We say, If this is so, then this, too, will likely be associated and may be understood.   Special creation carries with it no such range of implication; evolution, as we shall see in Section 4, is notably fruitful in this regard.

Section 3.   The Problem of Darwin

"Reason teaches that, at the beginning of things, a pair of each particular species was created." Thus definitely did Linnæus, the lawgiver of Natural History in the eighteenth century, answer the question regarding the variety of living things. It seemed to him as if the world of plants and animals had been ready-made for a clear-cut, precise system of classification ("Linnæan" classification, as we say). As each species was created separate and immutable, one could not possibly be transformed into another. But at the very time that these principles were most dominant, the advance of science in various directions was leading to another point of view.

The earliest, important steps were made in geology. While the catastrophic geology was still universally accepted, a Scotchman, James Hutton (1726–93), who had been studying the formations of his native country for many years, reached the conclusion that the mysterious causes called in by the "catastrophists" were superfluous and fictitious. Affirming that *the present is the key to the past*, he wrote an extensive work illustrating this thesis. Just as the crust of the earth is being changed to-day by the action of rain, rivers and tides, chemical decomposition and internal disturbances, so continents have always been altered and the most ancient strata built up. This is the principle of uniformitarianism (cf. von Zittel, p. 72) which was elaborated by Lyell and in its essential character became the keynote of modern geological investigation.   The following quotation from Playfair was inscribed on the opening page of Lyell's great book: "Amid all the revolutions of the globe, the economy of nature has been uniform and her laws are the only thing which have resisted the general movement. The rivers and the rocks, the seas and the continents have been changed in all their parts; but the laws which direct those changes, and the rules to which they are subject, have remained invariably the same." Darwin once wrote that Lyell's *Principles of Geology* "altered the whole tone of one's mind." And it has often been said that the doctrine of organic evolution is simply the application of uniformitarianism to the problems of biology.

Let us try to understand what is meant by that last statement. The existence of groups of animals having certain peculiar qualities was always more or less evident, until finally the opinion grew up that some of these groups, carefully defined as "species," were definitely immutable. The criterion of fertility was considered absolute, and since they could not have descended from one another, they must have been created separately. But, on the other hand, there were a great many obscure facts which were not illumined by such explanations, and which would at once generate questions in the curious mind, especially in such a mind as that of Charles Darwin. For example, careful observation and classification of fossil remains would reveal the fact that there were gradations in the fossil series, and that those higher in the series resembled contemporary beings more closely than those lower down. Why do animals in a particular region always appear to be related to those in the next region, so that the order of replacement is gradual? "*It was evident,*" wrote Darwin in his *Autobiography,* "*that such facts as these, as well as many others, could only be explained on the supposition that species gradually become modified."*

But now we are faced by the most difficult problem of all. Assuming for the moment that the thousands of existing species all have a common ancestry, what could be the explanation of such an inconceivably complex development? Why should there have been such an evolution? Until the "how" of the process had been discovered, it would be almost impossible to convince people of the process itself. Some solutions had been offered, but none seemed adequate. "That which we were all looking for," wrote Huxley concerning the investigators who were interested in the question before Darwin published *The Origin of Species* in 1859, "was an hypothesis respecting the origin of known organic forms, which assumed the operation of no causes but such as could be proved to be actually at work."

Unless such causes were forthcoming, special creation seemed to be the alternative; and the purposive or teleological character of each living thing became the only explanation which men might know for its existence. Each organism exists for some end. Insects were made to fertilize flowers, while cats exist to catch mice. It is the function of horses to serve men. In the same way every organ was made for a purpose — the eye to see, the ear to hear, the hand to grasp, and so on. For one who accepts this point of view, every fact of adaptation in nature, from the most immense to the most delicate, appears to be clearly explained. This is but a brief statement of the well-known argument from design which was elaborately worked out in Paley's famous work on *Natural Theology.*

The theory of special creation might, to be sure, be

held by those who read no purpose into the creation of the myriad forms, but the theory is usually associated with the belief that the reason why each thing exists is because it is destined to serve some end. This type of explanation gives great satisfaction, since, if it can be held without contradiction, it serves, better than any other, to answer the question, Why? The discovery of a final or ultimate cause sets the mind at rest, while proximate or efficient causes set one wondering as to their origin.

Darwin was not interested, however, in the discovery of a final cause, though nothing in his system or in the belief in evolution precludes the belief that, back of all the process which has brought the world to its present state, there exists one all-inclusive purpose. The Darwinian explanation of the presence of the forms which have existed or now live upon the earth had to do, not with the purpose, but with the mechanism, of evolution. His theory here, that of natural selection, was not his main, evolutionary theory, but only an explanatory element within it. He had perceived the origin of many of our domesticated plants and animals — the result of deliberate planning on the part of breeders and horticulturists. Here were countless examples of modification going on right before his eyes. But this was man-arranged, artificial selection; is there some such selection taking place in nature at large? If so, what are the agencies bringing this about? Now, Darwin had read Paley, but he also read Malthus on *The Principle of Population*. With his original belief in special creation shaken by such questions as we have already referred to, he began to brood over the assertion of Malthus, that the food supply increases arithmetically, whereas animals increase in geometrical proportion. If this is true, a constant struggle for existence will go on in the living world, and those creatures which are able to secure food and adjust themselves to their environment generally will survive, while the others will perish — the process known as "Natural Selection," or "Survival of the Fittest," "fittest" simply meaning capacity for adaptation, and not necessarily largest or muscularly strongest. Since offspring always tend to vary from the parental line (taking variation as a fact given) "favorable variations would tend to be preserved, and unfavorable ones to be destroyed. The result of this would be the formation of a new species. Here then I had at last got a theory by which to work." [1] These sentences mark the beginning of the triumph of the evolution idea. As man produced the types of domestic animals by artificial selection, the struggle for existence has produced changes in the organic forms, in nature at large. It was no longer necessary to invoke supernatural interference in order to understand such changes. It was no longer necessary to introduce a complete teleology in nature in order to explain nice adaptations.

In this chapter we are concerned primarily with the general theory of evolution, and not with the *factors*, or mechanism in nature, which brought about the evolution. It is entirely possible to be convinced of the fact, which is one problem, without having certain knowledge of the factors, which form another problem. But in order to come to a proper understanding of Darwin, it was necessary to dwell in some detail on the causal mechanism of natural selection just described, which led rapidly to the general acceptance of a belief that was as old as

[1] Darwin's *Autobiography*.

ancient philosophy. Many thinkers before Darwin had contended for evolution, and had offered evidence in support of their contention, so that his particular, unique contribution was the explanatory hypothesis of the mechanism of natural selection, or survival of the fittest. It is true that natural selection is by no means adequate to explain all of the complicated features of evolution, nor did Darwin ever argue that it was the exclusive cause. Such factors as the direct influence of environment and the effect of use and disuse of organs have not yet been sufficiently investigated. But whatever further conclusions are drawn, it seems certain that natural selection will always be regarded as one of the important factors.

From a period very early in his investigation, the work of Darwin became largely *deductive* — the problem of fitting into his hypothesis the concrete facts which came under his observation, with the result that the facts which might have led to the formulation of the hypotheses became evidences for their validity. What, then, are the implications of the suggestion that all living forms have a common ancestry? If this hypothesis is sound, we should be able to find many indications of interconnections between the various so-called "species." We should also behold interconnection between fossils. In the bodies of very different animals, there should appear telltale marks of their common origin. From various fields Darwin collected quantities of evidence which confirmed his hypothesis, and since his day there have been opened new fields of investigation which are only illuminated when we interpret them in terms of evolution. (The several kinds of evidence will be considered in the following section.)

At this point let us summarize briefly the method of Darwin. (a) Starting with the traditional belief in special creation and design in nature, he came upon such facts as the geographical distribution of animals and the peculiar relations of fossils. He was impressed further by the way in which breeders produced new varieties by deliberate selection. (b) Such observations seemed to imply modification of species, or diversified development from the same progenitors — the evolutionary hypothesis. But an explanation of this development was lacking, and he found it in the further hypothesis of natural selection, or survival of the fittest. (c) Finally, he discovered that the laborious examination of all manner of facts verified the evolution hypothesis; or, in other words, that from it the specific phenomena of animal and plant life were deducible.

Section 4. Evolution: A Growing World

Organic evolution means that the present is the child of the past and the parent of the future. It is not a power or a principle; it is a process — a process of becoming. It means that the present-day animals and plants and all the subtle inter-relations between them have arisen in a natural knowable way from a preceding state of affairs on the whole somewhat simpler, and that again from forms and inter-relations simpler still, and so on backwards and backwards for millions of years till we lose all clues in the thick mist that hangs over life's beginnings.[1]

Applicable to every living thing in the history of the earth, evolution is one of the most sweeping, all-inclusive generalizations ever conceived. Obviously, it cannot be completely established by direct observation or experiment, since human experience extends over such a

[1] *The Outline of Science*, vol. I, p. 56.

relatively brief period of time and a small part of the globe. But, on the other hand, it is based upon such a multitude of observed facts, constantly being added to, from so many different sources of investigation, that most scientists would probably be inclined to say that evolution is now as well founded as Newton's law of gravitation or the Copernican astronomy. It is this *cumulative character of the evidence* for evolution which becomes such a convincing confirmation. Not the presence of complete proof in any one field, but the fact that in every field evidence has been converging, and in none has it been incompatible with evolution, is the real argument supporting that theory. This fact deserves emphasis as it is a point in the methodology of thought which the evolutionary hypothesis illustrates with particular clarity.

In putting the hypothesis to the test, then, we may repeat the questions formerly asked concerning special creation, without reference to the subordinate problem of the mode or mechanism of the evolutionary process. Is evolution consistent with the known facts? Does it enable us to consider highly complex facts in simpler terms? Does it lead to further unknown facts? In this instance there will be no need of treating the answers separately. We shall see how a vast quantity of apparently unrelated phenomena are made intelligible by a single principle, and for the same reason how a group of originally independent sciences becomes unified. In this way do various distinct types of evidence point toward the same conclusion.

CUMULATIVE EVIDENCE AND EXPLANATION

(1) *Distribution: Palæontology and Geography.*

The examination of geological strata reveals an ascending order of fossil remains from the exceedingly simple to the most complex. Though there are imperfections in the record, there is no indication of completely new beginnings. The latest fossils resemble most closely existent organisms. From the observation of such order we infer genetic continuity. On exhibition in our various museums are concrete examples of genealogical series. Of these the horse pedigree is perhaps the most famous. Through nearly thirty stages, covering a period of approximately two million years, the modern horse is traced from a small animal of about the size of the fox, possessing several toes. Moreover, there have been predicted, and later found, intermediate fossil forms connecting large and now distinct groups, such as the archæopteryx and the pterodactyl, a flying reptile. This great accumulation of facts only becomes intelligible under the evolution hypothesis, so that Huxley was led to remark that palæontologists would have had to invent it if it had not already been put forward. And according to von Zittel, palæontology had a new beginning with the publication of *The Origin of Species*.

It will often appear that there is not the slightest relation between the animals of widely separated sections of a continent. But investigation of the intervening regions will show animals gradually varying between the two extremes. Interpreting these facts in terms of evolution, we conclude that they have all originated from a common center, being gradually modified as they were adapted to a new environment.

(2) *Comparative   Anatomy: Classification,   Homology,
    Vestiges.*

It is possible to draw up a "tree of life" which will
point to the general unity of the entire animal world.
Group merges into group in the most significant manner.   The natural connections between some of the
larger classes are continually being discovered.   In a
broad way, we can trace a line of descent from the one-
celled amœba to the highest vertebrates.   The possibility of zoölogical classification would be a profound
mystery without the development principle.

Homologous structures, according to the comparative
anatomist, are those which have a close resemblance
both in architecture and in manner of development.
For example, "the fore leg of a lizard, the wing of a
bird and of a bat, the burrowing shovel of a mole, the
flipper of a whale, the fore leg of a horse, the human arm
and hand," are all homologous structures. They seem
to be modifications of a single primitive type, the conclusion implied by evolution.

Useless and imperfect organs exist in all animals.
There are several incomplete bones in the leg of the
horse, including two functionless digits.   Whales have
vestiges of hind legs, hidden below the surface.   In human beings there are the muscles of the ears, the vermi-
form appendix, and occasionally "hare-lips," none of
which are of any value.   Such vestigial structures either
indicate nothing, or they point back to a prolonged evolution, to animals in which such organs were functional.

(3) *Artificial Breeding: Domestication and Experiment.*

It is difficult to deny the fact of evolution when we see

concrete examples of the process in the cultivation of plants and the domestication of animals. An observer of the preëvolution period, no matter how acute, would naturally see numerous fixed species among the many varieties of dogs, horses, pigeons, and so forth. But there is sufficient reason for affirming that our dogs are domesticated wolves, the many kinds of pigeons have descended originally from the wild rock-dove, and our beasts of burden have also had their more or less common progenitors.

Data drawn from the comparatively new science of genetics have verified further the hypothesis of evolution. The experiments often involve dozens or even hundreds of generations of a single species. Observations made under controlled conditions have revealed wide variations from an identical ancestry. Permanent and hereditary modifications have been brought about by abrupt changes of the environment. "Thus," as Professor Scott writes, "the experimental proof goes to show that the species of plants and animals are not fixed and immutable entities, but are capable of extensive modification even in the short time which is at the command of the experimenter." [1]

(4) *Embryology and Blood-Tests.*

There are striking resemblances in the embryonic development of animals in the same group. The embryos of reptiles, birds, and mammals, up to a certain stage, are not immediately distinguishable. At one point, the circulatory systems of all mammalians are essentially fish-like. In embryos, also, there occur vestigial structures, many of which, however, disappear before birth.

[1] *The Theory of Evolution*, p. 157.

In a highly abbreviated fashion the embryos seem to repeat the supposed history of the race. As species are seen to be related, so the individual, bearing numerous traces of his remote ancestry, ceases to appear as a distinctly new, sharply defined entity. Unbroken continuity is the outstanding feature of the organic realm.

There is a final class of evidence for evolution which differs in character from any known to Darwin, namely, the more recently discovered blood-tests. It is found in many cases that when the red blood corpuscles of a dog or a lower monkey are brought into contact with the serum or liquid portion of the blood of a human being the corpuscles are dissolved; but when the red blood corpuscles of a higher anthropoid ape are brought into contact with human serum they remain unaffected. This condition is paralleled in the case of a horse and an ass, a hare and a rabbit, an orang and a gibbon, a dog and a wolf. There is a slightly different reaction known as the precipitin test which has been performed by Professor Nuttall of Cambridge University sixteen thousand times with a large variety of blood sera. These two types of experiment are further indications of the general unity of all animal life and they point out specifically the degrees of relationships between the groups of animals, including the relationships between man and the higher apes. In this way, not only is the evolution hypothesis further substantiated, but an entirely new field of investigation is illuminated, which, without that hypothesis, would be incomprehensible. Add to this the multifarious facts of palæontology, geographical distribution, comparative anatomy, genetics, and embryology as integrated by the evolutionary interpretation, and we may understand somewhat how far-

reaching in its consequences a profound theory may be.
Literally, evolution has created new sciences while it has
remade old ones.

THE EFFECT OF EVOLUTION ON CLASSIFICATION

But more immediately in connection with our study
of scientific principles, it is important to note the effect
of evolution on the former conception of biological classification. That conception, as most thoroughly developed by Linnæus, was based on the doctrine of special
creation; the same position was taken by Linnæus' contemporary, Cuvier, one of the keenest observers in all
the history of science.   According to them, the organic
world was naturally divided into a certain number of
sharply defined, unrelated classes.   For them, the apparent connections between some of the classes is only
ideal, and not genetic.   "Specific features are constant,
and remain so even in domesticated breeds."   Thus,
careful definition and accurate classification, which are
the first stages in scientific investigation, became the
end and ideal of biological science in the eighteenth century.   This was the inevitable consequence of the false
foundation upon which biology then rested.   Not even
genius, such as that of Linnæus or Cuvier, could advance
far without a sound hypothesis, both as a guide for observation and as a principle of explanation.   "Nature,
it has been said, gives no reply to a general inquiry —
she must be interrogated by questions which already
contain the answer she is to give; in other words, the observer can only observe that which he is led by hypothesis to look for; the experimenter can only obtain the result which his experiment is designed to obtain." [1]

[1] E. R. Lankester, *Degeneration;* cf. Creighton: *An Introductory
Logic*, pp. 278-82.

The doctrine of evolution has exposed the arbitrary character of the older classification. We have come to realize that there are no sharp lines in nature, that the various forms of life have numerous relationships, and that ultimately they are all parts of one continuous stream. We have come to realize that there are no separate groups resulting from special creation. For precisely this reason, the word "species," which has been used so often in this chapter, has not undergone definition; it cannot be strictly defined. There are no fixed, immutable species, as formerly imagined. Even the chemist has found that his divisions are not absolute, discovering that atoms break down to form other elements. The distinction often made in logic textbooks between "natural" and "artificial" classification is really misleading; all classification is more or less artificial, more or less approximate. Such terms as "species" and "genera" are not, as we have noted, descriptive of actual divisions in the nature of things; they are only convenient, practical instruments, by means of which the naturalist organizes his material. And as such, they are exceedingly valuable, being the raw material of biological generalization.

Section 5.   Some Psychological Factors in Biological Belief

The belief that each living thing existed by an act of special creation, and the belief that all creation had a purpose, including, ultimately, that of serving man himself, find support in some of the most deeply rooted tendencies of thought.

Man knows how he himself does things; he knows that he makes his tools, his home, his garments.   Each new object which aids him in his life is directly or indirectly the work of his hands. With this knowledge strong within him, what could be more natural than that he should think of all living things, and the earth itself as the work of some great artificer, man-like, but enormously more wise and powerful? This tendency of man to think of things in terms of himself is called "anthropomorphism," man-form-ism. It is hard, furthermore, to understand not merely how things came to be, but also how they came to fit together. When things suit man's convenience, he himself has usually brought them together in accordance with some plan. Many things in the world man is acquainted with, fit together with amazing serviceability. This fact cannot escape even a casual observer. What more natural, then, than that man, even in explaining this world, should think that all created things play a part in some great preconceived plans, and that each thing serves some purpose? Spinoza (1632–77) gave a classic expression to this idea in his *Ethics:* [1]

Men do all things for an end, namely, for that which is useful to them, and which they seek. Thus it comes to pass that they only look for a knowledge of the final causes of events, and when these are learned they are content, as having no cause for further doubt. If they cannot learn such causes from external sources, they are compelled to turn to considering themselves, and reflecting what end would have induced them personally to bring about the given event, and thus they necessarily judge other natures by their own. Further, as they find in themselves, and outside of themselves, many means which assist them not a little in their search for what is useful, for instance, eyes for seeing, teeth for chewing, herbs and animals for yielding food, the sun for giving light, the sea

[1] Appendix, Book I.

for breeding fish, etc., they come to look on the whole of nature as a means for obtaining such conveniences. Now, as they are aware that they found these conveniences and did not make them, they think they have cause for believing that some other being has made them for their use. As they look upon things as means, they cannot believe them to be self-created; but judging from the means which they are accustomed to prepare for themselves, they are bound to believe in some ruler or rulers of the universe endowed with human freedom, who have arranged and adapted everything for human use." [1]

Thus, as Spinoza says, man is apt to see a purpose in the order of creation which serves himself as its pinnacle. Pride is a great motivator of belief. For this reason each creature might well be thought of as specially placed on earth for man's use. This tendency is called "anthropocentrism" — man's tendency to orient all things from himself as the center. This psychological tendency is one of the reasons for the enduring appeal of special creation and for the opposition to evolution.

The believer in evolution, who may be, to be sure, convinced on other grounds, sometimes finds in his desire to believe the doctrine an additional motive for its acceptance. Perhaps the best example of this psychological rather than logical element in belief is to be found in those persons or groups who pursue in their conduct the theory of the survival of the fittest, carried over into the ethical field of conscious and responsible human relations, with all the crudeness of its operation in the non-conscious and non-evaluating realm of nature. Valid standards for human ethics are not discoverable in the non-human world. The uncritical belief that the survival of the fittest is everywhere nature's law seems to

[1] Cf. Hume, *The Natural History of Religion.*

such persons justification for their conduct; and justification is a constant human need.[1]

In the scales for weighing belief neither man's tendency to such self-justification, nor his habit of viewing things in terms of likeness to himself, nor his fondness for making all things serve him, should weigh heavily — they may be causes, but scarcely reasons, for belief. Evidence rather than desire is a reliable guide. Into figures there can creep few biases. Even there, however, bias may appear in interpretation.

very good

Section 6.   Misconceptions of Evolution

However carefully the principle of evolution may have been formulated, misinterpretations were bound to follow as it became involved in general application. Among scientists themselves the implications of an hypothesis are frequently carried beyond their logically justifiable bounds. But when an idea derives its name from the common speech and makes a serious appeal to the popular mind, the danger of perversion is indefinitely greater. This is especially true of the doctrine of evolution. A large part of our thinking, often quite unconsciously, is "evolutionary." It has become the general tendency to study all phenomena in terms of origin and growth. The development of religious beliefs, political institutions, and moral customs is traced along with the genealogies of plants and animals. As might be expected, therefore, the strictly scientific notion of evolution has been variously misunderstood, and in the following sections we shall discuss two of the more common misconceptions.

[1] John Stuart Mill, *Essay on Nature;* Thomas Huxley, *Evolution and Ethics.*

EVOLUTION NOT SELF-EXPLANATORY

How exceedingly valuable evolution is as a principle of explanation, we have already observed in some detail. It has indicated relationships between multitudes of widely separated phenomena. We realize that ideas and objects, animals and institutions, do not soar up in sudden isolated fashion, but, on the contrary, are all parts of continuous series.

An evolutionary explanation is an historical description of events occurring in time. But *an historical description is not per se a causal explanation.* It is one thing to trace antecedents; it is quite a different thing to discover reasons for that particular succession. "There is an obvious and striking similarity between the evolution of man's inventions and the evolution of the shells of molluscs and of the bones of mammals, yet in neither case does a knowledge of the order in which these things arose explain them." [1] The fact that there should have been any changes at all is a profound, and often an insoluble, problem. This is simply the crucial distinction that we have already made between the *fact* and the *factors* of evolution. Granting this order, why has it been as it has been? Why did this occurrence precede that? Or, for example, why have our ancestors had certain beliefs?

If we ask why they so believed, it will not profit us to pursue antiquity again, unless by so doing we come upon the contemporaneous, experimental origin of that belief. For it is evident that if the belief had an origin, there was a time anterior when it did not exist, and its origin cannot, therefore, be explained solely in terms of that anterior time. Its origin points, not to continuity, but to action. It indicates, not that

[1] T. H. Morgan, *Theory of Evolution*, p. 4.

the originators of the belief had ancestors, but that, in view of their contemporaneous circumstances, they acted in a certain way. To explain the origin of anything, therefore, we cannot trust to the continuity of history alone. The continuity may carry us back to the beginnings of beliefs and institutions which have persisted and been transmitted from age to age; it may reveal to us experimental factors which have shaped beliefs and institutions, but which have long since been forgotten; but it can never, of itself, reveal the experimental origin of any belief or institution. That is, in principle, the limitation by which the explanatory value of historical continuity is restricted. To understand origins we must appeal to the contemporaneous experience of their own age, or to experimental science.[1]

Certainly evolution is a valid kind of explanation, but it is by no means the only kind. "To explain anything at all, it is necessary to keep in mind the questions to which the proposed explanation is relevant." In the previous chapter we discovered that a variety of explanations can be given for the same facts, depending on the specific questions that have been asked. A mechanical explanation, for example, is not incompatible with an explanation in terms of purpose. So we may consider a particular lyric as the consequence of the poet's unusual diet or his unusual lady, and neither explanation will exclude the other. The beauty of the lyric itself, as much as the beauty of a rose sprung from a refuse heap, is quite independent of its origin. In the same way, the truth of Schopenhauer's philosophy, or of Nietzsche's, or of Carlyle's, may be examined without reference to mental pathology. Though science originated in myth, it does not follow that contemporary science is mythical. If religion developed from ghost-

[1] Woodbridge, *The Purpose of History*, p. 69.

worship, modern religion is not therefore nothing but a modification of belief in ghosts.   The understanding of most phenomena is reached better by a contemplation of the latter stages than of the earlier, the contemplation of the oak rather than the acorn, the bird rather than the egg, the finished book rather than the fragmentary outline.   The conduct of conscious beings can be interpreted more intelligently by considerations of purpose than of physiology.   The knowledge of man's humble origin and of his bloody history is no justification of bellicose ideals and continuous wars among civilized peoples.

EVOLUTION NOT NECESSARILY PROGRESSIVE

In the briefest phrase possible, evolution means descent, with modifications which are usually adaptive. It is thus purely a scientific, descriptive term, with no moral or æsthetic implications.   It has no necessary connection with progress.   But that some such identification would be made is explained by the theory that the idea of evolution itself evolved from the idea of progress as "a gift from the philosophy of human nature to the philosophy of all nature." [1]   Progress was the dominant theme of revolutionary enthusiasm early in the last century, and somewhat later, evolution became the focus of discussion.   In the Synthetic Philosophy of Herbert Spencer and the poetry of Tennyson the two ideas are hopelessly mingled.

On the whole, we have been right in thinking of evolution as a movement from the relatively simple to the relatively complex.   This has involved finer adaptations,

---

[1] Cf. Benn, *History of English Rationalism in the Nineteenth Century*, vol. v, p. 13.

increased stability, and advance in intelligence.   The
human race is the latest stage of a prolonged and complicated process.   But there may be, and indeed there is,
in nature, evolution "downward" — that is, movement
from the more complex to the less complex — in a most
astonishing degree.   As Professor Lankester has pointed
out, there are three possibilities for any form of life: (1)
balance, in which it maintains more or less its *status quo*,
an even equilibrium; (2) *elaboration*, in which it becomes
more complex in structure; (3) *degeneration*, in which the
complexity of its structure diminishes and it becomes
adapted to more simple conditions of life.   Parasitism is
a manner of adaptation in which one organism lives off
another, inhabiting the food-canal, the blood-stream, or
the tissues.   It has been estimated that more than half
the animal kingdom is parasitic.

With regard to ourselves, the white races of Europe, the
possibility of Degeneration seems worth some consideration.
In accordance with a tacit assumption of universal progress
— an unreasoning optimism — we are accustomed to regard
ourselves as necessarily progressing, as necessarily having arrived at a higher and more elaborated condition than that
which our ancestors reached, and as destined to progress still
further.   On the other hand, it is well to remember that we
are still subject to the general laws of Evolution, and are
as likely to degenerate as to progress.   As compared with
the immediate forefathers of our civilization — the ancient
Greeks — we do not appear to have improved as far as our
bodily structure is concerned, nor assuredly so far as some of
our mental capacities are concerned.   Our powers of per-
ceiving and expressing beauty of form have certainly not increased since the days of the Parthenon and Aphrodite of
Melos.   In matters of the reason, the development of the intellect, we may seriously inquire how the case stands.   Does
the reason of the average man of civilized Europe stand out

clearly as an evidence of progress when compared with that of men of bygone ages? In such respects we have at least reason to fear that we may degenerate.[1]

Section 7. Summary

The foregoing comparison of the special creation and evolutionary hypotheses illustrates once more on a large scale all the methodological principles described in previous chapters, makes the meaning of those principles clearer, and adds new points to our account of reflection in the sciences. In comparing the Ptolemaic and Copernican astronomies the criteria of a good scientific hypothesis were found to be: (1) ability to explain all the facts, (2) simplicity, and (3) usefulness in prediction and further discovery. The analysis of the molecular theory in physics showed us what was meant by explanation.

In one sense the special creation theory is able to explain all the facts better than any evolutionary theory. For no description yet offered of the mechanism of evolution is quite consistent with *all* the evidence, whereas the Creator is by a single act of faith endowed with the power to produce anything He likes. But this greater inclusiveness of the special creation theory is procured by giving almost no account of the mechanism of creation, so that we cannot be said to understand it at all, much less to predict what further species it may be expected to produce. In the full sense of the word "explanation," therefore, the special creation theory may be said to explain nothing whatever. The only kind of explanation it gives is a sense of completed inquiry and rest in the contemplation of a supreme power that can

[1] E. Ray Lankester, *Degeneration.*

do anything.   The satisfaction which accompanies the final solution of a problem is here reached, but only by surrendering the problem, and without real illumination.

One should observe that simplicity in science must never be procured by turning away from facts.   Though the creation process may seem simpler than the evolutionary one, the latter has the tremendous scientific advantage of involving processes that have all been actually observed in nature, while all the elements of the former are hypothetical.   The special creation theory illustrates two tendencies of the human imagination which are dangerous to science.   One is the tendency to speculate rather than to observe; the other is the tendency of these speculations to take an anthropomorphic form, as if all beings were like men.   We have at once too much and too little imagination for science.   Scientific imagination must be free to conceive unfamiliar processes, and at the same time ready to test its conceptions by experience.   It must be bold, yet disciplined.

To illustrate these qualities of scientific imagination, and also to show how a broad generalization like evolution rests on evidence accumulated from many fields, was the special function of this chapter.   It may be pointed out, in closing, that the question of the ultimate origin of the universe was not involved in the problem, and therefore was not discussed.

QUESTIONS AND EXERCISES

1. Cite concrete examples of the special creation hypothesis from at least three ancient religions.
2. What is anthropomorphism?   Write an account of the living world from the point of view of some lower animal; assuming that they could reflect, how might an ant or a dog explain the existence of his fellows?   (See Clarence Day: *This Simian World.*)
3. What is meant by "explaining the past in terms of the present"?

In what two fundamental ways does the "scientific imagination" differ from the imagination manifested in popular mythology?

4. Name ten results of the process of natural selection, and show how they might also be used as evidence for the argument from design.

5. Why does Darwin stand out preëminently in the history of the theory of evolution?

6. Give some reasons for Darwin's success in a field where many other great men failed.

7. What were the three pairs of conflicting hypotheses in the evolution controversy?

8. What do we mean by evidence accumulating? Why is this an important matter for the support of an hypothesis?

9. What effect did the idea of evolution have on the traditional conception of biological classification?

10. Outline the phases of Darwin's investigation in terms of "the complete act of thought."

11. Does evolution always mean progress? Cite instances of degeneration in a nation; of an organism.

BIBLIOGRAPHY

Special Creation:

T. Huxley, *Science and Hebrew Tradition.* The Macmillan Company, 1893–95.

O. Schmidt, *The Doctrine of Descent and Darwinism.* D. Appleton & Co., 1898.

K. A. von Zittel, *History of Geology and Palæontology.* Charles Scribner's Sons, 1901.

The Problem of Darwin:

F. Darwin, *The Life and Letters of Charles Darwin.* D. Appleton & Co., 1888.

H. F. Osborn, *From the Greeks to Darwin.* The Macmillan Company, 1894.

J. W. Judd, *The Coming of Evolution.* Cambridge, 1912.

F. Cramer, *The Method of Darwin.* A. C. McClurg, 1896.

J. A. Thomson, *The Outline of Science* (vol. II). G. P. Putnam's Sons, 1922.

Evolution :

W. B. Scott, *The Theory of Evolution.* The Macmillan Company, 1921.

T. H. Morgan, *A Critique of the Theory of Evolution.* Princeton, 1919.

H. E. Crampton, *The Doctrine of Evolution.* Columbia University Press, 1919.

P. Geddes and J. A. Thomson, *Evolution.* Home University Library.

Evolution in Modern Thought. Modern Library, Boni and Liveright.

J. A. Thomson, *The Outline of Science* (vol. I).

Progress and Evolution:
E. R. Lankester, *The Advancement of Science.* London, 1890. (Contains essay on Degeneration.)
R. S. Lull, *Organic Evolution.* The Macmillan Company, 1917.
A. R. Wallace, *Social Environment and Moral Progress.* Funk and Wagnalls, 1913.
T. Huxley: *Evolution and Ethics.*

CHAPTER VIII

HOW REFLECTIVE THOUGHT DEALS WITH THE PAST AS ILLUSTRATED BY THE CRITICISM OF THE PENTATEUCH

Section 1. Character of Historical Inquiry

WE have seen how scientific inquiry deals with natural phenomena; that is, those facts of experience which can either be reproduced at will or observed repeatedly as they recur. Some scientific methods, however, will evidently fail us when we seek to ascertain events *in the past;* for, in the nature of the case, *past events do not recur* and cannot recur. Historical events differ from scientific events proper, in that they cannot be proved experimentally; for *they cannot be repeated.* No doubt one Indian war may be much like another; but no Indian fighter, General Miles, for example, ever did, or ever could, duplicate Custer's last fatal battle with the Sioux. Historical inquiry, therefore, must resort, either (1) to the after effects of events gone by — too often mere vestiges — or (2) to the testimony of eye- and ear-witnesses, all of whom, recent history apart, are now dead. Geology, the history of the physical earth, is virtually confined to the first resource; human history makes use chiefly of the second — the testimony of former witnesses.

Historical inquiry is thus dependent mainly upon written testimony, or documents. Hence it is, also, largely a literary and critical inquiry; that is, it is concerned with questions as to the age, correct test, authorship, teachings, and design of its documentary sources.

(1) *The Lower Criticism.* The determination of the true text of an ancient manuscript requires such special training that this kind of investigation has become a distinct branch of historico-critical inquiry. It is known as the "lower criticism," or at times "textual criticism," *criticism* being the accepted name for *careful inquiry into the past according to canons already approved in experience.* It is called "lower," not because it is inferior, but because it is concerned with the evidential foundations of the subject-matter. In most cases ancient books are now extant in the form of various manuscripts the wording of which differs not infrequently one from another. The original manuscripts were, of course, long since worn out or lost. Those of to-day are copies, and copies of copies, indeed the last links in a long chain of copies. All of these were made by hand; and even the best copyists are subject to error. Omissions have been made; additions, also, sometimes in the form of what are called "glosses." A "gloss" is a comment written upon the margin of the page by some reader, which a later scribe, supposing it to have been omitted, has copied into the body of the manuscript. In all such cases, which is the correct text? It is for the "lower critic" to answer.

(2) *The Higher Criticism.* All questions as to date, authorship, contents, and purpose fall within the field of the "higher critic"; that is, the inquirer concerned with the superstructure of record and thought reared by the author of the book. In this extensive task the higher critic is not without accepted canons of judgment to guide him; for historical criticism, learning partly from its own experience and partly from that of the courts of law, has established certain principles of documentary

evidence.   In practice these methods take the form of queries to be applied to each document, and are such as the following:

(*a*) What is the *content* of the writing? that is, What does the witness actually say?

(*b*) *Who* is the witness?   This question is not one of purely literary interest; it often has a most important bearing upon the witness's competency. To answer it is often much harder than an ordinary reader might suppose.   Ancient writers were not wont to put their names upon their manuscripts.   When the author's name is present, it has usually been placed there by a later hand, probably that of a copyist.   But did the copyist know who was the author?   If not, what were the grounds of his opinion on the subject?   A further difficulty arises from the fact that in ancient times the name attached to a book as its ostensible author was sometimes not that of the writer, but of some man of distinction in an age gone by whose putative authorship would be likely to give the book prestige and authority.

(*c*) Another question concerns the personal qualifications of the writer as to character, competency, and opportunity. Was he an eye- or ear-witness, or does his account rest upon hearsay?   If parts of the Pentateuch were written by Ezra (in the fifth century B.C.) it is obvious that they may not be good evidence as to what happened in the time of Moses, over a thousand years before.   But even eye-witnesses, as every court of justice knows full well, differ greatly in their powers of observation, and still more in their capacity to report events as they actually saw them.   For example, it has been shown that the three principal eye-witness accounts of so recent an event as the surrender of Napoleon III at Sedan vary in material respects, although one of the witnesses was the owner of the house in which the capitulation was signed, another a prominent German general, and the third the noted war-correspondent, Archibald Forbes.

In particular, it has been found that witnesses have a tendency both to perceive and to remember things, first, according to their expectations, second, according to their emotional bias, and, third, according to their private notions as to what would be the natural or reasonable way for things to happen. So criticism inquires, also, into the personality of the witness, which means not only his veracity, but also his mental tendencies. Was he a man of sober frame of mind, or was he imaginative in his thinking? Was he chiefly concerned with actual events — the facts — or was his main interest in the political or ethical or theological bearings of things?

(3) For most historical inquiries two kinds of evidence are available, *external* and *internal*.

(*a*) External evidence consists in such things as references to the writing in question, or quotations from it, by contemporary or shortly succeeding writers. In the case of most of the Old Testament books this kind of evidence is lacking. The books themselves are the only survivals of early Hebrew literature, and international culture in those days can scarcely be said to have existed.

(*b*) Internal evidence consists in all those critical indications which lie within the writing itself, such as the language used, the literary style, the opinions expressed or implied, and the historical and geographical references. For instance, when in Isaiah XLIV, 28 Yahveh is represented as saying of "Cyrus, He is my shepherd, and shall perform all my pleasure; even saying of Jerusalem, Thou shalt be built: and to the temple, Thy foundations shall be laid," etc., it is evident that that part of the book was not written by Isaiah, who antedated Cyrus by a century and a half. Nor, indeed, was it written before the captivity, for evidently Jerusalem was lying waste and needed to be rebuilt.

As an example of historical inquiry the problem of the origin and general structure of the Pentateuch, or first five books of the Bible, has been chosen for study, in the belief that it is a case which can be followed by any intelligent reader.

Section 2.   The Traditional and Critical Views of the Old Testament

At the beginning of the Christian era, the Jewish literature then current consisted chiefly of certain books which, because of their religious contents, were regarded as sacred and authoritative. They were known as the Scriptures, or writings. Later when taken collectively ecclesiastical scholars called them the canon, but the popular name for them became the Bible. These writings were divided by a writer [1] of the second century B.C. — probably not for the first time — into three groups, "the law and the prophets and the rest of the books." (1) Subsequent usage in the Talmud, New Testament, and Josephus shows that by the "Law" was meant the Pentateuch — Genesis, Exodus, Leviticus, Numbers, and Deuteronomy — all of which were attributed to Moses as author.   (2) By the "Prophets" was meant of course,

[1] The grandson of Jesus, the son of Sirach, who about 139 B.C. translated his grandfather's Proverbs into Greek.

the books of Amos, Hosea, and so forth, called the "Later Prophets," Daniel excepted, and also the more important of what we now consider the historical books, namely, Joshua, Judges, Samuel, and Kings. These were known as the "Earlier Prophets." (3) The third, or miscellaneous, group came to be called the "Sacred Writings," though in point of fact it was regarded as less sacred than the "Law" or even than the "Prophets."

These Biblical writings are accepted, not only by orthodox Jews, but by Mohammedans and virtually all Christian churches as true and authoritative, as are also the main Jewish literary ideas concerning them. For example, the Council of Trent, which in 1564 largely stereotyped the Roman Catholic creed, pronounced as follows: "The sacred and holy œcumenical and general Synod of Trent, lawfully assembled in the Holy Ghost ...receives and venerates with an equal affection of piety all the books both of the Old and New Testament, seeing that one God is the author of both. ... And it has thought it meet that a list of the sacred books be inserted in this decree," etc. At the end of the list the decree adds, "if any one receive not as sacred and canonical the said books entire with all their parts ... let him be anathema." In general the Protestant churches have concurred in these statements although the latter do not accept the so-called "apocrypha" as inspired.

This brief historical sketch reveals two connected, but quite distinguishable, things:

(1) The existence prior to the Christian era of a collection of books accepted as sacred, the first five of which (the "Law" or Pentateuch) current Jewish opinion assigned to the initial period of Israel's history and attributed to one author, Moses — Israel's origi-

nal legislator, and traditional liberator from Egyptian bondage.

(2) A remarkable consensus of opinion as to the supernatural character and authority of these books, an authority varying in degree usually in direct proportion to their reputed age. Thus the Protestant Westminster Confession declares concerning them, "All which are given by inspiration of God, to be the rule of faith and life." These opinions as to age, authorship, and authority constitute the traditional view of the Old Testament and of the Pentateuch as its oldest and most sacred portion.

Over against this age-long and cumulatively buttressed body of opinion the modern critic has dared to offer another account of the Hebrew Scriptures, and to advocate it as rationally superior. According to him the Old Testament is the *selected literature* of an ancient, developing people, the selective criterion (used more or less subconsciously) being that of religious and patriotic value.

(1) As in Greece and other seats of early culture, the literary beginnings consisted of songs, such as the song of Miriam, the song of Moses, and the song of Deborah. (Exod. xv, 1–19, 21; Judges v.) Professor Sanday characterizes them as "impassioned utterances of the natural man." They are strong in group loyalty, and breathe a lively devotion to Yahveh as the tribal God.

(2) The next type of writing to appear was that of *history*, or quasi-history, though much legal material was included in it. In the main the Pentateuch is a synthesized and edited collection of parts of three historical writings, parts selected by a fourth and later hand, a hand which added no little material of its own

and thus became the author of the Pentateuch as a whole.   Except in the case of Deuteronomy the parts selected from older documents do not correspond with the traditional divisions of the Pentateuch.

(a) One of the original sources used is now known as the *Elohist*, owing to the fact that, along with his other distinctive characteristics, the author, down to the Mosaic period, uses the name Elohim for the national God. His narrative — technically known as E — is annalistic. It includes many genealogical lists, and lays weight upon orderly development.   The author was a citizen of the northern kingdom, which means, of course, that he wrote after the time of Solomon, and is by no means to be identified with Moses.

(b) Another leading Pentateuchal author is known as the *Jehovist*, or *Yahvist*, because from the very first he calls the divinity by his tribal or covenant name of Yahveh.   His contribution is called J (Jehovist).   He gives another and strikingly different account of the creation. He treats the early history from the ethical and theological viewpoint of prophetism, and seems to have lived in the kingdom of Judah.   Manuscripts E and J originated apparently between the time of Solomon and the eighth century prophets (Hosea, Amos, etc.), and at a relatively early date were so combined that in places they are not now distinguishable.   So they are sometimes referred to together as J. E.

(c) The third historical factor is *Deuteronomy*, which made its appearance in the reign of Josiah in the latter part of the seventh century, B.C.   It contains much legal and ecclesiastical material, but is written largely from the prophetic point of view.   It was perhaps the outcome of a compromise between the prophetic and the

priestly parties.   Its aim was, on the one side, a stricter
monotheism and, on the other, a more equitable social
order.   It was apparently a product, and certainly an
instrument, of the notable prophetic reformation effected under King Josiah.   Its references to addresses
made to the people by Moses were literary devices for
claiming the authority of the great deliverer of old, an
authority which the author doubtless believed was on
his side; but there is no reason to think that he had
more than possibly an oral tradition to justify him.
The Book of the Covenant (Exod. xxi–xxiii) already
ascribed to Moses may have been a written source
utilized by the author.

(*d*) The fourth and all-inclusive section of the Pentateuch is primarily legal, and especially occupied with
ceremonial matters.   It is known as P, because it appears to have been the work of a priest, or of a partisan
of the priestly ideals and interests.   It dates from the
Jewish restoration in the fifth century B.C. under Nehe-
miah and Ezra, and Ezra probably was its author.   The
ceremonial law as proclaimed by him was a combination
of prophetic and priestly factors, factors which had
formerly been often at variance, but which the tribula-
tions of deportation and captivity had brought into
temporary accord.   Religious ritual and rules regulating it there had been, of course, from very early times,
and it had been increasing in amount for generations
prior to the fall of Jerusalem.   These ceremonial provisions Ezra incorporated into his edition of the Mosaic
law; but many of his rules appear to have had no standing in that law before his time, unless it be in the minds
of certain priestly zealots.   As a completed whole the
Pentateuch thus arose in one of the later stages of Hebrew history and by no means at the outset.

In this critical view of the Pentateuch the most fundamental contentions appear to be two: (1) In general its older parts are not now in their original form, but have been expanded or curtailed, cast and recast, in later times.   (2) The Pentateuch, and indeed most of our present Old Testament books, are composite, being constituted largely, and through various editing processes, of the older writings just referred to.

The opposition between these two views is evidently great.   To the conservative believer the critic seems to be unreasonable and presumptuous in thus challenging (as one such [1] says) "convictions which have come down unchallenged from the earliest Jewish age until what may be called yesterday."   John Stuart Blackie's remark about the criticism of the *Iliad* is cited: "We who stand on the recognized text have the tradition of long centuries in our favor. . . . Possession in literary, as in civil, matters is nine points of the law."   Indeed, the very concessions of the new interpreters favor the charge of presumption.   "The critic," says Professor Kuenen, "has no other Bible than the public.   He does not profess to have any additional documents, inaccessible to the laity, nor does he profess to find anything in his Bible that the ordinary reader cannot see. . . . Yet he dares to form a conception of Israel's religious development totally different from that which, as any one may see, is set forth in the Old Testament."

Nor is the critic able to appeal to archæology for support.   The monuments and other material remains of ancient times do not contradict the traditional view.   The opposition between the two views is thus not properly one as to the facts, but one as to the right interpre-

[1] John Kennedy, D.D.

tation of the facts. Opposite ways of thinking are involved. This thought opposition will appear more clearly if we follow the critic in a few of his reasonings.

Section 3.   Some of the Critical Arguments

All of these are appeals to *internal,* not external, evidence. In the first place, the critic points to the *composite character of the Pentateuch.* That the book of Proverbs is a collection of writings of various authorship probably no Biblical student will deny. The first nine chapters, attributed by the text to Solomon, and headed repeatedly with the words, "My son," are plainly different in style from the succeeding thirteen chapters, which have a fresh title and do not use that form of address. Other parts of the book are attributed to "the wise," to Agur, to King Lemuel, while the conclusion (an alphabetical acrostic) appears to be anonymous. Much the same is true of the book of Psalms. Five distinct hymn-books are plainly in evidence, each having a concluding doxology, and each made up apparently with no more regard for authorship than a modern hymn-book. Evidently literary compilation was nothing foreign to ancient Hebrew composition.

In the Pentateuch the composite structure is naturally not so obvious; but surely few who believe that Moses was its author will deny that verses 5 to 12 in the 34th chapter of Deuteronomy were written by a later hand than his. Even with the utmost good-will, one can scarcely believe that Moses wrote the account of his own death and burial, and then added, "*No man knoweth of his sepulchre unto this day.*" Such a remark could come with propriety only from one who wrote long afterward, with the admission of which truth, be it noted, the higher criticism of the Pentateuch has begun. It cannot stop there, however.

A composite character appears manifestly in the Pentateuch's inclusion of the songs of Lamech, of Balaam, of Moses, of Miriam, etc. It is almost equally evident in the duplicate and variant accounts of certain events. The first two chapters of Genesis offer us two descriptions of creation, descriptions which disagree in material respects. In the first account, man as a species ("male and female") is the last and crowning product of the creative process; in the second account, man *as male* is produced early in that process; and afterwards plants, animals, and finally woman, are created to keep him company. In the story of the flood, too, Noah is first directed to preserve two specimens (one couple) of *every* species, without distinction of clean or unclean; then, without suggestion of any divine change of mind, the command is to save *seven* couples of the *clean* beasts (Gen. VI. 19; VII, 2). Jacob's change of name is recorded twice, and the event located in different places, first at Peniel, second at Bethel (Gen. XXXII, 27–30; XXXV, 10, 15). Two explanations of the name Bethel (house of God) are furnished. One connects it with Jacob's vision of angels and the heavenly ladder *on his way to* the east; the other with his meeting with God *on his return from* the east (Gen. XXVIII, 10–22; XXXV, 9–15). The death of Aaron is recorded twice; and located once on Mount Hor, and once at Mosera (Num. XXXIII, 38; Deut. x, 6). So, too, the separation of the tribe of Levi for sacramental purposes is related twice, and with different accompaniments (Num. III, 5–8; Deut. x, 8). Three variant accounts of the laughter in connection with the birth of Isaac are given (Gen. XVII, 17; XVIII, 12; XXI, 6), two of

Hagar's expulsion from Abraham's tent (Gen. XVI, 4–14; XXI, 9–21), and two of Moses' reluctance to go to Pharaoh, in one of which it is promised that Moses shall be *"as God"* to Aaron, and in the other "as God to Pharaoh" (Ex. IV, 10–16; VI, 29 to VII, 2). The spies sent into Canaan are differently commissioned in two places, and the reports credited to them on their return are conflicting, one being highly favorable to the natural character of the country, while the other describes it as "a land that eateth up the inhabitants thereof" (Num. XIII, 2, 3, 21, and 17–20, 22, 26, 27, 32). There are three distinct references to the divine covenant name, Yahveh. According to Gen. IV, 26 (part of the J. document), this name was known to Adam's grandchildren,[1] whereas in Ex. VI, 2, 3, 6, 8 (part of the P document), God is represented as saying to Moses, "I am Yahveh, and I appeared unto Abraham, unto Isaac, and unto Jacob, as God Almighty, but by my name Yahveh[2] I was not known to them." Yet in Ex. III, 13–16 (the E document), the charge unto Moses is, "Say unto the children of Israel, Yahveh, *the God of your fathers* . . . hath sent me unto you. This is my name forever," etc.

Coincident with these differences in statement are differences in style, which critics regard as also pointing to multiple authorship. Our space limitations forbid their description here. Differences, too, in theological conception are not uncommon. Thus in the first account

---

[1] The name usually translated into English "the Lord" is in the Hebrew text, *Yahveh.*

[2] The word *Jehovah*, which appears here in the Revised Version, is due to the practice of pronouncing the consonants in Yahveh by means of the vowels in the Hebrew word for "the Lord," Yahveh having become tabu long before the Christian era.

of creation (the E MSS.) the process is by pure fiat, while in the second account it is by a kind of experimentation. After the human male had been formed and put in charge of the Garden of Eden, " Yahveh God said [apparently as a new discovery], It is not good that the man should be alone," whereupon the beasts and birds and woman were created. It was only then, too, it would seem, that Yahveh realized the need of names for these creatures, for then He "brought them unto the man *to see what he would call them.*"

A second argument alleges the *comparatively late date and non-Mosaic authorship of the Pentateuch as such.* The grounds of this contention could easily be given in detail, as in the sub-section above, did space permit. We shall have to confine ourselves to a few examples.

(1) The topographical references often indicate that the author was a resident of Palestine and not of the Sinaitic wilderness. In Deuteronomy 1, 1, he states that the words of Moses were spoken *"beyond Jordan* in the wilderness"— a description which implies that the writer was on the Canaan side of the river, which Moses never was. Moreover, his phrase for westward was *seaward,* which would not be correct at Sinai; and for southward it was "toward *the Negeb"* (or "parched land")— the dry steppe in the south of Judah. This again was an expression which a Hebrew would use only if he was a resident of Palestine.

(2) The historical books show that much of the Pentateuch was unknown to Israel prior to the time of Josiah, late in the seventh century, B.C. On the religious and ceremonial side the distinctive thing about Deuteronomy is its insistence upon the restriction of the sacrifices to Jerusalem and the Temple, and the destruction

of the "high places" or rival local altars. King Josiah yielded to this demand, but at first with no little astonishment. The people at large must have been astonished also; for the high places, with their associated pillars and poles, had been in use for the worship of Yahveh from the time of the patriarchs down. Samuel and Saul sacrificed to Yahveh repeatedly on the high places. So did the youthful King Solomon, going to Gibeon — described as "the great high place" of the time — and there Yahveh appeared to him (Judg. xi, 11, xx, 1; 1 Sam. vii, 6, 9–11, 17; ix, 12–14, 25; x, 3, 5, 13; xiv, 35; 1 Kings iii, 4, 5 ff.)   Elijah at Mount Carmel, as the very champion of Yahveh, "repaired the altar of Yahveh that was thrown down," and succeeded in bringing down upon it Yahveh's baptism of fire.   Thus an old Yahvist altar, *far from Jerusalem*, and from the Deuteronomic point of view utterly improper, is dramatically recognized by the divinity.   A little later, at Horeb, it is one of Elijah's chief grievances that "the children of Israel" had "thrown down" Yahveh's altars, which evidently were many, and none of them doubtless at Jerusalem in the neighboring kingdom of Judah. In other words, Elijah deplores as the triumph of heathenism the very acts which nearly three centuries later Josiah did in obedience to what purported to be the law of Moses!   (1 Kings xviii, 30, 38; xix, 14; 2 Kings xxii, 11; xxiii, 2–9.)

As the legislation of Deuteronomy exalted the Jerusalem Temple worship, so the legislation of Ezra exalted the priesthood, or clergy.   This also was evidently a new order of things.   Samuel belonged to no priestly or Levitical family; yet, even as a child, he ministered before Yahveh, wearing the ephod and the high-priestly mantle. He actually slept "in the temple of Yahveh, where the ark of God was" — a thing sacrilegious under the full Pentateuchal system — and on various occasions seems to have offered public sacrifices. (1 Sam. IX, 10–14, 19, 25; XIII, 7–12; XVI, 2–5.)

Such facts as the above, which are but a few out of many open to the observation of any careful reader of the Old Testament, have been the ready material of the hostile critic — the so-called "infidel" — for generations. Sometimes they are called "contradictions," sometimes the "mistakes of Moses"; and are cited as evidence of the untrustworthiness of the Bible. How should an intelligent reader regard them? The usual course of the religious believer has been not to regard them at all — to ignore them; which is plainly deserting the field to the enemy. To the historico-literary critic they are not proofs of the dishonesty of the Biblical writers, but simply evidences that those writers were lacking in trained historical judgment and used their documentary sources in an uncritical way.

Section 4. The Main Logical Methods of the Rival Schools

A. The Critical Methods.

From the survey just made of the *critical* arguments, fragmentary as it necessarily was, the general character of the inquiry must now be evident. *First of all*, it is manifestly an appeal to the facts of the subject-matter; *second*, it is an interpretation of those facts according to recognized historical canons. More particularly Old Testament critical inquiry is governed by the two great logical principles of science known as "positivism" and "scientific analogy." The latter principle has been considered in Chapter VI, and will be referred to later. Positivism is the cardinal rule of science that the most certain and the most authoritative elements of knowledge are the empirical facts; that is, the things vouched for by the direct evidence of the senses — our own senses or those of others. The other prominent factor in knowledge, namely, the ideas which the mind adds to these facts (explanations, laws, etc.), must be accommodated to the facts, not *vice versa*. For science ideas, no matter how venerable or imposing, are never coercive until the empirical facts make them so. Now, this is precisely the attitude of the higher critic to the facts of Old Testament history and life. He dares to maintain revolutionary conclusions in the face of ideas clothed with all the prestige of age-long opinion and ecclesiastical pronouncements, because those conclusions are the coercive results of a careful and unbiased examination of the historical facts.

B. *Methods of the Traditional School.*

Modern scholarship has gone over to the critical view primarily because of its scientific character; but, also, in no small degree because of its confirmed distrust of the intellectual methods of the older view. In so far as these are distinctive, they may be reduced to three — tradition, authority, and *a priori* reasoning.

(1) *Tradition* is the handing down from parent to child, or teacher to pupil, of observations and ideas of the past. This is done mostly by word of mouth; but not infrequently tradition's story, at some point in its course, becomes more or less fixed by being reduced to writing.

The present-day power of tradition appears to lie in

the strong influence upon the mind of ideas received by it in its early, formative period, when interest is keen and impressions deep, reinforced by continual social suggestion in the form of the expressed opinions of others, the recitation of catechisms, creeds, etc. This influence of the ideas of older generations, this functioning of the past in the present, is proper enough in childhood; for only through it can the new personality of the child come into vital touch with the life of society; but it is no longer to be approved when the mind reaches maturity and becomes capable of judging things for itself. Its factors are ordinarily strong determinants of conviction; but in the field of thought their condemnation is that they are as effective on the side of wrong as of right beliefs.

No doubt there are cases where tradition is a quasi-historical source, from which critical inquiry can derive certain probabilities as to past events otherwise unascertainable; but even this standing is not to be conceded to ecclesiastical tradition regarding the Old Testament. It fails to cite a single eye- or ear-witness in support of its major claims. Its evidence, when traced up, leads only to the opinions of men — Josephus, for example — who lived long after the events they mention, and who well may have known no more about them than any well-read man of to-day.

(2) Another main support of the traditional view is *authority*. Like tradition this is largely a matter of accepting ideas by social suggestion, and without any serious question as to their rational grounds. Authority stands primarily for what the psychologist calls "prestige suggestion" — the docile acceptance of ideas vouched for by men who are regarded as superior, either

in learning or ability or position.   Among such men are
the venerated heroes and teachers of the past, and at
this point authority and tradition merge; but the authoritative teacher may also be in the present, and his
deliverances relatively new and untraditional, as in the
case of the Pope's encyclical letter condemning "mod-
ernism."   Authority in belief may also be recognized
as residing in a great institution, such as the Roman
Catholic Church, or in a venerated book, such as the
Bible or the Koran.

Authority often owes much to the reinforcement of its
teachings by associated emotions and interests, as in the
case of religion and patriotism.   Some words, as Lowell
says,

> "have drawn transcendent meanings up
> From the best passion of all by-gone time,
> Steeped through with tears of triumph and remorse,
> Sweet with all sainthood, cleansed in martyr fires."

Such words naturally have a vitality, a sacredness, and
a compelling force, with which their mere rational cogency would never have endowed them.   Now, in the
wide sphere of active life and purpose these personal
and emotional — that is, essentially authoritative —
factors in received beliefs are often of large importance
and value; for, in the last analysis, life is more of a ven-
ture than an applied science.   In the field of reflective
inquiry, however, where conclusions are sought which
will fit in with all the rest of things in experience, these
warm human determinants are out of place, indeed, in-
truders; for they tend to override reason, and bias the
intellectual outcome in an irrational way.

There is, indeed, a qualified authority recognized in
science, the authority of the proved *expert;* but this,

although proper, since it has been earned by laborious research and the attainment of special competence, is merely relative. It has its limits, and is always subject to correction by the judgment of other experts in the same field. With this exception scientific inquiry now has no place for authority in intellectual matters, be it seated in exalted persons, in widespread vogue, in institutions, in books, or in creeds. For science it matters not in the least how many men have believed, and what notable religious leaders have taught, that Moses wrote Deuteronomy, if none of them was qualified to form a scientific opinion on the subject. Their views are to be classed with the opinion of the overwhelming majority of the race, past and present, that the earth is a flat disc.

The traditional view of the Pentateuch is, of course, abundantly supported by ecclesiastical authority represented in church fathers, prelates, councils, etc., and with impressive references to the penalty of anathema; but it can hardly be said to have any expert authority on its side. The nearest approach to that is the teaching of Saint Jerome — an eminent student of Hebrew who about 400 A.D. translated the Scriptures into Latin, making what is now known as the Vulgate version. Jerome himself, however, did not claim to be a Hebrew expert, but invited his critics, of whom then there were many, to "ask the most trustworthy Jew you can find, and see if he does not agree with me." That is, Jerome put into the Vulgate, not his own critical judgment, but the tradition of his Jewish teachers! Thus the second support of the traditional view proves likewise to be a broken reed.

(3) The remaining support of that view is *a priori* reasoning; that is, reasoning conditioned and controlled

a priori = reason controlled + conditioned by initial assumptions.

by initial assumptions. This in its place may be valid. In mathematics, for example, the reasoning is *a priori;* but then mathematics does not pretend to yield true conclusions about the actual world of objects and events, except in so far as that objective world corresponds with its own hypothetical world. Theological reasoning, however, is wont to start out with large existential assumptions; that is, assumptions with the standing, not of hypothesis, but of metaphysical and ethical certainties. For example, an American work on natural theology,[1] which had much vogue a generation or two ago, argues regarding the Scriptures as follows: A divinely inspired Bible is a "moral necessity, because the moral constitution of man implies, in order to its development, a written revelation." Man is "a cultivable being," but "no species of things can improve itself ... the culture must come in all cases from a nature higher than their own." [2] Essential to the process of improvement from above is a knowledge by man of God's moral nature, which can be produced only through a written revelation. "Without revealed truth, reason has no data, faith is mere credulity, and conscience is misdirected." Thus "the moral constitution of man demands a revelation *ab extra* — from without — as its complement."

So much for the apologist. It is evident that, if his initial assumptions are granted, there is much force in his plea. Man's need of guidance and of incitement by something higher than himself is assuredly great. But how does this need, however sore, prove the existence of

[1] J. B Walker, *Philosophy of the Plan of Salvation,* New York, 1841.
[2] This is an Aristotelian idea. It is found also in the New Testament; cf. John III, 3.

what will satisfy it? Evidently only on the author's confident assumption that the world has a supreme moral Governor, who is intent upon bringing men to their highest possible development. That is, this theological writer starts his argument with *a theory of history*. Now, it is doubtless true that some working historical theory must underlie an account of events, if it is to be properly history and not mere annals; but what kind of a theory? The traditional view holds that it should be paternalistic, assuming a purposive and superintending Providence to be in charge of human affairs; and it chooses this theory apparently because it is interested chiefly in moral and religious ends — the guidance of practical life and the increase of peace and hope. The critical view, on the other hand, being swayed by an intellectual rather than a moral interest — a desire to learn how things actually happen in the world[1] and to frame a coherent and credible account of events — adopts the naturalistic theory, according to which the history of every people is a natural development, an unfolding of its nature — that is, of group life and thought — under the conditioning influences of the environment and of historical circumstance. From this point of view, which has opened up discoveries in the study of other ancient peoples, Hebrew literature is to be presumed, in the absence of serious evidence to the contrary, to have arisen in ways similar to the literature of other ancient peoples — those of Babylon and Greece, for example — and is to be interpreted by the same gen-

---

[1] The temper of the critical view was well expressed by a wise moralist nearly two centuries ago: "The constitution of nature is as it is." "Things and actions are what they are, and the consequences of them will be what they will be; why, then, should we desire to be deceived?" (Bishop Butler, Sermon VII, last paragraph.)

eral canons. A true understanding of it demands that we reconstruct imaginatively the historical situation in which its various parts, or books, arose.

Does modern scholarship, then, regard historical accuracy as more important than moral welfare? By no means; but it holds that, *when historical results are the ends sought,* considerations of moral welfare are irrelevant. To appeal to them for interpretation of statements of fact is illogical. Mention has been made already of the fundamental scientific principle known as "scientific analogy." It consists in the accepted rule of science that, whenever possible, phenomena are to be explained by ideas known to apply in the field of investigation; and that no ideas imported from another field are to be *trusted* for interpretive purposes until their value in the new field has been established experimentally. According to this rule, Aristotle, in maintaining that the planets move in circular orbits, because the circle is the most perfect curve, invited the error into which he ran; for there is nothing to show that perfection is a principle of control in astronomy.

The like remark appears to apply to the paternalistic theory of history. Until the actuality of a superintending Providence has been established, the use of that idea for historical and literary explanation is unscientific. On the practical side, the doctrine of Providence may be a proper article of faith and, through its stimulus to moral endeavor, may be a useful determinant of life; but, so long as it *is* faith and not knowledge, it cannot be used as a proof or support of anything claiming to be knowledge. Intellectually it is merely an hypothesis, and cannot possibly prove that other hypothesis, the Mosaic authorship of the Pentateuch; for to justify one

scientific analogy = phenomena are to be explained by known factors + so new ideas are to be trusted until they have been proved experimentally.

hypothesis by another is very like the blind leading the blind.

It thus appears that the third main support of the traditional view, namely, *a priori* reasoning from theories rather than established truths, falls to the ground, and falls, too, even when it is well articulated in itself. Modern thought is evidently quite justified in adopting the critical view; for its results have been reached by scientific processes, while the supports of the traditional view dissolve like pillars of fog under the clear light of impartial inquiry.

In the case of most historical books it would not be needful to carry this discussion further; but we cannot and should not ignore the fact that in the western nations of the world the Bible is generally regarded as much more than a book of history. It is held to be a prime authority in morals and a saving guide in religion. But can it, and should it, continue to be so regarded if, as an historical record, it is subject to like errors with other ancient histories? Not a few have been quick to answer in the negative, and to deny it all moral or religious authority. This view, in the face of the countless testimonials to the Bible's value on the part of humanity's best and ablest, ancient and modern, is a hasty and far too sweeping judgment. If the Bible contains errors, and errors really integral to it, it evidently cannot be received by intelligent men as literally inspired by God. Two other ways, however, of recognizing and retaining its power and value remain:

(1) It may be held that the Scriptures *contain* "the word of God," that is, a divine revelation. Some believers who adopt this formula admit historical inaccuracies, but charge them to the human side of the

Bible, and claim inerrancy and authority for the divine side, namely, its moral and religious teachings. Unfortunately, these latter teachings, also, can be shown to be defective in places, sometimes seriously so. Thus no clear intellectual line of demarcation between man's and God's contributions to the Bible appears to be possible. Naturally enough traditionalists and radicals alike pronounce this theory of human and divine collaboration worthless, since it fails to show what parts of the Bible have any sort of divine backing. In reply, its more liberal defenders maintain that if no hard-and-fast scientific rule is furnished by it, yet for practical purposes the test of Coleridge is sufficient, that philosopher having held that those parts of the Bible are inspired "which find me"; that is, those which aroused within him an adequate spiritual response.

(2) The other theoretical way out is to renounce frankly all claim to special divine participation in the production of the Hebrew (and Christian) Scriptures, and to claim for them simply a first place in the spiritual literature of the world, a literature which it is possible to believe discovers intuitively and reflects convincingly divine truths and purposes of utmost moment to men. Such a claim is possible only for certain selected parts of those Scriptures (parts to be determined by Coleridge's test); for much of their contents have to do with matters of only passing concern, and some of them are below the level of other ethical and religious writings. From this point of view the Bible owes its unique position in the religious world, partly to its high insights expressed in everyday speech, and partly to the fact that so many generations of men of aspiration have approved those insights and witnessed to them in, and

sometimes with, their lives. Coleridge's test of spiritual truth, mentioned above, is evidently not a scientific one; for it does not appeal to a standard which is, or can be, *common* to all trained minds. On the contrary, it appeals to the *individual* mind. The teachings which actually awoke within him a spiritual response were doubtless dependent for their effect upon his emotional sensitiveness; and this is by no means alike in men of equal intellectual competency.

QUESTIONS AND EXERCISES

1. Give a concrete example of the difference between external and internal evidence.
2. State and justify the critical inferences in the following sets of Biblical references:
   a. Exod. xxi, 1–6, and Deut. xv, 12–18, compared with Lev. xxv, 39–46.
   b. Deut. xii, 1–14, Exod. xxvii, 1, 2 Chron. iv, 1, compared with Exod. xx, 24–26, 1 Sam. ix, 10–14, 19, 25, and 1 Kings iii, 2–5.
3. It is stated in the Talmud that "Moses wrote his own book . . . Joshua wrote his own book and . . . Samuel wrote his own book". What inference regarding the authorship and date of Joshua is to be drawn from Josh. xxiv, 29 ff., and from a comparison of Josh. xi, 23, xv, 63, and Judges i, 21, with 2 Sam. v, 4–10, and xxiv, 18 ff.; and by comparing Josh. x, 13 with 2 Sam. i, 17?
4. What is to be inferred as to the date and authorship of the books of Samuel from 1 Sam. xxviii, 3; xxvii, 6; xxx, 23–25; and 2 Sam. vi, 8? Compare the accounts of *how Saul became king* in 1 Sam. chaps. viii to xii (especially chaps. viii, x, 17–27; and xii with chaps. ix, x, 16, xi, 1–11), pointing out significant differences and drawing conclusions as to the origin of the book. Do the same with the *story of David* in 1 Sam. xiv, 52, xvi, 14–23, xviii, 5–11, 20–30, comparing these passages with chaps. xvii to xviii, 4, 13–19.
5. In June, 1916, the British Government reported the death of Lord Kitchener in the Atlantic Ocean; yet no witnesses testified to it, still less did any attendant physician certify to it. Why, then, should we believe the report? Are we violating the principle of positivism in doing so? If not, why not?
6. If a friend, who had just attended a widely and pictorially advertised prestidigitation performance, assured you that he had seen the performer actually swallow a thirty-inch sword, in what ways, without impeaching his veracity, could you account for his statement and belief?

7. A classmate of the present writer assured him that the absence of teeth at the sides of a horse's mouth was clear evidence that the mouth was designed to hold the master's bit: what scientific principle was violated in that claim? Explain the principle, and show its reasonableness.

8. Make a brief outline of the argument in this chapter, and show how it leads up to the conclusions on pages 101, 102, 103, 104. (Any logical criticisms will be welcomed.)

BIBLIOGRAPHY

G. B. Gray, *A Critical Introduction to the Old Testament.* Scribner's, 1913.

W. H. Bennett, *A Primer of the Bible.* Henry Holt & Co., 1898.

George Adam Smith, *Modern Criticism and the Preaching of the Old Testament.* A. C. Armstrong and Son, 1901.

S. R. Driver, *Introduction to the Old Testament.* T. & T. Clark, 1913.

C. A. Briggs, *The Higher Criticism of the Hexateuch.* Scribner's, 1897.

W. Robertson Smith, *The Old Testament in the Jewish Church.* D. Appleton Co., 1892.

A. L. Jones, *Logic, Inductive,* etc., part III, chap. III. Henry Holt & Co., 1909.

J. T. Shotwell, *An Introduction to the History of History,* Secs. I and II. Columbia University Press, 1922.

David Hume, *Enquiry concerning Human Understanding,* Sec. x.

CHAPTER IX

REFLECTIVE THOUGHT IN THE FIELD OF VALUES

Section 1.　The Value Situation: Mediate and Immediate Values

HITHERTO our illustrations of the principles of sound thinking have all been drawn from those sciences which deal with the various aspects of our universe from the purely descriptive point of view, apart from all considerations of good or bad, better or worse. We have pursued this course because our primary interest has been to examine the way in which scientists who have actually achieved knowledge have gone about that quest, and because it is in astronomy and mathematics and physics and biology that they have been most successful. Here, if anywhere, we can find those principles of discovery and testing actually displayed. With a clear realization of the part they play in the realm in which we can truly claim that knowledge is an accomplished fact, we can approach the difficult field of human relationships with some assurance that we may find a path through the maze.

So far, in our analysis of the typical act of thought, we have taken for granted, as given, the goal we had in mind. The solution of a presented difficulty was the aim at which all of our suggestions were directed, and by their success in reaching that solution they were judged. Throughout we have assumed that that solution was something unquestionably desirable to arrive at, and all of our suggestions have been measured by their value as means to the attainment of that end. One suggestion was good, another bad, one was better than several others, as it effected the end which had all along stimulated our action, whether that end was the arrival in a certain place at a certain time, or the explanation of the movements of the heavenly bodies. The kind of value possessed by these suggestions is known as "mediate" value; that is, they are valuable as they serve as *means* to some end beyond themselves. It is obvious that the whole process of reflection which we have hitherto so closely examined is concerned with the measuring of various "mediate" values; nor is it too much to say that the whole of science is fruitful in so far as it enables us to decide with certainty just what are the best means of achieving certain desired results.

Natural or descriptive science stops here, and does not go on to ask the further question of what results are to be desired, to be preferred to others. Science in itself furnishes none of the ends of action; in so far as the knowledge of the scientist is concerned, it is immaterial whether what we know of high explosives is used to build a great reservoir to make the desert blossom as the rose, or to construct giant shells to snuff out the lives of an entire city. As a man the scientist may, nay, must, make some preference; but the grounds for that preference are not to be found in physics.

How are these preferences themselves to be dealt with reflectively? Let us take a simple example. If we are bent upon getting downtown in the quickest possible time, it is easy to decide that the subway is a better mode of conveyance than the top of a bus, and it is no difficult matter to prove it to any one. If we desire to get downtown in the most comfortable way on this fine

day, it is again easy to decide and to prove that the bus
is the better method. So long as we accept the aim
of either speed or comfort and raise no further question,
we can arrive at a valid conclusion, easily tested, in accordance with all the principles developed so far in this
book. We have only to judge of bus and subway as
means to the end we have already accepted. But suppose that we are in no special hurry, and yet do not
desire to waste any time unnecessarily; how are we to
decide whether we shall make the speed or the comfort
our goal? It is good to ride on the top of a bus; it is
also good not to waste an afternoon. Which is it better to do?

Our decision could be made in several ways. We
might toss a coin. We might accept the preference of
our companion. We might say, "I haven't ridden on a
bus for some time; I think I'll try it to-day." But, in
any of these cases, we should not be choosing reflectively, and we should not be able to prove that our choice
was the better one, as we could prove which was quicker
and which was more comfortable. Is there any way of
proving that in this case speed is the better choice? Is
there any way of proving that to build a reservoir is better than to construct giant shells?

In the face of this problem of evaluating competing
goods, and of working out some method which will give us
valid grounds for preferring one to the other, those who
have given most consideration to the question are by no
means agreed. It may well be that very often it is impossible to make such a preference anything more than a
merely personal liking; it may well be that in many
cases we cannot deal reflectively with such evaluation of
ends. But one thing at least does seem fairly clear,

that, if reflection can enter into the matter at all, it must do so in certain definite ways. If we are to decide reflectively, when goods are compared with other goods, we cannot attempt to choose between them until all of the consequences that will flow from their acceptance, and all of the other values which are implied in them, have been carefully developed so far as lies in our power. Reflection can do very little if it tries to compare competing goods directly. We could set speed over against comfort, and be torn between them for so long as we wished; but, if we stopped there, we could get little basis for decision. We might, of course, feel that comfort made a greater appeal to us than speed, and hence choose the bus. But we could not prove to our companion that we were right; he would have to accept our preference as a brute fact. But if we regard the two courses in the light of the further consequences with which they are bound up, and which must follow if either is chosen, then we are in a better position to make an objective judgment. We can then realize that the extra half-hour spent on the bus may make it impossible to go to the play to-night; that, after all, the bus seats are very tiring; that if we took the subway we could stop in at the station and inquire about trains; and having before us, as it were, the complete pictures of what is likely to follow in either case, we can not only decide that it is the second rather than the first state of affairs which we desire to bring about, but we can also prove to our friend that he, too, wants to go to the theater, and hence accepts speed as the better end in this instance.

It thus seems possible to evaluate various courses of action only when we are in a position to know how they will lead to or affect other things or actions which, for the time being at least, we accept without further question. Ends can be evaluated reflectively only when they are regarded in the light of still further ends to which they may contribute. Other things being equal, that end is the better end which the better effects still further good. In this further good there must, of course, be included the immediate satisfaction of desires which is attendant upon the acceptance and enjoyment of any good; and, if I do like to ride on the bus much better than on the subway, the satisfaction I should derive from taking the bus must play an important part in the completed picture of the effects of taking it. This immediately satisfying quality which objects possess is known as their "immediate" or "intrinsic," as distinguished from their "mediate," value; a good can satisfy us both in itself, and also through its effect in producing a further good which can satisfy us in itself. Thus it is pleasant to ride on a bus, even if one does not care to go anywhere in particular; and a bus can also get one to a theater which will offer a pleasant afternoon. But it is usually impossible to choose between goods merely on the basis of this inherent satisfaction which they offer. The contention has been that, when it comes to measuring the relative value of two courses of action, we can come nearest to objective certainty when we take account of their mediate, as well as their immediate, aspect; when we see the whole picture and not the bare sketch.

The outcome, then, of our examination of the principles of the process of evaluation has been to make it but a special case of the typical act of reflective thinking. It is true that most things possess an immediate value, either positive or negative; that they are in themselves good and intrinsically satisfying, or the opposite. It is true that in many cases this immediate good may be that aspect of them which on first consideration makes the strongest appeal. But it is at the same time true that, if we considered this intrinsic appeal alone, we should never be sure that we had really decided most wisely; and since, in the nature of things, such an appeal must remain private and of little objective cogency, if we are to decide rationally and intelligently we must not stop with first appearances, but must go on to elaborate upon all the consequences of the various possible courses, to choose clearly some end which we will adopt as a standard, and to ascertain which of the courses will best effect that end.

It is obvious that the unquestioned ends which are accepted as the outcome of the process of elaboration are but preferences, in the sense that they are assumed to be good without further proof. When two men conflict upon these preferences, there can be but one way of reaching agreement. These preferences must themselves be subjected to elaboration and clarification, until it is made plain that the acceptance of one or the other will bring with it some still further good upon which the two disputants can agree. Suppose, as in the case which forms the basis of one of the following chapters, two men disagree about the legislative enactment of a maximum working day for women. If each contented himself with insisting upon the correctness of his own position, they might argue all day without producing any effect upon each other's convictions. But in actual practice each would try to show just what his solution would bring with it, and in the course of that elaboration the two would probably agree upon some other good which both wanted to bring about. In this case, both would admit that the general health and welfare of the community was an end upon which they could agree. It would then be a comparatively simple matter to establish by the citing of statistical and experimental evidence whether an eight-hour day did or did not effectively promote the general welfare. Thus, what had at first seemed to be a problem in evaluating ends could be turned into a mere question of testing two alternative means to an end, and that could be decided upon the basis of the knowledge we possess of industrial life.

If two men could reach no agreement whatsoever upon any thing that both considered good, then, of course, it would be impossible to choose reflectively between their proposals; the final choice would needs be based upon their irrational preference for one of the alternatives. Frequently reflection does find itself thus impotent to effect any agreement; and in such cases of conflict, when the circumstances preclude an agreement to disagree, it may become necessary to appeal to unreasoning force, either through a majority vote, or through recourse to arms. Two nations can thus fly at each other's throats when they both decide that the safety and glory of their own race is an ultimate good, and refuse to think of the effect of a victory upon the human race as a whole. But even here, where through lack of any accepted standard reflection finds itself unable to effect a process of ultimate evaluation, through the elaboration and clarification of the various choices it can eliminate the necessity of such an appeal to force before all the returns are in. It might well prove that the patriot would prefer his country to perish upon the altar of national glory; but at least in making such a choice he could be brought to realize the full price such victory would entail.

If this process of elaboration is to be succeeded by a genuine process of evaluation, however, in which alternatives are tested in the light of some more ultimate standard, that standard must be accepted by both parties. In any given process of evaluation, some preferred end must remain unquestioned. Just how fundamental that preference must be depends upon how fundamental is the conflict between competing goods; the choice between tennis and rowing as sports is much easier to make than the choice between a democratic and an aristocratic way of life. But, in any case, the preference must be pushed back until some good is reached which in the ensuing process of evaluation remains unquestioned.

Thus, when it becomes necessary to choose between two ends which offer themselves, three things are involved. First, those ends must be carefully elaborated until the complete picture is before us. Secondly, some further end must be agreed upon. Finally, those competing ends must themselves be treated as means, and evaluated as they serve to effect the further end. Reflection can thus clarify ends and evaluate means; but the acceptance of a standard for that evaluation remains something into which reflection cannot enter. That is a fundamental preference to be made upon a basis of experience and acquaintance.

Section 2. The Dogmatic and the Reflective Methods of Evaluation

We have described the process of evaluation in simple terms, as though it were the most obvious thing in the world to apply the principles of reflective thinking to any conflict between values. But unfortunately it has not always been so, and even at the present time it is but rarely that men will consent to employ reason in this all-important field. Far too frequently they accept certain types of act as good or bad in themselves, and then refuse to admit even the possibility of a test in the case of conflict, through reference to further consequences. This is the utter negation of reason, and means the removal of the field of values entirely from the realm of reflection. These absolutely good or bad acts are accepted, in theory at least, either on authority, as divinely bestowed in some sacred code of laws, or else as intuitively perceived to be binding. In any case of actual conflict, the question is not whether one choice would effect what, on rational consideration, seems to be the best result; it is which commandment is to be applied. Those acts that are commanded have been commanded, and obedience must be unquestioning; those truths which are self-evident it would be sacrilegious to subject to scrutiny and reflective criticism.

It may very well prove that, when these objectives that are accepted as absolutely good are evaluated reflectively, they will prove worthy of the confidence that men have placed in them. In fact, as we have already seen, no evaluative process can take place without some standard accepted, for the time being at least, as unquestionably good. Yet so often have the aims which men thus dogmatically imposed upon themselves and others resulted in evil and suffering, that it appears that to regard any values as quite removed from the possibility of further criticism is exceedingly apt to mean that they are incapable of any rational justification whatsoever. We shall have occasion to examine the function which such standards do perform in the evaluative process; but here we must assume that the more that process can be made genuinely reflective and the less we must take refuge in a dogmatic statement of preferences, the more likely we are to arrive at objective truth about values.

A different way of attacking the same problem is to say: "Let us forget for the moment that you say this must be done, and I say that must be done. Let us try to find out if we cannot agree on something of which we should both approve, and which we could both try to get. If we can agree on this good thing, then perhaps we shall not find it so hard to argue intelligently about the best way of getting it." If such an undertaking were carried on, each advocate might tell why he thought the end he desired was good. Its implications would be pointed out. All of the further consequences it carried with it would be displayed as things which would have to be accepted if it were taken. Thus an attempt might be made to show just what values were bound up with that end. When its consequences had thus been clearly put before both disputants, they might well say, "We agree on this as our goal; now let us see how we can best secure it."

These two methods of evaluating goods we have called the "dogmatic" and the "reflective" ways. The dogmatic method holds that there are certain things that are beyond all peradventure of doubt right and good, and that they should be aimed at, be the consequences what they may — *fiat justitia, ruat cœlum*. The reflective method holds that, however good things may be in themselves, if it become necessary to choose, that choice must be made in the light of further goods.   In this distinction "dogmatic" is not used in any depreciative sense; assuredly the more reasonable mode may be, at times, to adopt the dogmatic position.   But that cannot alter the fact that such a position does exclude reflection.

No more illuminating example could be found to illustrate these two methods of dealing with values than the contrast between the two great historic series of arguments in favor of the general principles of democracy, the absolutistic and dogmatic assertions of the natural rights school, as found in the classic American Declaration of Independence and the French Declaration of the Rights of Man, and the equally classic arguments of the Utilitarians.   We quote the admirable summary of Bryce.

"We hold these truths to be self-evident, that all men are created equal, that they are endowed by their Creator with certain inalienable Rights, that among these are Life, Liberty, and the pursuit of Happiness, that to secure these rights, Governments are instituted, deriving their just powers from the consent of the governed."   (American Declaration of Independence, 1776.)

"Men are born and continue equal in respect of their rights.

"The end of political society is the preservation of the natural and imprescriptible rights of man.   These Rights are liberty, property, security, and resistance to oppression.

"The principle of all Sovereignty resides essentially in the nation.   No body, no individual, can exert any authority which is not expressly derived from it.

"All citizens have a right to concur personally, or through their representatives in making the law.   Being equal in its eyes, then, they are all equally admissible to all dignities, posts, and public employments.

"No one ought to be molested on account of his opinions, even his religious opinions."   (Declaration of the Rights of

Man made by the National Assembly of France, August, 1789.)

These two declarations, delivered authoritatively by two bodies of men at two moments of far-reaching historical importance, contain the fundamental dogmas, a sort of Apostles' Creed, of democracy. They are the truths on which it claims to rest, they embody the appeal it makes to human reason. Slightly varied in expression, their substance may be stated as follows:

Each man who comes into the world comes into it Free, with a mind to think for himself, a will to act for himself. The subjection of one man to another except by his own free will is against Nature. All men are born Equal, with an equal right to the pursuit of happiness. That each man may secure this right and preserve his liberty as a member of a community, he must have an equal share in its government, that government being created and maintained by the consent of the community. Equality is the guarantee of independence.

These axioms, being delivered as self-evident truths, antecedent to and independent of experience, require no proof. They are propounded as parts of the universal Law of Nature, written on men's hearts, and therefore true always and everywhere.

While the Declarations of the Natural Rights of Man made at Philadelphia and at Paris were resounding through the world, there were other thinkers who, like some Greek philosophers more than two thousand years before, were drawing from the actual experience of mankind arguments which furnished another set of foundations on which democracy might rest. Testing the value of a principle by its practical results, they propounded a number of propositions, some of which may be given as familiar examples.

Liberty is a good thing, because it develops the character of the individual, and conduces to the welfare of the community. When one man, or a few men, rule over others, some of the subjects are sure to resent control and rebel against it, troubling the general peace. No one is good enough to be entrusted with unlimited power. Unless he be a saint — perhaps even if he be a saint — he is sure to abuse it.

Every man is the best judge of his own interest, and therefore best knows what sort of government and what laws will promote that interest.   Hence those laws and that government will presumably be the best for a community as a whole which are desired by the largest number of its members.

Two men are presumably better able than one to judge what is for the common good.   Three men are wiser still, and so on.   Hence the larger the number of members of the community who have the right to give their opinion, the more likely to be correct (other things being equal) is the decision reached by the community.

Individual men may have selfish aims, possibly injurious to the community, but these will be restrained by the other members of the community whose personal aims will be different.   Thus the self-regarding purposes of individuals will be eliminated, and the common aims which the bulk of the community desires to pursue will prevail.

As every man has some interest in the well-being of the community, a part at least of his own personal interest being bound up with it, every man will have a motive for bearing his share in its government, and he will seek to bear it, so far as his personal motives do not collide therewith.

Inequality, by arousing jealousy and envy, provokes discontent.   Discontent disturbs the harmony of a community and induces strife.   Hence equality in political rights, while it benefits the community by opening to talent the opportunity of rendering good service, tends also to peace and good order.

To sum up, government by the whole people best secures the two main objects of all Governments — Justice and Happiness, Justice, because no man or class or group will be strong enough to wrong others; Happiness, because each man, judging best what is for his own good, will have every chance of pursuing it.   The principles of liberty and equality are justified by the results they yield.[1]

Why does the absolutist demand liberty and equality? Because they are Natural Rights with which all men are

[1] Bryce, *Modern Democracies*, vol. I, pp. 43–45.

born. They are not subject to doubt. They are indelibly graven on the heart of every right-thinking man. They are beyond proof. They just *are*. Why does the man who reflectively considers consequences demand the same things? Because they conduce to the welfare of the community, to the general peace, to justice, to the common happiness — all of them things which even the opponents of democracy desire to effect. The first group state their demands categorically, and enforce them with their swords; the second explain why theirs will produce results which their opponents profess equally to advocate, and appeal to reason rather than to arms.

It is significant that in France, where the absolutistic Natural Rights theory was made the defense of democracy, and was opposed by a similarly dogmatic divine right theory of autocracy, the political change was achieved only by a bloody and violent revolution. Between men committed irrevocably to such contradictory beliefs about values, there was no way but force. On the other hand, in England, which on the whole adopted the opposing type of defense, the same change was accomplished peaceably and not wholly irrationally. Each side, accepting as its ultimate aim the common good, was able to claim that its system of government best effected that aim, and the autocrats and the democrats, being about equal in strength, could each demand that the other listen to their arguments. Reason here had at least a certain chance to develop its case.

It is, of course, quite possible to defend autocracy upon purely reflective and empirical grounds. It is worthy of note that many present-day writers attack democracy and favor some form of monarchy in government, with aristocracy in social structure. Some of their arguments against democracy are reviewed by Delisle Burns:

If there is a choice of leaders by the common man, either he chooses some incompetent person whom he can understand, and thereby ruins society, or he makes democracy impossible by choosing an exceptional man who cannot easily be controlled by the average intellect. Again it is said that no democratic organization can possibly give due power to minorities. . . . Thirdly, democracy is said to be irreconcilable with social organization for rapid and effective group action. . . . Finally . . . it is argued that the majority of men are not capable of original action and full personal responsibility.[1]

These arguments imply, on the whole, that the good of the majority is the ultimate aim, but that democracy is an ineffective means to its attainment. Other writers go still further, and deny that the good of the majority is the best end; "rather a few highly developed," they say, "even at the expense of suffering in others, than a vast rabble of mediocrities." These latter writers no longer admit the ultimate aim which the democrats profess, and hence make rational argument with democrats impossible unless some further end, some type of life, can be agreed upon. But if there is any common ground whatsoever, it is possible to introduce reflective thinking into the great field of values just as into every other branch of knowledge.

Section 3. The Reflective Elaboration of Ends

We have already outlined the general method which reflection must follow if it is to accomplish any fairly definite and objective results in the field of values. We have seen that the first service which reflection can per-

[1] *Political Ideals*, pp. 297-98.

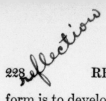

form is to develop the various courses of action or goods which are competing for our acceptance. It can reveal to us many of the further consequences which they will each entail. This process is essentially that of the fourth stage of the complete act of thinking, the stage in which the implications of the various suggestions are carefully elaborated. And, like that stage, it depends essentially upon the knowledge at our disposal of the causal patterns that do obtain. What will follow if we do perform certain actions? What things are valuable as means to further goods? We must possess this preliminary knowledge before we can either clarify our ends or evaluate them through reference to some further standard.

This process is exceedingly complicated, for the knowledge we need in this field is very hard to come by. We shall, therefore, in this section indicate some of the main difficulties in the way of obtaining that knowledge, and attempt to suggest ways by which those obstacles may be surmounted. We must not assume, however, that the way will be easy or clear, or that we can hope to attain that same measure of general agreement, even upon causal relations, that the natural scientist regards as the prerequisite of any definitely established body of knowledge. The reasons for the comparatively chaotic confusion in which the whole field of human relationships, with which the problems of evaluation so largely deal, finds itself to-day, will become clear as we advance. For that field at present forms a marked contrast with the achievements which the natural scientist so proudly records. Despite the fact that human intelligence has been reflectively occupied with the problems of the relations between man and man for a much longer time, than with those of our physical environment, and that many more men have devoted their attention to them; despite the fact that the pathfinders, from the great Greeks, Socrates and Plato and Aristotle, down, who have sought to blaze a way here, have most certainly not been inferior to any of the pioneers of natural science — it is unquestioned that these so-called social sciences have had little share in the growth characteristic of our knowledge of nature since the Renaissance, and that we are still pretty much where the Greeks left us two thousand years ago.

When the intellectual history of this time comes to be written [says H. G. Wells], nothing, I think, will stand out more strikingly than the empty gulf in quality between the superb and richly fruitful scientific investigations that are going on, and the general thought of other educated sections of the community. I do not mean that scientific men are, as a whole, a class of supermen, dealing with and thinking about everything in a way altogether better than the common run of humanity, but in their field they think and work with an intensity, an integrity, a breadth, boldness, patience, thoroughness, and faithfulness — excepting only a few artists — which puts their work out of all comparison with any other human activity. . . . In these particular directions the human mind has achieved a new and higher quality of attitude and gesture, a veracity, a self-detachment, and self-abnegating vigor of criticism that tend to spread out and must ultimately spread out to every other human affair.

James Harvey Robinson gives an even more striking example:

When we compare the discussions in the United States Senate in regard to the League of Nations with the consideration of a broken-down car at a roadside garage, the contrast is shocking. The rural mechanic thinks scientifically; his only aim is to avail himself of his knowledge of the nature and

workings of the car, with a view to making it run once more.
The Senator, on the other hand, appears too often to have little idea of the nature and workings of nations, and he relies
on rhetoric and appeals to vague fears and hopes or mere partisan animosity.   The scientists have been busy for a century
in revolutionizing the practical *relation* of nations.   The
ocean is no longer a barrier, as it was in Washington's day,
but to all intents and purposes a smooth avenue closely connecting, rather than safely separating, the eastern and western continents.   The Senator will nevertheless unblushingly
appeal to policies of a century back, suitable, mayhap, in
their day, but now become a warning rather than a guide.
The garage-man, on the contrary, takes his mechanism as he
finds it, and does not allow any mystic respect for the earlier
forms of the gas engine to interfere with the needed adjust-
ments.[1]

What is the reason for this startling contrast?   Why
do we apply intelligence to the repair of our automobiles
and refuse to apply it to the much more important human relationships?   Is it merely, as multitudes would
have it, that we lack the will, and that a simple resolve
to be intelligent, to employ reflective thinking, if it could
only be carried out, would result in as revolutionary
changes in social conditions as has the application of
scientific thought to our control over the forces and resources of Nature?   Need we only to repent and be converted?

Assuredly, our souls need repentance, and there cannot be laid too great emphasis on the necessity for the
most intense application of reflective thinking to the
problems of man.   That is why we have examined and
formulated the methods that have in the natural sciences proved so successful.   But we must recognize, if
we would hope for anything like the results that have

[1] *The Mind in the Making*, p. 8.

been therein achieved, that the field of human relation-ships presents difficulties beside which any in the natural sciences seem simplicity itself. The backwardness of the social sciences is not due to any neglect by the pathfinder, for it is probable that the amount of reflective thinking devoted to these problems far exceeds that spent on the interpretation of nature. It is due to causes which are in the nature of things ineradicable, and, unless we de-sire these difficulties to remain insuperable, we must frankly recognize their existence and endeavor to coun-teract them.

We have seen that the prerequisites for the formation and testing of suggestions are a body of exact and classi-fied knowledge of the general laws or patterns we may expect to discover, comparative freedom from prejudice and preconceptions, and the possibility of exact and careful experimentation. In the field of values none of these essentials is to be discovered. We have very few definitely established laws upon which we can count in social phenomena, we have very intense loyalties and prejudices, and we have practically no means of experi-mentation on an adequate scale. Hence it is exceed-ingly difficult even to evaluate goods as means to further goods. We lack the primary knowledge of what certain courses of action will actually accomplish.

The first and most obvious obstacle in the building up of a definite body of knowledge here is the difficulty of discovering general laws that will simplify the initial confusion and complexity which greet us in every field of investigation. At first glance nature, too, seems singularly complicated, and the riotous profusion of form and process in a forest seems to the ordinary man chaos itself. Yet it takes but the most elementary knowledge for that confusion to shape itself into a harmonious order; forms are seen to resemble each other, processes to repeat themselves with unfailing regularity. The pattern of causal relationships is, indeed, many-colored, but the same design is repeated through the whole range of nature, and when once its essential motifs have been discovered, we know what to look for at each spot. There is a pattern that enables us to predict with fair accuracy and precision what events each new moment will bring forth, and the utilization of that knowledge has verily extended the bounds of human empire over nature.

Not so in the field of human activities. If there be any pattern in the warp and woof of man's social experience, it has been so obscured by loose ends and tangled skeins that men have hitherto been unable to trace it. The complexity in the field of human affairs consists not so much in the chaotic profusion of the individual facts of that experience, for in this it differs little from the realm of nature; it lies rather in the inability of man to find any simple laws upon which those facts can be strung. This makes it well-nigh impossible to predict what will occur, and without prediction man is at a loss to control.

It is both a cause and a result of this condition that mathematics, so successful in the interpretation of nature, seems quite impossible of application to human nature. The loss which the inability to use this invaluable tool entails is incalculable. It means that accurate measurements are precluded; in society we are to-day where the physicist was as regards heat before he had invented a thermometer. It means that we cannot formulate our social hypotheses with the precision lent by mathematics. It means that we are unable to elaborate them deductively and arrive at further exact knowledge. It means that in the last analysis we find ourselves at a great disadvantage in testing them. There is, however, one method by which the facts of social phenomena seem to lend themselves to quantitative treatment: that is the newly discovered science of statistics. By the aid of statistics we can measure in the large what we cannot in the small; and it seems probable that, with the increasing application of the statistical method, that accuracy which mathematics gives may be able to increase our knowledge and understanding of the complexities of the social sciences. So important is this, and so hopeful appears the possibility of overcoming this tremendous difficulty in the way of reflection, that a special chapter will be devoted to the method of handling such problems by statistics.

It must not be forgotten, however, that, when all has been said, there enter so many incalculable elements into the actions of human beings that it is still quite impossible for us to tell, in any individual case, just what will be the outcome of any particular act which they perform. We can predict with fair accuracy how many men will commit suicide and how many men will marry in a given community in a year; but such a general statement will not satisfy our demands in the field of human relationships. We wish to know whether John Smith will commit suicide or marry; and that we cannot predict. We are really asking for much more refined knowledge in the field of values than we ever ask for in natural science. There individual differences are matters of little concern; here they are all-important. Since our demands are so much greater, it is not surprising that our results are less satisfactory.

But it is not merely the actual difficulties of the subject-matter that have kept back the social sciences; even if we knew how to do what we wished, we should still find ourselves bound up in a network of old associations, of traditions and tender memories, of blind prejudices and hatreds. The natural scientist is investigating a field in which after all the average man has very little interest, and he is for the most part quite free to follow facts whithersoever he finds that they lead. His conclusions do not conflict with beliefs held dear by men from time immemorial, for the simple reason that they lie in a realm which the average man has never experienced, and in which, consequently, he has no beliefs at all. It is far different with human relationships. Here every man has a vital interest; the beliefs here are bound up with emotional associations and interests which make every change a mutilation of the living flesh. If even the natural scientist has in the past found his way blocked by such established beliefs; if a Galileo feels the censure of the Church for maintaining that the earth moves, or if a Darwin and a Huxley are subjected to the taunts and jibes of the unthinking for declaring the record of the past, how much more will the man who finds it necessary to revise the fundamental ways in which men live feel the sting of social disapproval and hostility!

In the first chapter mention was made of the numerous obstacles that strew the path of the investigator in any field, the masses of prejudice and preconception, the still more powerful inertia of habit and tradition that prevent a frank and free investigation of truth. It needs but to be pointed out here that it is in the social sciences that it is most difficult to avoid them. Even the enlightened mind can never wholly escape their influence, and many of the greatest pathfinders have retained far more of traditional ideas and prejudices than they would care to admit even to themselves.   It is a great mistake to regard those men who often stand in the way of scientific progress as consummate villains because they cannot tear themselves loose from the mass of inherited beliefs in which their minds are embedded. To the ardent seer of new visions of life made more perfect, it is exceedingly difficult to avoid attributing the most sinister of motives to all those who still feel the grip of the old.   But this in itself is but to give way to a deep-rooted tendency of the human mind that enters in to obscure judgment: the desire to regard all who intellectually disagree with one as morally bad.   Which of us is there who is himself without such sin?   Nothing is more disheartening than the fitful flashes and shadows of the mind that is thoroughly convinced of its own enlightenment, the genuine bigotry of the emancipated. It is inevitable that beliefs endeared by long association, perhaps learned at the mother's knee, should seem compelling in the face of disagreeable facts whose only value is that they are true; who of us, however much he may be convinced by his reason of the futile horror of warfare, can fail to feel a martial thrill as the band plays, the flags fly, and the soldiers come marching down the street?   Prejudices and selfish interests offer perhaps the greatest single obstacle to the achievement of knowledge in the social sciences; and yet they must be accepted as inevitable factors in the situation, with which men must reckon, and to remove which they must devote much of the precious time that might have been spent in the direct ascertaining of knowledge.

Moreover, in the third place, there is this much of reason on behalf of the conservatives, that in the social sciences it is extremely difficult to experiment patiently in the laboratory. In fact, there exists no laboratory. The maxim of *experimentum in corpore vili* has no meaning, for no *corpus vile* exists. No human being is cheap enough to risk the danger of failure. Hence the necessity of carrying on social experimentation in the realm of the imagination, where a single false step will not result in hardship and suffering. And the imaginative foreseeing of consequences is in human relationships so much more difficult than in the natural sciences that it is commonly said that no plan of social change is worth anything until it has been tried out. When a great nation like Russia elects to engage in social experimentation upon an enormous scale, we may be intensely interested, and watch with the utmost sympathy, but we cannot help regretting the inevitable failures and mistakes which must precede even an eventual success. We can only do the best we can, experiment on a small scale, proceed slowly, test carefully so far as we are able, and endeavor always to project into the future every possible consideration before we set about the actual verification of our suggestions.

These are the difficulties which have made it so hard to find in the field of social relationships the fundamental causal patterns upon whose discovery depends all evaluation of means, and ultimately of ends also. We can elaborate and evaluate only as we can perceive the consequences and implications of our choices; and in society we are never sure what will be the result of a given act. Before we can go much further, we must discover definite causal patterns, with all the accuracy statistics can furnish. We must rid ourselves of prejudices and preconceptions and allow reflection a fair chance. And we must experiment patiently and carefully, in actuality and in imagination.

Section 4.   The Reflective Criticism of Standards

But after all the most serious problems which the consideration of values in human relationships presents to us lie not in our inability to state with any certainty just what will be the consequences of one of our acts or choices; difficult as is the actual amassing of classified knowledge in this field, it is not absolutely insuperable. Modern psychological and statistical methods have enabled us to discover far more of the patterns of the social life of men than we had dreamed possible a few years ago. If agreement can be reached upon the desirability of aiming at some definite state of affairs, it is usually not impossible to establish with a fair degree of certainty that one proposed course will be more apt to bring about that state than another. Thus, to refer again to the example of the chapter on law, when once men have decided that the health and welfare of the community as a whole is an end to be preferred to the high profits of private individuals, it is not so very difficult to prove by statistical observation that unrestricted hours for the labor of women are much less apt to effect that end than the legislative enforcement of an eight-hour day. Could men once agree on the kind of liberty and equality which a government should secure, it is not impossibly hard to determine whether certain measures will or will not be more effective instruments toward that attainment. So long as certain ends remain unquestioned, it is relatively easy to evaluate the various proposed means for getting them.

But supposing the question is raised, What kind of liberty and equality is best? Supposing the more ultimate ends in terms of which we are evaluating our means are themselves subjected to scrutiny? Supposing we ask the relative importance of liberty and authority in social activities, as we do in the chapter upon ethics, and endeavor to clarify just what we mean by liberty and by authority? It is when we attempt to make such an evaluation reflectively, and to get away from a purely irrational appeal to force or instinctive preference or perhaps mere blind chance, that we encounter the most serious obstacles of all.

All of the difficulties we have seen in the endeavor to discover what are really purely objective facts in the field of human relationships are present, intensified a thousandfold when we seek the better and the worse. Such moral judgments are so bound up with the very characters of men that even to discuss them involves the risk of passionate misunderstanding. For it becomes a question of men's ultimate preferences, those things which they hold to be most dear, and in the very nature of the case the frank and free doubting and discussion which are essential to the discovery of any sort of knowledge become well-nigh impossible. To convict a man of error in his aims and ideals, in his judgment of what is worth while, is far more than to convict him of an intellectual mistake; it is to brand him with moral obliquity and sin, to pass judgment upon the whole man. Who of us does not feel that the individual who differs with us upon the fundamental preferences, who refuses to acknowledge the sanctity of private property, or who sees no harm in the permanence of warfare — who does not feel that such a man is, indeed, beyond the pale? It is rare, indeed, that two men can engage in any discussion in which they find themselves differing thus radically without allowing the heat of passion to obscure the light of reason. To suggest even the need of criticizing and testing the commonly accepted standards of conduct is the surest way to incur the stigma of moral laxity.

But even if the investigation can be kept upon a plane into which there enters no personal recrimination, the logical difficulties themselves are appalling. We have already called attention to the fact that the immediate value of any course of action — that quality it possesses of affording intrinsic satisfaction — must play a most important part in the complete picture of the effects following upon it. But of all the consequences of an act, it is most difficult of all to foretell the amount of immediate satisfaction it will bring with it. Hard as it is to determine the total objective effects of, say, a single lie which a man tells to get himself out of a tight place, it is infinitely harder to predict the importance he will assign to the avoidance of that momentary embarrassment to-morrow morning or next week. It has been the advice of wise men from Plato down to endeavor so far as possible to escape from the immediate present and to look at our acts as they will appear to us a month or a year hence. But the pleasure of the moment is strong, and the appeal of future good is notoriously weak. *Video meliora proboque, deteriora sequor* — what is this but the cry of humanity that immediate satisfaction, even though temporary and evanescent, outweighs more permanent good? The cynic who said, "There is but one thing in the world more terrible than not getting what you want, and that is getting it," was a profound observer of human striving and aspiration. For the gratification which the satisfaction of immediate desires will bring is the most unpredictable thing in the world, and nothing is more universal than for anticipated pleasure to turn to dust and ashes when it is finally in one's grasp. Just in so far as allowance is made for the respective satisfactions which it seems various goods will bring with them, an element is introduced into such deliberation about values which makes any strictly objective calculation impossible. And yet not to take it into account would be the most irrational course of all.

The only basis for giving to such pleasures their proper weight in the developed picture is that of actual and repeated experience with them. Only he who knows both the better and the worse can be a judge of which is the better; only he who has eaten of the fruit of the tree of the knowledge of good and evil can engage in moral deliberation. It is, for example, the inability of the average respectable moralist to comprehend the appeal which the worse course can make, as well as the better — it is his lack of a sympathetic acquaintance with all of the values entering into the problem — that makes the great mass of what ordinarily passes for moral guidance and exhortation quite worthless. But when a man can say, like Augustine, "I have tried both — I have dwelt amidst the flesh-pots of Egypt, and I have journeyed through the wilderness into the Promised Land, and I tell you that all the delights of iniquity are as naught to the enduring worth of righteousness" — when a man has experienced both, he can speak as one possessing authority, and his words will be hearkened to for generations.

It may well happen that men disagree upon the appeal of various goods for lack of actual experience with

them. No one who had never heard a single symphony
of Beethoven performed would be accepted as a competent judge of the respective merits of Beethoven and
Irving Berlin. We laugh at the Frenchman who tried
to prove that Victor Hugo was a greater poet than
Goethe, when we learn that he could not read a word of
German. And yet not a day passes that we do not
make ourselves some judgment of value upon an equally
meager experience. To a man who is manifestly basing
his opinion upon some such one-sided knowledge of the
facts, we can only say, as Pascal said to the dissolute no-
bility to whom he was trying to prove the worth and
value of the Christian religion at its best, "Try it, taste of
its fruits, and then decide whether human life is not the
richer for it and the poorer without it."

John Stuart Mill well expresses this fact, that only he
who has tasted the higher as well as the lower forms of
satisfaction is a competent judge of which is the more ap-
pealing, in a passage in his *Utilitarianism* that has become classic:

Now it is an unquestionable fact that those who are equally
acquainted with, and equally capable of appreciating and en-
joying, both, do give a most marked preference to the manner
of existence which employs their higher faculties. Few human creatures would consent to be changed into any of the
lower animals, for a promise of the fullest allowance of a
beast's pleasure; no intelligent human being would consent
to be a fool, no instructed person would be an ignoramus, no
person of feeling and conscience would be selfish and base,
even though they should be persuaded that the dunce, the
fool, or the rascal is better satisfied with his lot than they are
with theirs. They would not resign what they possess more
than he for the most complete satisfaction of all the desires
which they have in common with him. . . . It is better to be a
human being dissatisfied than a pig satisfied; better to be

Socrates dissatisfied than a fool satisfied. And if the fool, or the pig, are of a different opinion, it is because they only know their own side of the question. The other party to the comparison knows both sides.[1]

In the last analysis, the final test of the relative worth of values must be experience, just as the final test of any truth must come down to an experienced agreement with fact. That is why in any process of evaluation there must be an initial agreement on some thing as good, on some standard as valid. Could the scientists not agree upon certain observed facts, there could be no science; could men not agree upon some standards, there could be no reflective choices of competing goods.

Yet it still remains true that many men would disagree, even after a thorough experience of various values, as to the relative importance to be assigned to each in any ultimate standard of what constituted a good life. It often happens that the process of clarifying ends results in a more marked disagreement than at the outset. Men who could fight together for the ideal of democracy might well quarrel with each other if they came to analyze precisely what they meant by that vague and generous concept. Yet even if they finally came to blows themselves, they would know more clearly what they were fighting for, and that conflict would be fraught with a more genuine significance. The Northern and the Southern Colonies fought England twice in defense of their liberty; then for a generation their statesmen engaged in a process of clarifying just what they meant by that liberty. That led to the Civil War; but at least the liberty which was at stake in that conflict possessed a richer meaning than the vaguer liberty of the Revolu-

[1] *Utilitarianism*, chap. II.

tion. And, after all, both North and South did agree on most of the essential points, and the very fact of the final clarification on the field of battle has made possible a much fuller coöperation since. The chapter on ethics is to deal with an issue in which all these points are brought out clearly.

But this fact of what constitutes perhaps an ultimate disagreement on important preferences, which cannot be settled by an appeal to experience because experience differs from man to man, does lead to the most profound difficulty of all in any consideration of values.

Judgments are assertions about matters of fact or about the relations of ideas; they are true or false, and if true for one, they are true for all. But preferences, it may be objected, are not true or false; they are personal traits; and, although a preference may be shared by many people, it is none the worse for being peculiar to one individual. Our judgments of value, it may be urged, are really nothing more than expressions of taste; and, if the proverb that there is no disputing about tastes is not quite an axiom, it can hardly be denied a large measure of truth. An argument can always be brought to an end if we agree to call the point in question "a matter of taste," and though it would doubtless be a mistake to attach too much stress to a convention by which we are accustomed to avoid continuing a debate that has begun to seem unprofitable, we can hardly deny the fact any significance at all. A man who says that New York is more populous than London can be convicted of error with a conclusiveness not to be hoped for if he says that the view of New York from the bay is more impressive, or less impressive, than the view of London from the Thames. Of the latter statement we may say that it all depends on what you find impressive; one man may prefer mere bigness, another architectural harmony and the presence of historical associations, and who is to judge between them? If I prefer ripe olives to green olives, and you prefer green to ripe, neither of us, probably, is prepared to call the other wrong, though each may be convinced that his own taste is the more refined. If we differ on the relative merits of Æschylus and Shakespeare, there is more room for debate, and perhaps slightly more hope of agreement, but certainly we cannot expect a demonstrative conclusion on either side. Even if we take a judgment which seems to admit of no dispute, such as that *Othello* is a greater tragedy than *The Easiest Way*, proof seems impossible to find; more people will pay to see the latter, and to what quarter are we to look for an authoritative condemnation of their judgment?

The same sort of criticism may be extended to moral judgments. The statement that murder is wrong seems to command assent almost as universal as that lead is heavier than water. We can, however, assent to a statement only when we know its meaning, and when we begin to examine the assertion that murder is wrong we find that it has no such unmistakable significance as the assertion about lead and water. The terms of the latter are absolutely specific, and within reasonable limits we can be quite sure when a substance is lead or water. To define "murder," however, is by no means a simple affair. To kill a man is not murder unless it is done with malice aforethought and in the absence of justifying circumstances. Homicide in self-defense or in war is not generally regarded as unjustifiable, nor is a man a murderer when in anger he strikes a blow not in-

tended to be fatal. We cannot, in other words, identify
an act of homicide with murder until we have made sure
of a set of circumstances at least part of which, the
frame of mind of the alleged murderer, is in the nature of
the case uncertain. We have virtually prejudged an
act as immoral in calling it murder, and the moral judgment that murder is immoral is to that extent tautolo-
gous and not a true judgment at all. If this, probably
the least doubtful of all moral judgments, thus turns out
to be uncertain in its application, there seems to be little
probability that any other of our precepts for conduct
will stand on a firmer logical footing, and this we find
upon examination to be the truth. Bribery, deception,
theft, are all doubtless wrong. But these are vague
terms: Is a man who to keep his position refrains from
expressing unpopular opinions accepting his salary as a
bribe for betraying the truth? Is he deceiving his employer and securing money under false pretenses? We
cannot answer these questions in the affirmative until we
have decided in the light of all the circumstances that
the act is wrong, and our alleged moral certainties turn
out in consequence to be little more than statements that
what is immoral is immoral. It can scarcely be maintained that such judgments are of the same logical
standing as the Pythagorean theorem or the law of
gravitation.

This conclusion about the validity of moral laws is
enormously reinforced when we discover the variations
in moral standards in time and place. We should consider nothing more outrageous than to burn a man alive
rather than to permit him to differ with us on a matter
of opinion. This, however, was regarded not so many
centuries ago as not only a permissible method of con-

troversy, but also as a moral and religious duty if the controversy were about matters of serious importance. The moral skeptic is therefore led to generalize: to say that anything is wrong is to say that it displeases me, and to say no more. "Cruelty is immoral," "Boasting is vulgar," "'Way Down East' is a bad play," "Men should not use perfume," and, "It is barbarous to put maple-syrup on lobster-salad," are all, from the point of view of logic, indistinguishable.

To these arguments of the complete moral skeptic, it must be admitted, there can be made no conclusive and irrefutable reply. But neither can any conclusive reply be made to the skeptic in any field, not even to the man who assails that vast edifice of observation and inference we call scientific truth. When all has been said in favor of skepticism, it remains clear that men must act, that some acts are better than others, and that some basis of discrimination must be used. The skeptic is right in maintaining that at some point all our knowledge, of sense-fact, of mathematical truth, of inference, of values, rests upon unproved assumptions. Yet it is obviously the part of reason to make these assumptions as fundamental as possible, to choose those that appear the least uncertain, and to introduce them only when reflection has reached its limits. To maintain that, because ultimately it is a matter of preference that wanton taking of human life is bad, we should slay the man next door, would be as foolish and impossible as to maintain that, because men lie and the senses deceive, every statement is as good and as true as any other.

Nor is it by any means certain that disagreements are as absolute as the moral skeptic affirms. When men have actually experienced several different goods, there

stand whether it is better to steal or to buy the fruit; we have learned that stealing is bad, and that principle remains for us unquestioned. In all the practical exigencies of life these principles remain given, the points of reference by which all doubtful cases can be decided; in a sense so far as that problem is concerned, they are accepted as absolute. As such they facilitate immensely the solution of difficulties, summing up as they do large bodies of experience, classifying our values under general heads. We should be as helpless without them as would the scientist without his accumulated and classified body of established beliefs on which to rely. And yet there is a very real danger that these general principles, important and useful as they are if they are rightly regarded as summations of past experience, may come to be looked upon as fixed and unalterable, not themselves amenable to further testing. They may be removed entirely from the field to which reflection is applied, and become the fixed dogmas of the orthodox moralist.

As John Dewey so well puts it:

Morals must be a growing science if it is to be a science at all, not merely because all truth has not yet been appropriated by the mind of man, but because life is a moving affair in which old moral truth ceases to apply. . . . Principles exist as hypotheses with which to experiment. Human history is long. There is a long record of past experimentation in conduct, and there are cumulative verifications which give many principles a well-earned prestige. Lightly to disregard them is the height of foolishness. But social situations alter; and it is also foolish not to observe how old principles actually work under new conditions, and not to modify them so that they will be more effectual instruments in judging new cases. Many men are now aware of the harm done in legal matters by assuming the antecedent existence of fixed principles under which every new case may be brought. They recognize that this assumption merely puts a premium on ideas developed under by-gone conditions, and that their perpetuation in the present works iniquity. Yet the choice is not between throwing away rules previously developed and sticking obstinately by them. The intelligent alternative is to revise, adapt, expand, and alter them. The problem is one of continuous, vital readaptation.[1]

This adaptive process, the continuous application of principles to particular cases and the accompanying revision of those principles, so important in every branch of human relationships, is the especial subject of the chapter upon the law that is to follow. Therein will be considered the problems that arise in the application of such general maxims as have been developed in the course of centuries and enshrined in the body of our law. They form a group of standards which, taken collectively, comprise the very essence of our civilization. They are the principles which have emerged through long experience. The lawyers have developed a most interesting technique for applying those general principles which are accepted by the public opinion of the country and embodied in its legal system, to the many particular cases of competing values which are brought before them for judgment. Of course, such general rules must be modified to fit each particular case and each particular problem; and how this is done we shall endeavor to ascertain.

In summary, then, the field of values presents great difficulties, not only in the meager knowledge we can actually obtain about the functioning of the factors in human relationships, but even more in the arriving at pro-

[1] Dewey, *Human Nature and Conduct*, pp. 239–40.

visional standards by which any courses of action may be judged. The most promising method for reflection to follow is to elaborate suggestions until there does emerge some further standard by which they can be judged; and then, applying what knowledge is at our disposal, to try to evaluate our conflicting courses of action in the light of the consequences that appear to flow from them.

QUESTIONS AND EXERCISES

1. Give several examples of choices which involve merely the evaluation of means, and illustrate the reasoning leading to a decision.

2. Give several cases in which it is necessary to choose between competing ends. In how far can these choices be made reflectively? To what extent does irrational preference enter?

3. A man is confronted with the alternatives of stuffing a ballot-box or seeing a very undesirable candidate elected. Elaborate both possibilities to bring out all the implications of each. Does it then become clearer which choice is to be preferred? Do you arrive at any definite criterion?

4. Make a list of things whose chief value lies in the immediate satisfaction they bring. Make another list of things whose chief value lies in the further goods they effect. Is there in either list anything which could not on occasion be placed in the other list?

5. How would you set about proving to your friend that he ought to hear a symphony concert to-night instead of going to the movies? Trace the three stages in the process in some detail.

6. Mention a few of the precepts of conventional morality that could probably maintain themselves in the light of reflective criticism, and indicate the general lines of their defense. Mention some that you think could not, and give the reasons that would influence you to abandon the latter.

7. What standards did the Utilitarians agree upon in their arguments for the revolutionary principles?

8. What further end might democrats and aristocrats agree upon to test out their respective theories?

9. Name a few definite causal patterns that have been discovered in the field of human relations.

10. Enumerate the chief difficulties in the way of developing a genuine social science. How might they be removed?

11. How would you set about to determine the respective satisfactions which two courses of action might bring?

12. Name a few moral standards that have proved useful classifications

of values. Illustrate the need and the process of revision and adaptation.

13. How would you prove that it was not wrong to dance? That it was wrong to take human life wantonly?

BIBLIOGRAPHY

On the Process of Evaluation:
   J. Bentham: *Introduction to the Principles of Morals and Legislation.*
      Oxford University Press., 1907.
   John Stuart Mill: *Utilitarianism.* Everyman's Library.
   John Dewey: *How We Think.* D. C. Heath & Co., 1910.
            Human Nature and Conduct. Henry Holt & Co., 1922.
On the foundations of Democracy:
   J. Bryce: *Modern Democracies.* The Macmillan Company, 1921.
   J. Bentham: *Anarchical Fallacies.*

CHAPTER X

MEASUREMENTS FOR USE IN SOCIAL DECISIONS

Section 1. Two Ways of Choosing a Career

MANY persons are consciously anxious to choose a career in which they will be happy and successful. They would like so to live that they would find personal satisfaction and give to society the benefit of whatever talents they possess. Frequently such anxiety is not felt by the persons directly concerned, but is keenly present in the minds of their parents or advisers, or in the desires of statesmen to know how a community or a nation may help its citizens to make the best use of themselves and to contribute most to the common good.

When, however, we consider the reasons which lie back of the advice given to a boy on his life plans we find very frequently that desire to raise the family prestige, the father's estimate of the monetary returns of the prospective career, the mother's fondness for an uncle who followed that calling, the ease of preparation for that vocation, the feeling that "this kind of job is as good as any other," and dozens of similar guesses and whimsies are the sole bases for a decision. In business, when men are selected for different positions, "systems" of an equally inexact character are often followed. Some firms will have only blond salesmen, others only men with dark complexions, some tall men, some men with sharp noses.[1] To use such methods of vocational

[1] C. S. Yoakum, "Basic Experiments in Vocational Guidance." *Journal of Personnel Research*, vol. I, no. 1, May, 1922.

choice or of placement is to abandon reason completely and to disregard our need for exact knowledge in matters requiring a well-founded belief.

It is clear that we need more than exact knowledge in order to decide on a career. Some, unhappily many, persons are so poor in this world's goods that they cannot follow the course of life which would mean most to them and to society. Such poverty may not prevent a person of the very highest natural or native ability, capacity, or endowment from reaching his goal, but it is undoubtedly a barrier which many cannot surmount.

Suppose that we consider, however, a boy whose parents are able to provide all needed advantages. What would he and they need to know? First, a great deal more information than we now possess about the exact requirements of the different careers open to men. We might call such information "career specifications." These would include a great variety of items of varying specificity, but they would in most cases include at least indications of the requirements in intelligence, ability to get on with other men, ability to take responsibility, and the advancement and income which might be expected.

Next we should have to know whether the boy had abilities to match the "career specifications." Such knowledge would be hard to get. Obviously the immature boy might not have all of these abilities, yet perhaps he would develop them by the time they should be required. We should need to be able to measure present ability, and to predict future ability. If we could secure precise "career specifications," measurements of present ability, and predictions based on ability at present possessed, we should be able to approximate a reasoned decision.

Section 2. Individual Differences [1]

There are many questions raised by the last sentence of the previous section. One may be: How do we know that abilities differ so greatly in individuals that so careful an analysis as is proposed will be significant? During the last sixty years psychology has been at work endeavoring to find out whether individuals differ in capacities, those potentialities with which they come into the world. Such potentialities we may call native; they cannot be created by nurture of any kind, though they may remain undeveloped because nurture is lacking. To-day practically all psychologists believe that there are native differences, and that there is a wide range in the possession of those human traits which no artificial development can bring forth. Psychologists do not agree on the accuracy of our present measures of these abilities, nor on the exact analysis of these traits into their separate parts, as, for instance, into intelligence, aggressiveness, courage, etc.

All would admit that it is possible to determine how well each person in a group of four hundred does a particular task, and nearly all would say that such tasks may be set as will reveal native ability and be at least some indication of future development. One of the most striking examples of the range of accomplishment known is the record of testing in the army. The chart on page 256 shows us grades made by men in a wide range of occupations when they took a standard test which was interpreted as a measure of mental alertness, of so-called intelligence.

Men vary widely also in traits which we call moral

[1] See Chapter 1, Section 3.

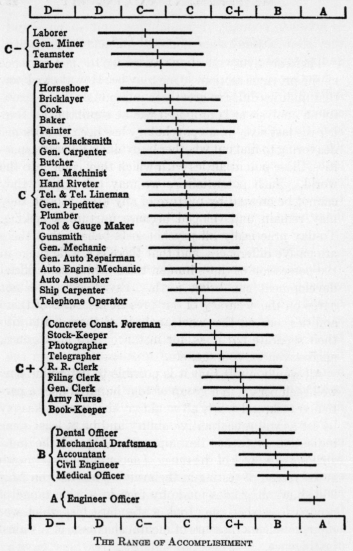

THE RANGE OF ACCOMPLISHMENT

Grades shown by army tests

Reproduced from C. S. Yoakum, "Basic Experiments in Vocational Guidance," *Journal of Personnel Research*, vol. I, no. 1, May, 1922. Taken from *Psychological Examining in the United States Army*, edited by Robert M. Yerkes, National Academy of Sciences, vol. 15 (Washington, 1921), p. 829.

— honesty, courage, dependability, and so on — and they show a wide range of ability in manual dexterity and in sensitiveness to things of beauty.

Another question which may be asked is whether an individual shows the same dominant ability and the same amount of it, relative to the amount shown by his fellows, throughout his life. That is: Do the traits discernible in a boy of ten appear in the same relationship in a man of thirty. To this we must answer that we do not know surely, but "all the experiments to date tend to prove that the relative mental capacity of the child determines his relative mental capacity as an adult." [1]

Section 3.   Some Requirements of Measures

The assertions which have just been made rest on investigation and experiment. Psychologists have studied human behavior and have tried to use the same caution as other scientists and to reach the same kind of quantitative basis as has advanced scientific study in other fields. The determination of quantities has been the method of testing out the suggestions which have arisen as hypotheses and, as is so generally the case, the attainment of exact data has given rise to new theories.

To say that measures are used to determine quantities is to say what every one admits. All will agree, too, that when one knows "how much," one is able to carry on comparisons. Not every one, however, realizes the difficulties involved in the use of measures as aids to well-founded beliefs. It is worth while, therefore, to state some of the elements essential to measurement. First of all, if we want to compare quantities, we must have a

[1] C. S. Yoakum, "Basic Experiments in Vocational Guidance," *Journal of Personnel Research*, vol. I, no. 1, May, 1922.

numerical basis; we must count and have ten of *a*, and five of *a*, and three of *a*, and so on. When we want to measure intellectual ability, we devise a task and set every one about this same task in which degrees of success must be expressed in figures. This raises a second point: We measure indirectly. When we measure intelligence, we are really counting scores; as when we measure temperature, we are measuring the height of a mercury column in a tube. We must always define what we are directly measuring and then define the thing for which it stands. A third point is that we must have constant units agreed upon (by convention) which are qualitatively alike, so that they can be added and otherwise handled quantitatively. The unit of the Fahrenheit scale is one one-hundred-and-eightieth part of the difference in the height of a column of mercury as it rises in water from freezing to boiling, but for the Centigrade scale it is one one-hundredth of that distance. Fourth, in making measurements there must be some point of reference agreed upon by convention just as the units are. In measuring temperature, for instance, the point of reference for Fahrenheit is thirty-two degrees below freezing, while for Centigrade it is the freezing point itself. When all these conditions are met, it is possible to say, for example, that in this instance measured there are ten units with *x* taken as the point of reference in the count, while in that instance measured there are eight units with *x* the point of reference. With such knowledge exact comparisons can be made.

Section 4. Putting Measurements into Relation

In the chapter on experimental methods we saw that one of the methods was called concomitant variations.

antecedent + consequent

It could be employed when two factors varied in a constant relationship. Now, in making measurements we are often interested in being able to tell from one measurement made what we may expect concerning other elements which have not in that particular instance been subjected to measurement. Such referential knowledge cannot be based on guess, but must rest on previous investigations where many instances in which quality A is measured have been examined also for the quantitative amounts of quality B. Suppose, for instance that we have a group of 100 with a college entrance score of 125. We then find out how many of these finish the Freshman year without failing a course. Perhaps 95 members of the group turn out to have passed all the courses. To get greater accuracy, suppose we increase the count and discover that, in a thousand cases of men receiving 125 as entrance score, 930 pass all Freshman work. We should then feel justified in saying that we have established a relationship between an entrance score of 125 and success in Freshman studies. If, then, we wanted to make reasonably sure that 93 out of 100 men admitted to college would pass, we should insist that they all have scores of 125. In other words, by knowing the score 125, we could predict that another element would be in co-relation; namely, success in Freshman courses. Statisticians, working in education or in economics or in health departments, or in any of the sciences where the knowledge of relationships and their predictability is essential, have reduced the expression of correlation to a numerical statement. If one element always varies directly as the other, this perfect positive correlation is expressed by saying that the coefficient of correlation is 1. If one element always varies inversely as the other, this perfect inverse correlation gives a coefficient of correlation of –1.   If the variations in one element bear no relation, direct or inverse, to those of the other, this lack of relationship is signified by a coefficient of correlation of o.   Correlation is an excellent example of the truth brought out in Chapter II that to include a thing in a class carries with it the implications of that class.

Section 5.   The Application of Measurement to an Individual Case

Let us now look back at the case of the boy seeking advice as to his career.   If he should think he wanted to be an engineer, and as a Freshman in college was taking calculus and physics and passing well, we might say to him that out of 100 men who passed these subjects 85 graduated in the minimum time from their engineering course.   Such an approach to accuracy we could attain. This information would not tell the student anything in quantitative terms about the likelihood of success in actual engineering practice.   We should notice, moreover, that we still could not tell him that *he* would be one of the 85.   Such statistical treatments deal with groups, and do not predict as to specified individual members of a group.   But suppose we knew more about engineering and found that there were among other types designing engineers, operating engineers, and salesmen engineers.   We should want to find out success correlations with the student's subjects and each type. Did we aim at the maximum advice, we should want to know in the greatest detail all the duties of the kind of engineering he proposed to enter, and also the qualities of mind and character (including desires) which the work demanded.   We should need to study each type of engineering very carefully and, from the analysis of the qualities in a large number of successful engineers in a defined kind of work, determine the traits most con-stantly associated with success in its various ranges. These we should express in quantitative terms. We should then want to determine again in quantitative terms his possession of these qualities. We might then be able to tell him into what group, with a specified cor-relation with success (externally and personally satis-factory), he would fall. It is unnecessary to say that we are far, far removed from such an ability to predict. But we are, nevertheless, able to point out lines of prob-able failure and success with a certainty which is of an altogether and completely different sort than could be claimed by him who chose his salesmen by the color of their hair, or advised his son to go into a profession be-cause of its financial return.

Section 6.   The Social Utility of Measurements

If the student whom we have considered had been well advised and he had entered a profession in which he would have gained happiness and success and had helped effectively to carry on the work of the world, we should have been using exact information to some pur-pose. We should have been discovering a causal pat-tern in social phenomena, as Chapter IX put it.

There is opportunity in education for the use of exact measures on a scale so great as to dwarf any individual instances. When the measuring of individual differ-ences in ability and interest finally reaches a complete-ness and accuracy now only dreamed of, we shall doubt-less be able to direct students into a wide variety of types of education rather than send them through one stereotyped curriculum. We shall be able to advise, furthermore, as to the probable profit of continuing the education beyond a certain point, for we shall be able to tell with considerable accuracy how much a person with a specified amount of ability may hope to gain from continued study in a certain line.

The application of exact measurements to the accomplishment of students is important for school systems, as well as for individuals, for, when we know how much students of x ability do in School A, we can compare the effectiveness of School B which is also training students of x ability. In this fashion, school administration is given some tangible basis for the criticism of its standards.

In the study of various political mechanisms, as, for instance, the referendum, success can within limits be studied quantitatively; and in economics the equation of wage and the cost of living is an excellent example of the quantitative treatment of a public problem of the greatest importance. Insurance is another instance of the practical application of the statistical method or the determination of probabilities for groups. Statistics have, indeed, been advanced partly because of their utility in the insurance field.

In all of these applications of a quantitative method what we are doing is making increasingly clear the actual situation with which we are dealing. We are making a more exact observation and classification possible. The difficulties of such quantitative treatment in the field of human life, with its great variability, its rapid changes and its responsiveness to a tremendously complex multiplicity of stimuli from within and without, far exceed the limitations under which quantitative measures in the field of physics suffer. But the advantages of exact knowledge in individual and social decisions are readily appreciated, and the statement of Chapter I, that we need human engineers, may now, perhaps, be better understood.

QUESTIONS AND EXERCISES

1. *a.* If some one should question the effectiveness of the referendum as a means of finding out public opinion, why would an advantage in determining the validity of the question be gained by a study of the vote on measures referred for public expression of acceptance or rejection?
   b. What kinds of information should such a study seek?
   c. What would be the end which referendum would serve, and under what circumstances would it be considered an effective means?
2. On the basis of what findings through exact measures would it be desirable, when financially possible:
   a. To establish high schools of widely different curricula?
   b. To establish schools for the mentally retarded and mentally precocious?
3. How could physical fatigue be measured exactly? Show why such measurement might be valuable for law makers, safety engineers, production managers in business.
4. *a.* In the mobilizing of an army from private citizens, why would a knowledge of the mental ability and of the kind and degree of trade craft or professional skill be important?
   b. How would you go about testing degrees of skill in telegraph operators?
5. If you were a manufacturer of cotton dress goods, and wanted to know what color in gingham to manufacture, what steps would you take to find out the answer to your problem?

BIBLIOGRAPHY

D. C. Jones: *A First Course in Statistics.* Bell, 1921.

W. F. Ogburn: *Methods of Direct Legislation in Oregon.* Quarterly Publications of the American Statistical Association, June, 1914, p. 136.

Harold Rugg: *Statistical Method Applied to Education.* Houghton Mifflin Company, 1917.

H. Secrist: *An Introduction to Statistical Method.* The Macmillan Company, 1917.

L. M. Terman: *The Measurement of Intelligence.* Houghton Mifflin Company, 1916.

E. L. Thorndike: *An Introduction to the Theory of Mental and Social Measurements*, 2d ed. Teachers College, Columbia University, 1913.

E. L. Thorndike: *Educational Psychology.* 3 vols., Teachers College, Columbia University, 1913–14.

B. D. Wood: *Measurement in Higher Education*, World Book Company, 1923.

Robert M. Yerkes, Editor: *Psychological Examining in the United States Army*, National Academy of Sciences, vol. 15. Washington, Government Printing Office, 1921.

C. S. Yoakum: "Basic Experiments in Vocational Guidance," *Journal of Personnel Research*, vol. I, no. 1, May, 1922.

CHAPTER XI

REFLECTIVE THINKING IN LAW

Section 1.   The Non-Reflective Growth of Law

THE institution and practice of law, like all other institutions, is only in part a reflective process.   It has its origins in the most primitive and unconscious forms of human behavior and social organization.   Mankind, in its blind gropings, in the half-conscious process of feeling its way out of primitive brutishness, had created unwritten laws and was governing itself according to them long before it became aware of the fact.   Indeed, so closely inwoven into the fabric of social life are these rules and customs that those who first reflected upon them naturally attributed them to the Creator himself or to whatever forces were supposed to control human life and destiny.   Even long after it had ceased to be intellectually fashionable to attribute these laws to the designing will of some superhuman spirit, men still regarded them as part of the universal framework of nature, calling them "laws of nature."   According to this theory human society is supposed to be under the government of laws not of its own making, and therefore not of its own unmaking; laws similar to the "natural laws" of which the scientists speak, which are as immutable and eternal as Nature herself.

But as knowledge of human history and of human nature advanced, men became conscious of the fact that these laws are man-made and self-imposed, that they were a long time in forming, and that the forces of habit and gregariousness operating for the most part unconsciously had succeeded in moulding society into more or less stable patterns, whose guiding principles could be discovered and formulated. With this insight attained, the imagination of man was liberated and given constructive power. Once man discovers that he has been blindly and unconsciously shaping laws and customs, he is enabled to proceed consciously or reflectively. He becomes aware of his own responsibility and undertakes the process with foresight. Thus the intelligent use and control of laws becomes possible, and the making and practice of law becomes a chapter in the social organization of reflective thinking.

ITS IMPORTANCE FOR REFLECTIVE LAW

Though the operation of legal codes is now for the most part a highly organized system of reflective thinking, it cannot be understood unless its non-reflective origins are kept in mind. Underlying the processes of legislation and judicial decision, which are or ought to be reflective, there are principles and precedents which come from nobody knows where, and there are others whose origins are known, but known to be much earlier than the invention of modern systems of legislation and jurisprudence. Conscious legislation, in fact, would be almost a superhuman task were it not for this great body of recognized modes of procedure which centuries of experience have established, and which can be reformed and reformulated, but cannot be abolished. The conscious art of legislation never begins with a clean slate, so to speak; it cannot create a social order; it can but redirect a social order already in operation. Intelligence in the legal sphere, as in all spheres of human activity, is forced to work with material not of its own making; and it is creative only when it makes the best of the material in hand, instead of wandering about in search of material more to its liking. More specifically this implies that the law, in so far as it is a system of reflective thinking, is a continuous attempt to apply approved and established modes of conduct to new and uncertain situations in such a manner as to insure their mutual reinforcement. Reflective law must avoid both of two extremes: if it merely follows the established traditions, it loses its value, for it ceases to be reflective; if it ignores the established traditions and attempts to construct a social order of its own based on "reason" alone, it loses its applicability, for its orderliness is dialectical instead of social. Reflective thinking in law is chiefly concerned with finding the proper mean between these extremes. Bacon's famous dictum is nowhere so important as in law: "the wit and mind of man, if it work upon matter, . . . worketh according to the stuff and is limited thereby; but if it work upon itself, as the spider worketh his web, then it is endless, and brings forth indeed cobwebs of learning, admirable for the fineness of thread and work, but of no substance or profit." [1]

A statute or a decision to be effective, must be generally consistent with traditional principles: it must conform to the general force of custom and to "the spirit of the common law" sufficiently to be capable of assimilation. The customary penalties and sanctions, the established modes of enforcement, and the general approval or disapproval of public sentiment are factors which no legislator can disregard. Within certain limits these stabilizing forces, often operating uncon-

[1] *Advancement of Learning,* I.

sciously, are sufficient to "make or break" a law. Any legislation which is content to ignore these forces, or even to scorn them as irrational, is certain to find the tables turned: it will find itself isolated, ineffectual, and to that extent irrational. This does not mean that legislation must slavishly follow custom, which would be anything but reflective procedure; but it does mean that legislation must be willing to work *upon* custom, and in general conformity with established practices and moral sentiments, instead of attempting to operate on an *a priori* basis, be it ever so "logical."

A second important limiting factor in reflective legislation is the fact that legislation, since it is of necessity general or universal, and since it deals with social facts that are continually changing and thus rendering old generalizations more or less ambiguous, can define its object with only a very limited degree of accuracy. If each situation could be dealt with on its own merits, if it were a "law unto itself," legal thinking would be logically simpler and might be more intelligent; but then we should not have *laws*. For the whole purpose and essence of law is to enable us to deal with particular issues as particular examples of a general type or class. Intelligent control would be out of the question, were it not possible to discover general types and to deal with them as such. But such general types can be formulated only within limits. To begin with, social institutions and problems cannot be classified with mathematical precision; and even if they could, they change so continually, and, in modern society especially, so radically, that, even with the utmost care in defining the scope of a law, ambiguities creep in almost immediately and usually grow worse as time passes.

And here we come upon a fundamental difference between the logic of the natural and of the moral sciences. The "laws" which the natural scientist discovers have little in common, save the name, with laws in the legal sense. A scientific "law," being merely a descriptive formula of the behavior of natural objects which can be accurately and mathematically described and calculated, is immediately applicable as long as these objects behave as they do. The "application" of physical laws consequently requires chiefly technical skill in working with ready-made formulæ. But human laws are seldom capable of such accurate formulation, nor are the conditions under which they operate so constant. Natural laws have no power to govern, nor do they make Nature more orderly than she happens to be. But human laws, in so far as they operate at all, actually do govern; and they govern not merely in that they are prescriptions of what men should do rather than descriptions of what they actually do, they govern in the sense that they become guiding principles for the handling of new situations, modes of controlling what would otherwise be "chaotic" and unintelligible. Indeterminate cases are determined by them; new situations are "brought under" them. If every situation had one law, and that obviously *its* law, the legal profession would be more like a card index and less like a science. If in medicine each symptom meant a definite disease, and each disease had a single cure, we might have automatic mechanical physicians. But as it is, the lawyer, like the physician, is forced to make diagnoses, to select proper remedies and to use his judgment. It is this problem of discovering how law can be applied to an uncertain case that makes the reasoning of the lawyer both so intricate and so useful.

Hence one of the most serious problems for law is the problem of the classification and definition of particulars by means of group concepts. If the concepts are too inclusive, the law will be applied where it was not intended to apply, resulting in stupidity and injustice; if the concepts are too exclusive, the law will be interpreted as inapplicable and consequently become ineffectual. For example, if all promises were legally obligatory, much injustice would be done; if, on the other hand, the conditions under which contracts are legally obligatory are too narrowly drawn, men will avoid making contracts, and the law becomes ineffectual. The law must "draw the lines," but to draw them clearly and suitably is a difficult task. Many a law is side-tracked because, if "construed strictly," it makes unfair discriminations, and, if "construed loosely," it includes too many cases to be enforcible. Such dangers legislators and judges must continually keep in mind.

Section 2. The Legal "Act of Thought"

The whole legal process, from the first agitation for a certain line of legislation or judicial decision to the final assimilation or rejection of the statute (or decision, as the case may be) in the established body of the law of the land, is really a single act of reflective thought, though it take several decades or centuries to complete it. In fact, the field of law gives us one of the best illustrations of the vast amount of social organization and coöperation necessary for the carrying on of systematic thinking. Legislatures, with their numerous committees, bureaus and boards, lawyers, judges, courts, detective agencies, investigating commissions, to say nothing of all the associations for the promotion of various types of legislation, are, or at least ought to be, so much social machinery for reflective thinking in law. Thinking machinery is probably the most intricate machinery there is. All we can hope to do in this chapter is to outline the chief steps in the process, and then to describe a concrete case which illustrates some of the more important of those steps.

The process falls into two main divisions: (1) the making of laws, (2) their testing or application.

THE REFLECTIVE MAKING OF LAWS

The two conditions discussed above, the power of custom and the need for controlling particular events by general rules, furnish the setting and fix the problem for reflective legislation. The first raises the problem of finding effective means of enforcing a law — the problem of "sanctions"; the second raises the problem of defining the scope and purpose of a law. The difference between a genuinely reflective and a superficial making of laws lies in the amount of care and thoroughness with which these problems are faced.

Hence the care with which the problems are analyzed and the precision with which laws are formulated. Hence the numerous hearings before committees on proposed bills, the submitting and resubmitting, until the scope of the bill has been defined sufficiently. The various drafts of a bill may be defined as so many hypotheses, each of which has to be tested until one is finally accepted. When, after all this analysis and experimentation with rival "hypotheses," a bill finally passes and becomes a law, we are apt to regard that as the termination of the reflective process. We regard the measure as finally validated, verified, accepted, and the problem as

solved. In some cases this is no doubt true. Some
laws are put into practice readily, work smoothly, no
questions are asked, and the matter may be regarded as
"settled"; and a few others immediately pass into obliv-
ion, are never applied, and become "dead letters." But
in the great majority of cases the process of verification
merely begins with the enactment of a law. The problem merely "changes hands"; it passes out of the jurisdiction of the legislator and into that of the lawyer and
judge. Here fresh difficulties arise, for here the practical testing begins. The lawyers, not the legislators,
have the task of applying the law, and usually in the
course of this task unforeseen problems arise. The real
"making of laws" is continued by the judge after the
legislator has finished with them; and the judge's decisions are subject to the same dangers and difficulties,
when they in turn become law.

It might be that reflective thinking in law would be
more efficient if the process were not so rudely interrupted by a change of hands. Much valuable experience might be capitalized which is now lost, if, as is the
case in the common law, those who make laws were also
responsible for their application. Be that as it may, the
fact is that there is this general division of labor in legal
thinking. The result is that the courts, even in addition
to the common law, which is mostly court made, actually "make" more law than the legislature. For, in
spite of the painstaking analysis of the legislators, or
more frequently because of lack of it, the lawyer soon
discovers ambiguities in the application of a law or conflicts between one law and another which call for a
decision. These decisions, which are made by judges,
really are but a further definition and systematization

of laws whose meaning and application were left ambiguous by the legislators, and they operate in much the same way that the original laws do. They form a body of "interpretations" which are used as precedents. If a legal case is seen to be in one or more respects identical with a previous case, the decision of the previous court is cited as precedent. Law could, of course, make little progress if the same problem had to be argued afresh each time it arose, instead of taking the decisions arrived at as precedents. Precedents may be called in question if for any cause the reasoning which supports them is thought to be fallacious; but otherwise they are simply accepted as authoritative opinions. The only problem which arises in such situations is whether or not the present case and the case on which the precedent rests are really identical; and this is usually not so easy to determine as one might suppose, so that sometimes it happens that the use of precedent raises more problems than it avoids. But on the whole, the use of precedents is not only a convenience, but an absolute necessity, for it is manifestly impossible to argue the validity of a whole legal system every time a legal case arises. In any argument there must be some things taken for granted.

The judges, as interpreters of law, may or may not coöperate with the original legislators. They probably have their own ideas about what the law *should be*, and their interpretation of what the law *is* is consciously or unconsciously influenced by these ideas. This is especially true when party issues and tactics enter into the situation. The consequences of the "change of hands" in legal thinking become most obvious in constitutional law; for constitutions are of necessity most vague and general, and judicial "interpretations" of them are consequently most vital.

So far we have spoken of laws as originating in legislatures and as being perfected (or perverted, as the case may be) by the courts. But only one half of the law, and, historically speaking, the less significant half, originates in the legislature. In most countries courts were in existence long before legislatures, and, even in those cases where they were established simultaneously, the courts recognize the validity of a body of procedure which arose independently of the statute law of the land. This is known as the "common law." Its sources vary in different countries. In the United States it is based largely on the body of custom which was recognized by English courts, on precedents established by English courts, and to a much lesser extent on feudal law, laws of the Puritan congregations, etc. Many of the laws still in operation have their origin in the customs of English merchants which came to be known as "the law merchant" and which was bodily incorporated into the English common law. Some laws even go back to a Roman household, or a mediæval ecclesiastical order, or the decisions of a feudal baron. Some of the elements in these sources are non-reflective, resting as they do on mere custom or tradition; others are just as reflective as any statute of a legislature. But whether they be reflective in origin or not, they are reflective in their operation to-day. Cases continually arise which involve no statute and which are therefore decided on the basis of the common law. But the common law, especially when it rests on ancient procedures, is indefinite in its application, even more so than statute law, and must be "interpreted" and adapted to modern social conditions. The common law is thus being continually redefined, clarified, and extended. This growth of the common law, in so far as it is deliberate, is a process of lawmaking coördinate with legislation in the narrower sense. The judge both makes and "applies" laws. This fact makes the "judicial process" and the legal profession a much more complicated affair than it would be if all law were statute law, but, logically speaking, the reflective thinking involved in the making of the common law is quite the same as that involved in the making of statute law, so that the analysis of legislation made above is to be understood as applying to "judge-made" laws as well as to the enactments of legislatures. We have begun our analysis of the "legal act of thought" with the legislature rather than the courts because it is a social instrument or institution devised specifically for the purpose of reflective lawmaking, whereas the lawmaking function of the courts, at least of modern courts, is a secondary or acquired function, the prime purpose of the courts being to administer or apply the law. But legal theorists have been traditionally divided into two groups, those who think that all law ought to be statute law, in order that legal practice may be held continually responsible to the particular social facts and problems which the legislator has in mind, and those who think that all law ought to be common law, in order that it may form a consistent body of universal rules of procedure.

The law with which the lawyer is required to deal is thus made up of distinct systems, each of which has its own origins and field of operations. We have distinguished three such systems: (1) the common **law,** (2) statutes, (3) judicial "interpretations" of statutes, which tend to become incorporated into the common law. With this brief analysis of the making of laws, we pass to the second phase of the legal "act of thought," the application or practical testing of laws; the first is the inductive phase, the formation of a general rule to meet the demands made by certain particular situations; the second is the deductive phase, the application of this general rule to other situations which test its validity.

THE REFLECTIVE APPLICATION OF THE LAW

From the foregoing it is evident that when the lawyer and judge ask the question, "What *is* the law in this case?" the answer is usually not found by merely looking it up in the index, as it were; it requires genuine reflective thinking. Of course, there are always cases brought to a lawyer for which "looking it up" in the precedents suffices. Where the law is explicit and precedent unequivocal, the solution of the problem is comparatively simple as in the eviction of a tenant for nonpayment of rent. In such cases the lawyer may be regarded as a skilled mechanic rather than as a reflective thinker: he merely applies the legal machinery which automatically solves the case. The practice of law is in such cases purely deductive, and the reasoning involved differs in subject-matter only, and not in form, from that involved in a geometrical demonstration or proof. This involves thinking, to be sure, but, as this type of thinking has been analyzed in previous chapters, we pass on to more distinctively *legal* thinking.

The distinctively reflective side of the legal profession comes out in those more important cases where precedents conflict, where terms are ambiguous, where social facts have changed so as to render doubtful the applicability of the law, and in general where the law does not automatically apply itself. There are four general types of problems which confront the lawyer as he tries to apply the law as it is. The first is the problem of defining and clarifying the exact meaning and application of the law. The factors which underlie this problem have been discussed above when we were considering some fundamental difficulties in legal thinking, namely, the confused and changing social facts which law attempts to regulate, the consequent difficulties of precise definition and classification, the inability of legislators to foresee all the ambiguities which will arise in the operation of a law, etc. The lawyer avails himself of all possible means in meeting this problem. He first consults authoritative precedents for the accepted meanings of terms and interpretations of laws. These may be adequate; but more probably he is faced with conflicting precedents, in which case he may resort to experience directly and try to determine meanings by examining the facts of the case at hand; or, on the other hand, he may resort to some more fundamental authorities than judicial precedents, to moral principles, traditional usage, authoritative legal writing, or the like.

A second type of problem is the need of correlating and harmonizing the vast number of laws of various times, by various legislators, and under various codes. Legal systems, being the products of centuries, have various roots and conflicting tendencies. These must be interrelated and codified so as to make them as consistent as it is possible to make them. Absolute consistency is here out of the question, but so is absolute contradiction.

A third type of problem, closely allied to this, is involved wherever various lines of interpretation and of reasoning are possible and where choice must be made between them. Reasons for preferring one to another must be thought out, and methodical systems of interpretation developed for such cases. Since two or more interpretations are logically possible, the reflective judge is forced to choose between them on the basis of their respective usefulness, applicability, conformity to custom, and the precedents which they may establish for other decisions. "The law," in short, is never as simple as the words imply.

One principle or precedent, pushed to the limit of its logic, may point to one conclusion; another principle or precedent, followed with like logic, may point with equal certainty to another. In this conflict we must choose between the two paths, selecting one or the other, or perhaps striking out upon a third, which will be the resultant of the two forces in combination, or will represent the mean between extremes. Let me take as an illustration of such conflict the famous case of Riggs v. Palmer, 115 N.Y. 506. That case decided that a legatee who had murdered his testator would not be permitted by a court of equity to enjoy the benefits of the will. Conflicting principles were there in competition for the mastery. One of them prevailed and vanquished all others. There was the principle of the binding force of a will disposing of the estate of a testator in conformity with law. That principle, pushed to the limit of its logic, seemed to uphold the title of the murderer. There was the principle that civil courts may not add to the pains and penalties of crimes. That pushed to the limit of its logic seemed again to uphold his title. But over against these was another principle, of greater generality, its roots deeply fastened in universal sentiments of justice, the principle that no man should profit from his own iniquity or take advantage of his own wrong. The logic of this principle prevailed over the logic of the others. . . . The judicial process is there in microcosm. We go forward with our logic, with our analogies, with our philosophies, till we reach a certain point. At first we have no trouble with the paths; they follow the same lines. Then they begin to diverge and we must make a choice between them. History or custom or social utility or some compelling sentiment of justice or sometimes perhaps a semi-instinctive apprehension of the pervading spirit of our law, must come to the rescue of the anxious judge, and tell him where to go.[1]

The fourth type of problem arises, not from the laws, but from the facts themselves. A lawyer, especially in criminal law, is often as much concerned with the problem of *what the facts are in the case* as with what the law is in the case. This introduces us to a whole new set of legal intellectual machinery: the jury, the witnesses, evidence, cross-examination, the analysis of motives, the question of sanity of the criminal, etc. The processes are quite familiar, and will be seen to be instruments of observation and analysis of facts — a topic discussed in previous chapters. The more highly these instruments are developed and the more extensively they are utilized, the more reflective the thinking becomes, and the more adequately and justly can the law be applied.

SUMMARY OF THE ANALYSIS OF LEGAL THINKING

This bare outline of legal thinking may suffice to indicate the essential traits of the process; the illustration which follows is intended to exhibit the same process in

[1] Benj. N. Cardozo, *The Nature of the Judicial Process*, pp. 40–43. A very clear and interesting case of two equally valid interpretations, in which that one happened to be chosen by the courts which later led to many difficulties — difficulties which the other would have avoided — is described in an article by Dean Harlan F. Stone, *Columbia Law Review*, June, 1922.

concrete form. If this process is concerned well, it avails itself of all the instruments of reflective thinking which other sciences employ. By careful observation, testing of evidence, and experimental investigation, it seeks to discover the facts, as any natural science does, by precise definition and classification, it seeks to build up a unified system of concepts, as any dialectical science does; and by the clarification of human ends and ideals, it passes judgment on human conduct, as any moral science does. Legal thinking is thus seen to be characterized, not so much by peculiar *methods* of thought, as by its complex *subject-matter*.

Section 3. A Case of Reflective Thinking in Law Analyzed

To give concrete meaning to these theoretical considerations, we shall describe a typical legal case — typical in so far as any case can be typical of certain fundamentals in legal thinking; it is not technically typical of all cases, for, being a case in constitutional law, it is not typical for criminal law, equity, and other branches of the law. It concerns the problem of regulating the hours of labor for women.

We are really not starting at the beginning of the problem if we assume that it exists ready-made and well defined for the legislators. For whom does the problem exist? Who raises it? How is it raised? Ordinarily we say the problem originates in "public opinion," and that public opinion directs the legislator's attention to it. This may be the case, but more usually the problem is raised by interested groups or associations. The groups undertake investigations, publicity campaigns, and propaganda. If these are successful, "public opinion" may be aroused, and finally the legislature may take cognizance of the problem. If these groups are "influential" (e.g., a newspaper, or "Wall Street"), they may succeed in getting the attention of the legislature long before the general public is aware of it, and, indeed, if the problem is technical and of only limited interest it may be legislated upon without ever becoming a matter of "public opinion." But in any case the activities of certain interested groups are necessary to bring the problem to the consciousness of the legislator. In fact, so great is the noise of those who are whispering in the ear of the legislator, that only the persistent presentation of the problem, and its increasing acuteness, may expect to draw the attention of the over-burdened law maker.

In our particular case, it might be supposed that the women who toiled overlong under unhealthful and inhuman conditions were first to demand legislation. Not so. Indeed, it may be doubted whether most of them had any further thought than making the best of a hard life. But certain organizations, following the lead of others in Europe, and of International Associations for Labor Legislation, began agitating the regulation of working hours for women. Among the societies aiding this movement were the National Consumers' League, the Russell Sage Foundation, Women's Rights Party, United States Industrial Commission, United States Bureau of Labor, various labor unions, and similar bodies. Some of these were Government institutions, but most of them, certainly the earliest of them, were private enterprises. The societies either directly employed or received the coöperation of numerous scientists, physicians, economists, etc.

After years of investigation and propaganda carried on by these groups, several State Legislatures finally passed laws attempting some sort of regulation. To confine our attention to one of these, let us see what happened to such a law passed by the State Legislature of Illinois, June 17, 1893. The law is entitled "An act to regulate the manufacture of clothing, wearing apparel, and other articles in the State, and to provide for the appointment of State inspectors to enforce same, and to make an appropriation therefor." Among other things it provided that "No female shall be employed in any factory or workshop more than eight hours in any one day or forty-eight hours in any one week."

On a certain day of February, 1894, a Mr. Ritchie was arrested on the charge of employing a woman more than eight hours a day. He waived jury trial, and, upon being fined five dollars by the Justice of the Peace, appealed to the Criminal Court of Cook County, where a similar procedure took place. From this court he appealed by "writ of error" to the Supreme Court of Illinois. Obviously the question at issue was not whether this man was guilty under the law, for his guilt was admitted; the question was whether the law itself was "in error," or whether it was consistent with the constitution of the State of Illinois. The ruling of the court was that the statute was inconsistent with the principles laid down in the constitution, and consequently the judgment of the Criminal Court of Cook County was reversed and the case was remanded to that court with directions to dismiss the prosecution. The significance of the case was, of course, not that Mr. Ritchie escaped the five dollars fine, but that it was henceforth useless to arrest similar offenders against that act, and thus the whole act was rendered void and ineffective, and the will of the legislators, and of the groups immediately responsible for the legislation, was frustrated.

Now let us return to our case, to analyze the reasoning involved. The following extracts are taken from the opinion of the court, as delivered by Mr. Justice Magruder, and are arranged under topical headings to suggest the structure of the argument: [1]

(1) The location of the main points at issue: (a) right of contract, (b) police power:

The main objection urged against the Act, and that to which the discussion of counsel on both sides is chiefly directed, related to the validity of section 5. It is contended by counsel for plaintiff in error, that that section is unconstitutional as imposing unwarranted restrictions upon the right to contract. On the other hand, it is claimed by counsel for The People, that the act is a sanitary provision and justifiable as an exercise of the police power of the State.

(2) The precise definition of terms involved in the first point: (a) "right to contract" and "employment."

Does the provision in question restrict the right to contract? The words, "no female shall be employed," import action on the part of two persons. There must be a person who does the act of employing, and a person who consents to the act of being employed. Webster defines employment as not only "the act of employing," but "also the state of being employed." The prohibition of the statute is, therefore, two-fold, first, that no manufacturer or proprietor of a factory or workshop shall employ any female therein more than eight hours in one day, and, second, that no female shall consent to be so employed. It thus prohibits employer and employee from uniting their minds, or agreeing upon any longer service during one day than eight hours. In other words, they are prohibited, the one from contracting to employ, and the other

[1] Ritchie v. The People, 155 Ill. 101–17.

from contracting to be employed, otherwise than as directed.
"To be employed in anything means not only the act of doing
it, but also to be engaged to do it; to be under contract or or-
ders to do it." (United States *v.* Morris, 14 Pet. 464.) Hence
a direction that a person shall not be employed more than a
specified number of hours in one day, is at the same time a direction that such person shall not be under contract to work
for more than a specified number of hours in one day. It follows that section 5 does limit and restrict the right of the
manufacturer and his employee to contract with each other in
reference to the hours of labor.

(b) "Liberty and property rights."

Is the restriction thus imposed an infringement upon the
constitutional rights of the manufacturer and the employee?
Section 2 of article 2 of the constitution of Illinois provides
that "no person shall be deprived of life, liberty or property,
without due process of law." A number of cases have arisen
within recent years in which the courts have had occasion to
consider this provision, or one similar to it, and its meaning
has been quite clearly defined. The privilege of contracting
is both a liberty and a property right. (Frorer *v.* The People, 141 Ill. 171.) Liberty includes the right to acquire property, and that means and includes the right to make and enforce contracts. (The State *v.* Loomis, 115 Mo. 307.) The
right to use, buy and sell property and contract in respect
thereto is protected by the constitution. Labor is property,
and the laborer has the same right to sell his labor and to contract with reference thereto, as has any other property owner.
In this country the legislature has no power to prevent persons who are *sui juris* from making their own contracts,
nor can it interfere with the freedom of contract between
the workman and the employer. The right to labor or employ
labor, and make contracts in respect thereto upon such terms
as may be agreed upon between the parties, is included in
the constitutional guaranty above quoted. (State *v.* Good-
will, 33 W. Va. 179; Godcharles *v.* Wigeman, 113 Pa. St. 431;
Braceville Coal Co. *v.* The People, 147 Ill. 66.) The protection of property is one of the objects for which free govern-

ments are instituted among men. (Const. of Ill. art. 2, sec. 1.)
The right to acquire, possess, and protect property includes
the right to make reasonable contracts.   (Commonwealth *v.*
Perry, 155 Mass. 117.)   And when an owner is deprived of
one of the attributes of property, like the right to make contracts, he is deprived of his property within the meaning of the
constitution.   (Matter of Application of Jacobs, 98 N.Y. 98.)
The fundamental rights of Englishmen, brought to this country by its original settlers and wrested from time to time in
the progress of history from the sovereigns of the English nation, have been reduced by Blackstone to three principal or
primary articles: "the right of personal security, and the
right of personal liberty, and the right of private property."
(1 Blacks. Com. marg. page 129.)   The right to contract is
the only way by which a person can rightfully acquire property by his own labor.   "Of all the 'rights of persons' it is the
most essential to human happiness."   (Leep *v.* St. L., I. M.
& S. Ry. Co. 58 Ark. 407.)

(3) Partial conclusion: Right of contract being a right
of liberty and property, is guaranteed by the constitution, subject to limitations which must be defined, viz.:
(*a*) "due process of law."

This right to contract, which is thus included in the fundamental rights of liberty and property, cannot be taken away
"without due process of law."   The words "due process of
law" have been held to be synonymous with the words "law
of the land."   (The State *v.* Loomis, *supra;* Frorer *v.* The
People, *supra.*) . . . The "law of the land" is "general public
law binding upon all the members of the community, under all
circumstances, and not partial or private laws, affecting the
rights of private individuals or classes of individuals."   (Mil-
lett *v.* The People, 117 Ill. 294.)   The "law of the land" is
the opposite of "arbitrary, unequal and partial legislation."
(The State *v.* Loomis, *supra.*)   The legislature has no right to
deprive one class of persons of privileges allowed to other persons under like conditions.   The man, who is forbidden to acquire and enjoy property in the same manner in which the

rest of the community is permitted to acquire and enjoy it, is deprived of liberty in particulars of primary importance to his pursuit of happiness. If one man is denied the right to contract as he has hitherto done under the law, and as others are still allowed to do by the law, he is deprived of both liberty and property to the extent to which he is thus deprived of such right. . . .

(b) "Reasonable" vs. "arbitrary" limitations.

We are not unmindful that the right to contract may be subject to limitations growing out of the duties which the individual owes to society, to the public, or to the government. These limitations are sometimes imposed by the obligation to so use one's own as not to injure another, by the character of property as affected with a public interest or devoted to a public use, by the demands of public policy or the necessity of protecting the public from fraud or injury, by the want of capacity, by the needs of the necessitous borrower as against the demands of the extortionate lender. But the power of the legislature to thus limit the right to contract must rest upon some reasonable basis, and cannot be arbitrarily exercised. It has been said that such power is based in every case on some condition, and not on the absolute right to control. Where legislative enactments, which operate upon classes of individuals only, have been held to be valid, it has been where the classification was reasonable, and not arbitrary. (Leep v. St.L., I.M. & S. Ry. Co. *supra;* The State v. Loomis, *supra.*)

(4) Conclusion: the enactment is void, because limitation of right of contract would be arbitrary.

Applying these principles to the consideration of section 5, we are led irresistibly to the conclusion, that it is an unconstitutional and void enactment. . . . We are inclined to regard the act as one that is partial and discriminating in its character. If it be construed as applying only to manufacturers of clothing, wearing apparel and articles of a similar nature,

we can see no reasonable ground for prohibiting such manufacturers and their employees from contracting for more than
eight hours of work in one day, while other manufacturers and
their employees are not forbidden so to contract. If the act be
construed as applying to manufacturers of all kinds of products, there is no good reason why the prohibition should be
directed against manufacturers and their employees, and not
against merchants, or builders, or contractors, or carriers, or
farmers, or persons engaged in other branches of industry,
and their employees therein.   Women employed by manufacturers are forbidden by section 5 to make contracts to labor
longer than eight hours in a day, while women employed as
saleswomen in stores, or as domestic servants, or as book-
keepers, or stenographers, or type-writers, or in laundries, or
other occupations not embraced under the head of manufac-
turing, are at liberty to contract for as many hours of labor
in a day as they choose.   The manner in which the section
thus discriminates against one class of employees and employers and in favor of all others, places it in opposition to the
constitutional guarantees hereinbefore discussed, and so renders it invalid. Section 1 of article 2 of the constitution of Illinois provides as follows: "All men are by nature free and independent, and have certain inherent and inalienable rights;
among these are life, liberty, and the pursuit of happiness.
To secure these rights and the protection of property, governments are instituted among men, deriving their just powers
from the consent of the governed."   Liberty, as has already
been stated, included the right to make contracts, as well with
reference to the amount and duration of labor to be performed, as concerning any other lawful matter.   Hence, the
right to make contracts is an inherent and inalienable one, and
any attempt to unreasonably abridge it is opposed to the
constitution.   As was aptly said in Leep *v.* St.L., I.M. & S.
Ry. Co. *supra:* "Where the subject of contract is purely and
exclusively private, unaffected by any public interest or duty
to person, to society or government, and the parties are capable of contracting, there is a condition existing upon which
the legislature cannot interfere for the purpose of prohibiting
the contract, or controlling the terms thereof."

(5) Analysis of the second main point: "police power." (*a*) scope of "police power."

... But it is claimed on behalf of defendant in error, that this section can be sustained as an exercise of the police power of the State. The police power of the State is that power which enables it to promote the health, comfort, safety and welfare of society. It is very broad and far-reaching, but is not without its limitations. Legislative acts passed in pursuance of it must not be in conflict with the constitution, and must have some relation to the ends sought to be accomplished; that is to say, to the comfort, welfare or safety of society. Where the ostensible object of an enactment is to secure the public comfort, welfare or safety, it must appear to be adapted to that end; it cannot invade the rights of person and property under the guise of a mere police regulation, when it is not such in fact; and where such an act takes away the property of a citizen or interferes with his personal liberty, it is the province of the courts to determine whether it is really an appropriate measure for the promotion of the comfort, safety and welfare of society. . . .

(*b*) This act not a public sanitary measure.

There is nothing in the title of the act of 1893 to indicate that it is a sanitary measure. The first three sections contain provisions for keeping workshops in a cleanly state and for inspection to ascertain whether they are so kept. But there is nothing in the nature of the employment contemplated by the act which is in itself unhealthy, or unlawful, or injurious to the public morals or welfare. Laws restraining the sale and use of opium and intoxicating liquor have been sustained as valid under the police power. (Ah Lim *v*. Territory, 1 Wash. 156; Mugler *v*. Kansas, 123 U.S. 623.) Undoubtedly, the public health, welfare and safety may be endangered by the general use of opium and intoxicating drinks. But it cannot be said that the same consequences are likely to flow from the manufacture of clothing, wearing apparel and other similar articles. . . .

It is not the nature of the things done, but the sex of the

persons doing them, which is made the basis of the claim that the act is a measure for the promotion of the public health. It is sought to sustain the act as an exercise of the police power upon the alleged ground, that it is designed to protect woman on account of her sex and physique. It will not be denied that woman is entitled to the same rights under the constitution, to make contracts with reference to her labor as are secured thereby to men. The first section of the four-teenth amendment to the constitution of the United States provides: "No State shall make or enforce any law which shall abridge the privileges or immunities of citizens of the United States, nor shall any State deprive any person of life, liberty, or property without due process of law, nor deny to any person within its jurisdiction the equal protection of the law." It has been held that a woman is both a "citizen" and a "person" within the meaning of this section. . . .

. . . The question is not whether a particular employment is a proper one for the use of female labor, but the question is whether, in an employment which is conceded to be lawful in itself and suitable for women to engage in, she shall be deprived of the right to determine for herself how many hours she can and may work during each day. There is no reasonable ground — at least none which has been made man-ifest to us in the arguments of counsel — for fixing upon eight hours in one day as the limit within which woman can work without injury to her physique, and beyond which, if she work, injury will necessarily follow. But the police power of the State can only be permitted to limit or abridge such a fundamental right as the right to make contracts, when the exercise of such power is necessary to promote the health, comfort, welfare or safety of society or the public; and it is questionable whether it can be exercised to prevent injury to the individual engaged in a particular calling. . . .

(6) Conclusion: the enactment is void, for there is no proof that it is a "police" measure; i.e., necessary to promote public health, comfort, welfare or safety.

. . . When a health law is challenged in the courts as uncon-

stitutional on the ground that it arbitrarily interferes with
personal liberty and private property without due process of
law, the courts must be able to see that it has at least in fact
some relation to the public health, that the public health is
the end actually aimed at, and that it is appropriate and
adapted to that end.   This we have not been able to see in
this law, and we must, therefore, pronounce it unconstitutional and void.

On the face of it this argument seems to have the following characteristics: (1) Certain rights are guaranteed
by the constitution to the citizens of the State.   Such
rights are liberty, the right of property, the right of contract, right against "partial and discriminating" legislation.   Also certain powers are granted to the government as the police power.   (2) All that the court
attempts to do is to determine whether a particular act
violates these rights or exceeds these powers.   (3) The
legitimate interpretation of debatable terms is largely
determined by precedent or authority; i.e., by previous
judgments of the courts or by recognized writers on the
law (e.g., Blackstone).   (4) The authority of the constitution and of precedent being unquestioned, the validity
of a law can be definitely determined by formal reasoning, without a study of the empirical conditions and consequences at issue.

But on closer inspection this logical simplicity van-
ishes.   In the first place, when we ask for definitions
of liberty, right of property, right of contract, police
power, etc., we find no general agreement.   Precedents
can be found on either side of the question.   Even so
apparently definite words as "to be employed" offer
difficulties in definition.   Does employment imply contract?   If so, does the "privilege of contracting" involve
liberty and property rights?   When the exercise of the

police power conflicts with rights of contract and property, which shall take precedence?   If these rights can be limited by legislation, what is "reasonable" and what is "arbitrary" limitation of these rights?   How may these questions be answered?   The judge is supposed to answer them by examining the meaning of the constitution.   Theoretically he is supposed to "interpret" the intention which the framers of the constitution had in employing those terms.   But practically that is impossible, since the framers of the constitution probably had as varied "intentions" as legislators have to-day.   Whatever their intentions may have been, most of them are impossible to discover, since no adequate account was left by the framers of the constitution.   Even if we had an authoritative version of their intentions, present conditions are so different from conditions at that time that they would have to be "interpreted" in the light of the present conditions.

To fall back on the precedents of the courts is only a specious solution to these problems.   For, in the first place, precedents can usually be found to support either side of a case.   Theoretically, too, to fall back on precedent is futile, for on what basis does the authority of the precedent rest?   If the judgment takes its authority from the constitution, it is subject to most of the limitations of constitutional authority, which have just been pointed out.   If it rests upon the judgment's "reasonableness" with respect to the case which it judges, the whole basis of authority is shifted from given principles to particular facts.   The validity of any judgment, then, rests upon its adequacy in view of the facts of the case, precedent or no precedent.   Add to these criticisms the fact that departure from precedent is itself sufficiently justified by precedent, and there seems to be little left in practice of the authoritative principle upon which constitutional law theoretically rests.

The dialectical or deductive form of law, therefore, conceals beneath its formal simplicity a vast amount of empirical thinking which is necessary to define the terms of the argument. In this case such terms as employment, health, comfort, public welfare, etc., needed to be empirically defined, and upon the meaning assigned by empirical considerations to them really rested the outcome of the case. It is possible to argue that an eight-hour law for women is a violation of the right of contract; the right of contract is a property right; a property right is guaranteed to the citizen by the constitution; whatever is inconsistent with the constitution is void; THEREFORE, the law is void. Although this looks like a perfect mathematical demonstration, it has the certainty of such a demonstration merely in form. Its certainty rests upon the precision of definition of its terms. What would happen to mathematics if a triangle were as difficult to define as the right of liberty? What would happen to physics, if horse-power were as vague a term as police power? No calculations could be made on the basis of such a terminology. A vague idea is not clarified by giving it a name. Consequently legal science may develop a complicated system of legal ideas, each consistent with the other, and the whole based upon constitutional principles, but this formal consistency will have only as much logical force as the ideas employed have precision of meaning.

Social and moral sciences, in general, have this disadvantage when compared with the mathematical and physical sciences. Mathematics is precise and certain, as we have seen, because it can deal with purely ideal symbols which are capable of absolute definition. Whether actual circles are really round or not makes little difference to it, for it deals only with ideal circles, which by definition are perfect. Physical sciences are, to be sure, engaged in the study of physical facts, but they deal with them in terms of quantitative measures which allow a very great precision. The science of law has neither of these advantages. It can deal neither with purely ideal data, nor with physical facts which admit of precise, quantitative measurement. It must deal with physical facts, and it must deal with their least definable qualities. Human wants and social needs are vague, fluctuating things. They would be difficult enough to define even in a static society. In a social environment which is continually and radically changing, these wants and needs are continually assuming new forms. The process of defining them must, therefore, likewise be continuous, reconstructive, and experimental. The definition of a circle, or a volt, is an entirely different process from the definition of the rights of a citizen. Nevertheless, the rights of a citizen need defining, and where the legislator fails to do so, the judge must do it.

To return to our case: the main argument of the case, as quoted above, when extracted from its constitutional and technical setting, runs about as follows: This act is an unreasonable infringement on the right of a woman to use her own judgment as to how long and under what conditions she shall work. If she wants to ruin her health, that is her affair, not ours. The law can interfere only when the PUBLIC health demands it. If it can be shown that for a woman to work more than eight hours a day at the manufacture of clothing is not only prejudicial to her health, but also to the health, safety, and welfare of the public, this interference on the part of the Government would be reasonable.

The chief point here is not whether the Government should respect individual rights, for both sides admit that; nor whether the Government should protect the public welfare or not, for both sides admit this also. In any act of Government these aims may be conceded. In the constitution they are formulated, but of necessity in the most general terms. People can tell in general what they want a government to do, but, when it comes to the particular application of that on which they are in general agreed, differences of judgment immediately arise. So here, the real question at issue is just how our general aims apply to this situation. That problem arises afresh for every new situation. Hence the necessity of a system of deliberative judgments as we have them in the courts.

In answering this type of problem the judge must turn from the constitution to experience. No amount of reasoning from principle will throw light on whether or not women's health is prejudiced by working more than eight hours; nothing in the constitution will tell whether or not the hours of labor for women affect the public health. The appeal here is to facts. And in this case the judge threw out the act because he thought no facts had been introduced to prove that the act really did what its defenders claimed for it. Formally, of course, he threw it out because it was unconstitutional.

Fifteen years later this same Mr. Ritchie was again haled before the same court to test the constitutionality of a similar law for regulating the hours of labor for

women in factories — this time a ten-hour law passed in
1909. (Ritchie & Co. *v.* Wayman, 244 Ill. 509.) An
entirely new bench of judges was sitting. The same
old arguments were raised about the right of contract,
liberty, etc. The defense rested its case largely upon
the decision and the argument quoted above. But the
prosecution, under the leadership of Mr. Louis Brandeis,
adopted entirely new tactics. Mr. Brandeis submitted
a brief of over one hundred pages, of which only two
pages were devoted to the technical legal aspects of the
problem.[1] The bulk of the brief was a mass of statistics
gathered from all over the world, of testimonies from
prominent physicians and physiologists, of reports from
labor commissions, and the like, all proving beyond
doubt the real point of the argument, namely, that usually the health of women is seriously undermined by the
fatigue and strain of long hours, and that these effects
were prejudicial to the health of their children and thus
to the welfare of the people at large.

To give the main features of this famous document
will show the type of facts of which law must take cognizance, and how they are made known. They were collected under the direction of Miss Josephine Goldmark,
and may be found in her volume entitled *Fatigue and
Efficiency.* The evidence contained the following items
among others:

  1. Testimonies of a number of physicians, factory inspec-
     tors, statistical bureaus, insurance companies, etc., to
     the effect that
     (*a*) Women in factories are more subject to fatigue and
        overstrain caused by speed, monotony, piece-work,
        etc., than men are.

[1] This brief was prepared for and first submitted in the case of Muller
v. Oregon, Supreme Court of U.S., October, 1907.

(*b*) Women are more subject to disease than men.

2. A detailed account of the effect of fatigue on nerves and muscles, with charts showing the effect of long-continued stimulation of muscles, the physiological functions of rest, etc.

3. Testimonies of experts, submitted in the courts of Europe, and of the United States, as to the bad effects of long hours on health, safety, relation between fatigue and disease, etc.

4. Statistics showing the relative frequency of industrial accidents, and the relative production for the working hours of the day, proving beyond doubt that increased accidents and decreased efficiency result from fatigue.

5. Testimonies regarding effect of fatigue and overwork on morals, infant mortality, health of the next generation, and the general benefit of society.

6. Testimonies regarding the benefits of leisure and recreation.

7. Reports from countries who had put into effect laws for shorter hours, proving the efficacy of such legislation to bring about the results desired.

8. Reports and testimonies showing that shorter hours do not eventually restrict the output, for the gain in efficiency and quality of output soon offsets the initial reduction of output.

9. Testimonies showing the ill effects of allowing overtime, and urging uniformity of regulation for all.

10. Statistics supporting the above from various industries, for example, laundries, mercantile establishments, millinery and dressmaking shops, restaurants, etc.

The presentation of these facts really determined the judgment of the court. "We take judicial cognizance of all matters of general knowledge" was the dictum of the courts. One wonders, of course, whether the reversal of the decision was really due to the introduction of these facts. It is possible that, had the same judges been sitting here who sat in the previous case, these facts might

have left them immovable. Or it might be that, even
if they had changed their minds in the meantime, the
change was due not to more facts, but to pressure of
public sentiment or party policy. There is abundance
of evidence to show that judges are very human in their
capacity to be influenced consciously or unconsciously
by "extraneous" forces. Political parties, for instance,
ever since the days of John Marshall, have realized the
importance of getting "their own men" on the bench.
But granting for the present that the judges in both
cases were skilled and conscientious legal logicians, the
case is significant and typical to this extent, that it indicates how and why the intelligence of the court is dependent on empirical facts, as well as on legal tradition
and formal reasoning. This does not mean, of course,
that the technical difficulties which had stood in the
way of the former act were simply ignored, and that the
constitution was made of no effect. It means that the
choice of rival interpretations of these technical matters
was determined largely by the empirical and practical
issues at stake. For instance, the earlier act was entitled "an act to regulate the manufacture of clothing."
Since the constitution gives no such general power of
regulation to the legislature, and since the title therefore
proved to be a stumbling-block in the courts, the enac-
tors of the second act emphasized the fact that it was
an act to protect the safety and welfare of the people,
which power was expressly granted to the legislature.
The questions of the right of contract, unfair discriminations, etc., were also decided in the light of these facts.
In the former case the right of contract was held to place
limits upon such use of the police power (precedents
were given); in the latter case the police power was held

to place limits upon the right of contract (precedents were given). Which of the two judgments would be made depended upon the relative importance which the different judges attached to the evil effects of long hours on the one side, or of loss of freedom on the other, rather than upon inconsistencies of argument. Similarly the matter of unfair discrimination was decided by the significance attached to sex differences, to conditions existing in factories and laundries, etc., rather than by appeal to an authoritative interpretation by constitutional principles. Thus the meaning of these concepts (right of contract, etc.) gets continually redefined in the light of changing conditions, and at the same time by using such concepts the changing conditions are subjected to some sort of order and coherency. These concepts or "principles," precisely because they are vague and capable of various interpretations, are useful in maintaining a flexible social order in the face of continual change and a general regularity and consistency in the face of a bewildering multitude of details. But when such principles are assumed to be fixed and definite, like mathematical axioms, and to give to law a demonstrative certainty, they confuse and obstruct social practice by concealing social uncertainty under such sham certainties. The law is, of course, deductive or demonstrative in form, for the applications of a law must be *demonstrated* to follow from it; and this implies that the form or structure of legal reasoning must be logical. But skill in formal reasoning alone will never make an able lawyer.

Formal reasoning is adequate only so long as it is possible to decide a case on the basis of unambiguous precedents. If the issue can really be defined and determined merely by deducing the inferences from accepted precedents, if the precedents adequately "cover" the case, the reasoning involved is purely dialectical. But this practically never happens, since history does not repeat itself accurately enough to enable a lawyer (unless his thinking is very superficial) to apply conclusions based on the past directly to a present case, without raising empirical problems. Reflective thinking in law has the difficult task of applying a rigorous dialectical discipline to a subject-matter which is both indefinite and fluctuating; if it sacrifices precision of meaning to formal consistency, it loses its honesty; if it sacrifices consistency to the drift of opinion, it loses its power. To think well on legal problems requires both "reason" and "wisdom"; for it involves both the intricacies of consistent argument and the intricacies of interpreting the meaning of concepts in the light of ever-changing facts and ideals.

QUESTIONS AND EXERCISES

1. Describe the various attitudes of people toward the policeman. What light does this throw on the ways in which law operates in society?
2. Analyze the process of making and testing laws in terms of the analysis of an act of thought given in the Introduction to the book.
3. What improvements in the process of legislation might be expected if it were exclusively in the hands of lawyers and judges? What dangers and disadvantages?
4. Analyze the thinking involved in the Eighteenth Amendment to the Constitution from the time it was first proposed until the decision as to the constitutionality of the Volstead Act.
5. What limiting factors must reflective thinking in legislation keep in mind?
6. What use do lawyers and judges make of authority and precedent? What similarities and what difference does this use of authority present compared with its use in the scientific thinking which you have studied in previous chapters?
7. What problems for reflective thinking are peculiar to the moral and social sciences, and how do they manifest themselves in law?

8. What is the difference between "law" in the legal sense and in the sense of "laws of nature"?
9. Make a list of the terms which Mr. Justice Magruder defines in the argument cited. How does he go about defining them? How would you go about it?
10. What elements of the argument of Mr. Justice Magruder were contradicted by the later decision against Ritchie? Can either of the two arguments be proved formally fallacious? What inferences would you draw from your answers to these questions about "judicial reasoning"?
11. In a similar case to the one cited in the text, a judge remarked that this argument would have more force if the women, not their employers, were clamoring for freedom of contract. Do you think this is a valid objection? What are your reasons for thinking so?
12. Read Cardozo's *The Nature of the Judicial Process*. What does he mean by "the method of philosophy" and the "method of history"?

BIBLIOGRAPHY

Benjamin N. Cardozo: *The Nature of the Judicial Process*. Yale University Press, 1921. (The best brief and non-technical discussion of law from the standpoint of reflective thinking.)

Munroe Smith: *Jurisprudence*. Columbia University Press, 1909.

W. N. Hohfeld: *Fundamental Conceptions Applied in Judicial Reasoning*. Yale University Press, 1919.

Roscoe Pound: *The Spirit of the Common Law*. Boston, 1921. (Especially chap. VII, " Judicial Empiricisms"; chap. VIII, "Legal Reason.")

Oliver Wendell Holmes: *Collected Legal Papers*. New York, 1921. (Especially pp. 25–32, 167–249, and 291–97.)

James H. Tufts: "The Legal and Social Philosophy of Mr. Justice Holmes." *American Bar Association Journal*, vol. VII, no. 7, pp. 359–63, July, 1921.

James H. Tufts: "Judicial Law-Making Exemplified in Industrial Arbitration." *Columbia Law Review*, vol. XXI; no. 5, pp. 405–15, May, 1921.

Sir Frederick Pollock: *Essays in Jurisprudence and Ethics*. 1882. (Especially "The Science of Case Law.")

Pierre de Tourtoulon: *Philosophy in the Development of Law*. Translated by Martha McRead. Being vol. XIII of the "Modern Legal Philosophy Series." 1922. Chapters VIII–XI inclusive.

CHAPTER XII

REFLECTIVE THOUGHT IN THE REALM OF ETHICS

Section 1. The Ethical Situation

IN Chapter IX the general problems, methods, and difficulties of evaluation were discussed. Since ethics attempts to evaluate human character and conduct, it encounters the difficulties which were seen to confront all reflective evaluation. In the first place, we saw that there are immediate values which cannot be measured by any standard common to a number of individuals, but which have to be judged privately, each individual gauging as best he can his own liking for the various alternatives between which he must choose. To measure values objectively, we must consider them in their mediate aspects, as means to the realization of certain ends; and our ability to do this depends upon our readiness to take certain ends for granted, so that we may apply objective methods to determine which means will best satisfy those ends. In general, we saw that the soundness of our evaluation depends upon our success in seeing all the implications of a decision, and in estimating correctly our desires with respect to them.

Has evaluation in ethics any peculiar characteristics distinguishing it from other kinds of evaluation? What reasons are there, if any, for giving separate attention to reflection in ethics? This question is one upon which mankind has reached no general agreement. To some ethics is a unique subject with methods all its own, while others hold there is no difference between the logic by which ethical questions are decided and the logic of any other field. There are also many intermediate positions.

Most people recognize that ethical problems have a special importance, even if they believe that the logic of ethical judgment is the same as that of any other field. In analyzing the process of legal decision, we have seen the very elaborate machinery which men set up to solve certain problems arising in their relations with one another. But the solutions reached by this machinery are not always satisfactory. People ask: Are the laws just? And even if the answer "yes" is returned, the very asking of the question implies a criticism of the laws, a reviewing of them in the light of standards which are regarded as more fundamental than they. The part which such standards may play in the judicial process has been suggested.

To arrive at certain ultimate standards, by which all else can be evaluated, is the cardinal problem of reflection in ethics. It is a problem which every one, who participates in social life, must solve in some fashion, well or ill. Every man, consciously or unconsciously, employs some set of ultimate standards, be they consistent with each other or inconsistent. Moreover, to question a person's ultimate standards is to touch him at a very tender point, namely, his moral consciousness.

In the chapter on evaluation we remarked that reflection is hindered in this field even more than in others by prejudices, judgments already formed in advance of the act of judging. Prejudices in ethics, being supported by the moral consciousness which we have mentioned, are of all prejudices the most powerful. All of us have been taught from our earliest years that some actions are right, others wrong, and, since it is of the first importance that our conduct should not be such as to bring ourselves or others into difficulty, this moral indoctrination has ordinarily been as thorough as possible. Erroneous opinions about physics or geography are not ordinarily considered serious except for the physical scientist, for a man may believe that the earth is flat without harming himself or any one else. Erroneous opinions about morals are another matter, and it is generally believed that every effort ought to be made to prevent any one from supposing that he is at liberty to appropriate the possessions of others without their consent, or to follow his impulses at every moment without restraint of any sort. It is not important, in other words, that more than a limited number of persons should possess mathematical and scientific knowledge, since such knowledge is required for only a fraction of our activities; but all persons at all times need guidance in their personal conduct, and every precaution is accordingly taken that no one is left unsupplied with moral convictions.

Furthermore, the beliefs on which our conduct is based are often such as to compel us to forego pleasures and satisfactions which we desire very much, and, unless we are strongly convinced of the truth of these beliefs, and of their universal applicability, we are likely to make exceptions to them in our favor whenever they conflict with our desires. The suspension of judgment, consequently, which is enjoined upon scientists and investigators in the field of abstract knowledge in general, is not thought an advantage when beliefs about conduct are concerned. It is thought that any one not entirely convinced that theft is wrong is dangerously likely to dispense with honesty in his personal practice. To call into question any generally accepted moral opinion is, therefore, to appear in the light of one seeking justification for moral lapses, or at least as the instigator of such lapses in others: moral initiative is indistinguishable from immorality. Under the circumstances, it is not surprising that the free discussion out of which comes progress in intellectual matters has not prevailed in the ethical field, and that the positive results elsewhere achieved are conspicuously lacking in ethics.

The conditions under which one ordinarily comes to the study of ethics are, then, as follows. Before he has ever reflected about right and wrong at all, he has had impressed upon him a code of rules for conduct, the validity of which, he has been taught, is not open to debate. These rules appear to be, in the main, a set of prohibitions, the more obvious purpose of which is to safeguard the welfare of others. Large numbers of the acts which he would naturally be prompted to perform are forbidden him, and the estimation in which he is held depends upon acceptance of these prohibitions so that his fellow men may prosper. To such an extent is this true that in the popular view morality is almost the same thing as self-denial and, especially, self-sacrifice. If I do what I wish I am not, perhaps, immoral, but neither in any positive sense moral, while if I yield my desires so that others may gratify theirs, my virtue is incontestable. The interests of the individual and the interests of society are in conflict, and the individual is moral in proportion as he sacrifices his welfare to the welfare of the whole. Should he decline to make the sacrifice, society will exact it: the policeman will deal with him if he disregards such of the social demands as are enacted into law, and public opinion will bring pressure to bear upon him in behalf of the remainder.

This system of repressions comes to appear, however, not merely as a thwarting of part of the individual's desires. It is also an assurance of satisfaction to another part of his desires. If I am prevented from interfering with my neighbor's interests, he also is prevented from interfering with mine. At the price of accepting duties, I acquire rights, and the two are correlative; I cannot enjoy the latter without submitting to the former. Here, again, some of the rights are guaranteed by law, and if they are threatened I can enlist the force of the state in my behalf; others are safeguarded only by public opinion. I can sue a man who refuses to pay his lawful debts to me; if I convey some information under promise of secrecy and the promise is broken, though I have no legal redress, the disapproval of the circle in which we move may be quite as effective a punishment as fine or imprisonment. Any moral and legal code whatever secures as well as circumscribes my field of interests.

Reflection on morals takes place when we begin to consider the justification of the moral code in detail. It starts often from a comparison of the moral standards of different times and different peoples. An individual on whom any existing set of moral rules did not press with excessive severity would be comparatively unlikely to question the justice of the customs of his people if he knew no others. Finding, however, that some of the things of which he is deprived by the laws under which he lives are not forbidden to the citizens of other countries, who in spite of their greater freedom do not come to disaster, he begins to question the necessity of the particular tabu, and finally raises the question of the justification of each and every prohibition. The price paid for security may seem exorbitant, or, if it is not exorbitant on the whole, the individual may wish to be shown in detail what will be returned to him for each particular act of self-denial. If we suppose him to decide that no adequate *quid pro quo* is in sight, is his first duty to authority, or is his liberty sacred? Must I always do what society regards as my duty, or may I take issue with society if I think its laws, written or unwritten, unjustified, and act on my individual opinion?

Questions of this kind lead to the formation of ideals, ultimate standards, in the light of which choices are made and justified. It is the conflict between these ideals which gives rise to the cardinal problem of reflective ethics. Between two ultimate standards is there any way of deciding which is the better? In previous chapters we studied cases in which old views gave place to new which were generally accepted, and by examining the reasons for these changes we gained some knowledge of reflective thinking. But in ethical controversies there has been much less general agreement as to which of the various proposed solutions is best. In mathematics or physics or astronomy it was possible to illustrate the nature of reflective thought by analyzing solutions which were undeniably solutions. Though no one supposes that in the Copernican astronomy the last word on the movements of celestial bodies is uttered, its relative satisfactoriness as against, for example, the Ptolemaic astronomy, is questioned by no one competent to judge. The logician, when he attempts to distinguish between the better and the worse in thought by discovering the characteristics in which the heliocentric theory differs from the geocentric, runs no risk of failing to identify the better theory.   But in ethics there is no such certainty. In considering a genuine ethical problem we are not at liberty to take any suggested solution as *the* solution, and compare it with alternative solutions.   There is no preeminently and indubitably satisfactory solution, and consequently no analysis of conclusive proof in ethics can be offered.

If this be true, what profit may we reasonably expect from the analysis of a controversy in ethics? Let us not answer this question without experiment.   Let us examine carefully the discussion of some important ethical problem, and see whether any kind of progress or development may be noted in the thinking, such as would give us some criteria for evaluating reflective thought in ethics.   It would be rash to say that all thinking was vain and profitless which did not reach a solution to its problem upon which every one could agree.   The early Greek scientists, like most pioneers in every field, did not succeed in proving or in gaining the universal acceptance of any of their major theories.   Yet they made progress in discovering the real problems of science and in suggesting the kinds of concepts by which those problems might be solved.   Perhaps we shall find a somewhat similar situation in the field of ethics.

The conflict between the ideals of individualism and of collectivism is the particular issue which we have chosen for our experiment.   The statement of this conflict has been foreshadowed in the introductory section; in the section which follows a more definite, though still provisional account of it will be offered.

Section 2.   Individualism vs. Collectivism

Every one is aware of a distinction between what he is permitted by society to do and what he is not permitted to do, and almost every one meets some situations in which he thinks it would be better from some points of view to do what he is not permitted to do.   For instance, a man may think it better not to pay a tax maintaining armaments, but the law requires him to pay it. The individualist is one who is impressed by the frequency and harmfulness of these dilemmas, and who, therefore, regards control by law or by public opinion as at best a necessary evil which should be reduced to the minimum possible.   The collectivist, on the other hand, believes that either from incapacity to judge of his own welfare or natural indifference to the welfare of others, or else for the sake of greater social efficiency, the individual requires guidance and control, and that extension of such control wherever it can be made effective is advisable.

I. THE CASE FOR INDIVIDUALISM

In the course of controversy it becomes necessary for both parties to state their ideals more explicitly.   Individualism, if pushed to the logical extreme, would deny the justification of any social control whatever.   We need not, however, pause for a discussion of a theory of anarchy in morals.   It is not seriously maintained by any one that we ought all to do what happens to please us irrespective of its effect on any one else; in other words, that there are no such things as obligations. For better or for worse, we are social beings, and unless we are prepared to feed, shelter, and clothe ourselves without help from anybody, and to limit our conversation to soliloquy, we must pay due regard to the conventions which make associated activities possible. Since we cannot live, or at least get more than a small fraction of the things we wish, without the services of our fellow men, we must offer a return for such services; and this consideration, in the individualist's opinion, both justifies and defines our obligations. Our bargain is within limits a good bargain, but we are obliged to make a return only for value received, and if we yield more we are allowing ourselves to be imposed upon and deprived of our rights. Correspondingly, we are entitled to ask of others only such deference to our wishes as we have earned by deference to theirs, and we are usurping authority that belongs rightly to them if we seek to control any of their actions or preferences that do not affect the fulfillment of our desires.

Such considerations are equally applicable to our private and to our public activities. Certain of our acts affect gravely the welfare of others, and for control of these the state exists, of which the characteristic feature is the power to use compulsion. Its rôle is limited to the preservation of our security; externally, to defense against aggression on the part of other nations; internally, against attack by other individuals. An ideal state in an ideal world would have no other functions than the maintenance of order and the enforcement of contracts. We ought to be compelled, that is to say, to do no more than respect the rights of others and discharge such obligations to them as we have contracted for. The state may tax us for the support of the judge, the policeman, and the soldier, but for nothing else.

The general distinction which the individualist draws

is thus between acts which affect ourselves only, and
those which affect others, and he is prepared to admit
interference, by the state or by public opinion, only
with the latter. This conclusion is reinforced by two
sets of arguments, the first drawn from a study of comparative ethics, the latter from the results of compulsion
on the character and usefulness of those subjected to it.
If we consider the codes under which people live and
have lived, we find a vast number of conflicting ideas,
along with a certain amount of agreement. All civilized
states maintain for their citizens a reasonable measure of
security: they protect the lives and property of those
who come under the jurisdiction of their laws. In addition, however, they impose restrictions and exact duties which vary from state to state, no one of which,
therefore, is essential to the existence of a stable community. Public opinion, going beyond this, adds to the
burden. Individuals are obliged not only to respect the
rights of others, as they ought to be: they are compelled
to order their private affairs in accordance with the ideas
of the majority of their fellow citizens; and this is wholly
unjustifiable. If we go further afield and consider the
moral codes of primitive peoples, we find that the sav-
age is subjected to innumerable prohibitions or tabus for
which no utility can be found. "His whole life, to its
minutest detail, is ordained for him by the voice of the
herd, and he must not, under the most dreadful sanctions, step outside its elaborate order."[1] Whom he may
marry, what he must wear, how he must conduct himself in the presence of his superiors, his inferiors, and his
equals, are matters rigidly determined by the custom of
his tribe. We find, in other words, that men in associa-

[1] Trotter, *Instincts of the Herd in Peace and War.*

tion, whether through legal or extra-legal means, constantly tend to interfere with actions on the part of their fellows that have no bearing on the proper concerns of the state; that authority is naturally disposed to be tyrannical, to meddle, and to enjoin upon the individual behavior inimical to his own welfare.

If we compare the life of civilized communities, in which the individual has won at least a measure of freedom from control, with that of the savages, where custom is all-powerful and brooks no exceptions, we find that it is only in the former that there is any trace of what we call "individuality." In the absence of this characteristic, it would hardly be too much to say, there can be nothing of real value. People are only happy in their own lives, or of interest in the lives of others, in so far as they are at liberty to develop in their own peculiar fashion, to display their distinctive gifts and become unique personalities. But compulsion, the individualist contends, is in its nature repressive; it forces those affected by it into a stereotyped mould, and allows no play whatever for individuality. A rich variety of types is not only more valuable from an æsthetic point of view; it is also more effective practically. A state has many and varied problems to solve, and requires in consequence extensive resources in human material to draw upon: if all people are alike, there can be no specialized functions, as there are none, or almost none, among savages. What is done under compulsion, furthermore, is badly done. A man acts effectively, as a rule, only when he is doing what he likes, when he is free to act or not to act according to his pleasure. Hence the superiority of private initiative to governmental direction. We secure spontaneity, inventiveness, resourcefulness, in a word, effectiveness, in every field of activity, only when we let people alone, permit them to do as they please. Hence that government and that public opinion is best that governs least: authority is always to be distrusted, and the eternal vigilance on the individual's part in scrutinizing law and convention is the price of liberty and happiness.

This argument, if it is justified, yields an ethical conclusion of general validity. It supplies us with a test for deciding which of the acts prescribed by society and the state are justly prescribed, and which are not; it enables the individual to judge of the extent to which he is morally bound to obey the commands of his people. It does not, of course, answer every question that may be asked about his conduct, since unjust laws may be obeyed on the ground of expediency; but it does answer an important part of the moral question in a way equally valid for all men. Nor, it must be added, does any science answer questions of practice in a final or conclusive manner. The most perfectly trained physician may err in the diagnosis or treatment of a case: the application of his knowledge may in a concrete instance always go astray. Universal validity, which is characteristic of the sciences, does not involve absolute finality or absolute certainty in application. The absence of these in our present state of ethical knowledge is, therefore, no bar to the inclusion of ethics among the sciences if it can furnish us with laws that may be both proved and applied to concrete cases to the same extent, as for example, the principles of medicine. Such, it is alleged, is the general statement that the individual owes only such services as society has earned by assuring his security, with the corollary that the degree of compulsion exerted by society far oversteps this limit, and ought to be resisted until it is reduced to the extent indicated by the general principle. This statement is true for every individual and for every community; it carries with it particular consequences of practical value, and its truth and value vindicate the claim of reflective thought to be applicable to the sphere of conduct.

We may summarize the contentions of the individualist as follows: Human interests naturally conflict, and their conflict can only be resolved by mutual concessions. Since we accept others' concessions, we are in duty bound to make concessions ourselves. By living in society, we tacitly accept the "social contract," the obligations of which society may with justice compel us to discharge. Over such of our acts as affect only ourselves, society has no jurisdiction, and if it attempts to control them it ought to be resisted. If it is well advised, it will make no such attempt, since we are not only happier, but also more valuable to it if we are left, subject to the above reservation, to do as we please.

II. THE CASE FOR COLLECTIVISM

Criticism of the above argument begins by making explicit the assumptions underlying it. It takes for granted, first, that actions may be divided into those affecting only the agent, and those affecting also his fellows; second, that there is a natural and essential conflict between the interests of different individuals, such that compulsion exerted upon one man in the interests of others or of society as a whole is necessarily abridgment of the freedom of the individual coerced; finally, that every one knows what he wishes, is the best judge of what will satisfy his desires. All these assumptions may be denied, and the collectivist does deny them all.

He asserts, in contrast, that all our desires and acts are indissolubly bound up with one another, and that if any of them are society's concern, all of them are. The state may set a norm for private as well as public life, exercise a positive as well as a negative function. If it is objected that this opens the way to unlimited exploitation of the individual in the interests of society, the reply is that no opposition exists between the interests of the two: society is not an external means to the ends of the individual, but we are in all literalness "members one of another." The welfare of society is directly and immediately a part of the individual's welfare, for without his relations to others he would not be even an individual. Finally, if the individualist contends that compulsion is still unjustified, since to the extent that the welfare of the man and the State are one no compulsion is needed, the collectivist replies that the individual does not, in the beginning, know his own welfare. What he supposes himself to desire is in many cases utterly unsatisfactory to him when he gets it, and what appears compulsion and the negation of liberty is really a direction of his energies into channels that have in the past been proved to lead to a real goal, and not to some illusory Utopia. When any one wishes anything contrary to what the law permits him, the argument runs, he may be sure that the end he has in view would not satisfy him if he could reach it. At best it could be had only at the sacrifice of some greater good which in his ignorance he has overlooked. True freedom and obedience to law are not, consequently, opposed, for law, when positive as when negative, interprets to each man his own will, and when he hearkens to it he hears the voice of his own best self.

The first point is one easily made. The individualist was unwilling to allow the state to compel or supervise education, to forbid the use of alcohol or drugs, to look after the health of the personal tastes of its people, because these things relate to the private life, and have nothing to do with the discharge of one's obligations to others. They have, however, much to do with the adequate discharge of such obligations, and the social welfare as a whole. Illiteracy, addiction to drugs, and in general a low level of culture and intelligence are injurious to each and all, and in preventing them to the utmost possible extent it is the claim of the collectivist that the state is increasing and not diminishing freedom. It is possible to be a slave to superstition, ignorance, ill-health, and vice, and the compulsion exerted by the state and public opinion to prevent these conditions rivets no fetters upon the individual, but rather breaks them. Abstract freedom of contract may in practice turn out to be servitude, none the less real because it is enforced by the "invisible lash of hunger." Liberty, in the only real sense, is something that must be assured by legislation, not by merely leaving the individual alone.

This conviction is deepened if we consider, not the conditions under which we can secure our ends, but the ends themselves. The individualist considers association between individuals as merely incidental to the acquisition by each of the things he wishes to enjoy, and the services he renders to society as always a subtraction from his total enjoyment. But if there were no society, no other persons in the world, the individual would be nothing, or at least there would be nothing to characterize him as a human being. He would have no interests to make his own, nothing to enlist his energies and provide an end in the achievement of which he could find his satisfaction. Vocationless, companionless, with nothing to do but find food and shelter himself from the elements, he would be precisely on a par with the animals. If individualism were true, a man living alone on an island would enjoy the most complete freedom, a conclusion which reduces individualism to absurdity. A freedom which turns out to mean freedom from all our deepest interests can hardly be distinguished from slavery. How is our man without a fellow different from a man undergoing solitary imprisonment?

If we take into account the social nature of man, then, his duties appear in a very different light. The actions exacted from him apparently in the interests of others are in reality in his own interests. The welfare of the social organism is his welfare, its injuries his injuries, and its destruction his destruction. The murderer not only sets an example and authorizes a practice of which he may be the next victim; he, also, whether discovered or not, confirms himself in the isolation which is harder than any other penalty to bear. The liar, if he is found out, cannot expect thereafter to have what he says believed, but what is worse for him is that he cannot himself believe others. A trivial example may illustrate the general principle. We may consider the rules of a game as intended to safeguard the interests of all playing it, as compelling each to give consideration to the claims of his opponents. On the individualistic view, I am restrained from cheating because unfair play would rob another of a deserved victory. The truth is that a game won unfairly is not won at all: it is I who am deprived of the victory, for I know, whether others know it or not, that the outcome did not reveal the best player. Law once more appears as the expression of my own will, and what it demands of me is what I truly wish to do.

The final argument for collectivism has been stated by implication in what has gone before. The individualist assumes that every man knows what he wants, but so far is this from the truth that we might with equal propriety say that no man knows what he wants. There is no one who, looking back into his past, cannot remember desires without number the satisfaction of which he now thanks heaven was denied him. The truth contained in the epigram, "There are two tragedies in life, not getting what one wants, and getting it; and the second is by far the worse," may be only a half-truth, but the individualist forgets it entirely. If we are capable of being educated at all, we soon learn to distinguish between our real selves and our momentary, impulsive, or unenlightened selves. Few of us are so fortunate as never to have had to say, "I was not myself when I did that." What we think we want at any moment is therefore no index to our real needs, and society, in compelling us to forego many satisfactions to which we feel ourselves drawn, is really enforcing the claims of our own enlightened will. This statement is, indeed, only a summary of the arguments already set forth: the social will is really our will, and it is only our own blindness that can persuade us to the contrary.

All these facts point to one conclusion. The individual, apart from the state of which he is a member, is nothing: he owes to the state, in consequence, his absolute and unconditional loyalty. He is most fully himself when he accepts the duties the state assigns him, knowing that its life is his, and that the hardships it seems to impose upon him are no more than every one submits to who restrains the impulses of the moment because they conflict with some greater ultimate good. Our moral duty is near at hand and unmistakable: it consists in discharging the duties of our station, and living in accord with the spirit of our people. Though every age and every nation has its own set of laws and traditions, and these are not all the same, we must not suppose them, therefore, to be in error; each is justified in its own time and place; and the individual cannot do better than to make those of his state his own.

III. AN ATTEMPTED SYNTHESIS OF THE CONFLICTING VIEWS: REDEFINITION AND CLARIFICATION OF THE ISSUE

This conclusion, so diametrically opposed to that reached in the preceding section, may seem to throw us back into the arms of the skeptic. He appears to be right who says that where good and bad are concerned there can be nothing but opinions; you may take your choice, for no opinion can be proved. Perhaps, however, the disagreement may not be so absolute as our first impression suggests: a criticism of both arguments may reveal at least a measure of concord.

If we admit the contention of the collectivist, that his opponent misconceived the nature of the individual, falsely opposed the individual's welfare to the welfare of society, and understood liberty, consequently, in too narrow a sense, we may still hesitate to accept his conclusion that no individual is ever justified in taking issue with the moral code under which he lives. As against an individualism which identifies freedom with the abil-

ity to disregard others entirely, except as means to our
ends, it must be admitted that relations to others are
part of the essence of the individual, and that action in
their interest cannot be regarded as necessarily involving self-sacrifice on his part.   It is doubtless true also
that we learn what we want only gradually, and that if
we had no society to instruct us — partly at least by
compulsion — we should never learn.   But when all
this is conceded, we may still feel reluctant to admit the
claim that the world is always wiser than any man, and
entitled, therefore, to demand absolute obedience from
all.   This reluctance may be defended on at least two
grounds, one, furnished by the answer to the question
how far the state does actually offer perfect satisfaction
to the wishes of every one, provided he learns to know
what his true wishes are; the other, furnished by a consideration of the history of moral progress.

Critics of the theory of the all-wise and all-powerful
state invariably urge that that theory considers the
state in its ideal form; finds that a perfect state would
supply the individual with opportunities precisely adjusted to his powers, that it would provide him with better instruments for the solution of his problems than any
he could possibly find by his own unaided efforts; and
that the theory then attributes these qualities to the
existent state and claims for *this* state the allegiance due
only to the perfect community.   A state in which perfect
justice and perfect wisdom were the rule could, it may
be, be permitted to determine absolutely the duties of its
citizens, reveal to them their real will, and claim their
obedience with no appeal to any other quarter.   But
the state as it actually exists is a set of institutions which
have gradually developed from forms that no one would

now consider perfect, and the traces of this ancestry have by no means disappeared. The position of woman in the family, for instance, has always been determined in a large measure by the fact that she was once a chattel, a part of her husband's possessions, to be regarded as permanently and essentially his inferior. This is the status that, if we take into consideration the past and by far the greater part of the world at present, has, in an overwhelmingly high degree, been assigned her by law and public opinion. No doubt in an ideal marriage the nominal possession of authority by either husband or wife would be a matter of indifference, since the desires of each would aim at nothing contrary to the welfare of the other. However, the conditions with which we are confronted are real and not ideal conditions, and under them we are not justified in expecting from fallible human beings the perfect insight, justice, and self-control that should be characteristic of any one wielding absolute authority. It may make a great deal of difference to a woman that she does or does not retain title to her property after she marries. And, in general, the will of the state is always exercised through individuals. It is only by a figure of speech that we can talk of the state's creating or regulating institutions. Actually, it is the individuals holding office who pass legislation and administer justice, and few will be found to maintain that legislatures and parliaments and their ministers always know better than the individuals for whom they legislate what is for the best interests of those individuals. When by the fortunes of war Alsace and Lorraine were added to the German Empire, it is not immediately obvious that their inhabitants had no real will but to renounce their allegiance to France, or that in England in the eighteenth century, when theft of any article exceeding five shillings in value was punishable by death, the criminal who paid that penalty agreed in putting so high an estimate on the debt he owed society.

Similarly, when we consider the history of progress as a whole, we find that everything now considered an advance was fiercely contested by law and public opinion at the time it was first proposed, and that he who advances beyond the moral standards of his time is in the eyes of his contemporaries as much a criminal as he who lags behind. The circumstance already mentioned, that every possible pressure is brought to bear upon each individual, at the time when he is most susceptible to suggestion, and least capable of criticizing it, to make him accept the moral standards current in his community, justified suspicion of any blanket endorsement of things as they are in the moral world. In general, we may say that the collectivist argument, if at any time in the past it had been accepted in its entirety and acted upon, would at that moment have brought progress to an end. Every great advance has been the work of individuals who entertained beliefs at variance with the accepted code of their time, and had the courage to act upon them. Socrates and Jesus are the stock examples; and if any one chooses to say, as has been said, that the conservative is the imitator of the dead radical, it is not altogether clear with what words he is to be answered.

An individualism which takes its stand on the foregoing considerations thus escapes the force of the collectivist polemic. It may grant that freedom is opportunity to strive for a more than personal end in an ordered social world, and at the same time contend that the individual may not only select, but to some extent create, the ideals to which he yields allegiance. Again, though he does not know at the start, and indeed never completely knows, what his own will is, and though society through its laws and institutions does much to teach him, there is no law and no institution which was not hammered into its present form out of a more imperfect form, no change which was not resisted by the collectivists of an earlier day. If the word "tradition" be used to cover the whole heritage of the past by which we are directed into fruitful and significant ways of living, the individualist of whom we are at present speaking can say of it, as has been said of so many things, that it is a good servant but a bad master. As an instrument its value cannot be overestimated, but its value *is* instrumental, and when made into an end in itself, when withdrawn from constant criticism and reconstruction, it at once becomes an engine of enslavement. And since it is in response to the desires of individuals that the testing and reconstruction goes on, the center of gravity remains in the man and not in society.

Section 3. Results of the Controversy

Has the foregoing controversy brought us further than we were when we started? The ethical skeptic may appear to have the last word, since neither of the disputants seems able thoroughly to prove his case, nor have they advanced to any third position upon which they are in complete agreement. Nevertheless, a change in the arguments advanced for individualism and collectivism has come about through the discussion. The attention of each party has been drawn to values in its opponent's position, and in a measure each party has tried to incorporate these values of its opponent's view into its own position.   Thus, the individualist is forced to recognize that men must coöperate in order to live, and that individuals are after all in large degree social products.   What he now holds out for is that certain kinds of variation and liberty are highly desirable, and he sees that the next step in the development of his position is to make clear to himself and to others what kinds of variation and liberty these are, and under what conditions they can be best secured.   The collectivist, on the other hand, sees that groups are growing, developing things, not given as perfect, and that individual variation is in part the manner by which they grow.   In the light of this discovery he will now be apt to consider what kinds of group regulation best insure those values which he originally desired and those of which the individualist has made him cognizant.

From a consideration of this instance we may draw some general conclusions as to the kind of progress possible through reflection in ethics.   In the first place, reflection brings to our attention values which we might otherwise overlook.   Secondly, reflection leads us to a better understanding of ourselves, to a defining of our real aims, a clarification of our desires.   If we still find ourselves in disagreement with others, it is nevertheless satisfying to see more clearly the reasons why.   Plato's *Dialogues*, Aristotle's *Ethics*, the Hebrew Prophets, the *Meditations* of Marcus Aurelius are regarded as great monuments in the field of ethics just as are the works of Copernicus and Newton and Darwin in science.   These ethical classics are in many ways conflicting in their points of view, and there is no method of detecting which is better as in science.   In calling them all classics we mean to recognize more than their literary excellence, however; we mean that each has thought through to its foundations some genuine desire of man, expressing it, therefore, truly, "as a possession forever." This is the kind of clarification which reflection introduces into ethics.

A third value which reflection brings in ethics arises from this clarification of ideals. By banishing vagueness, revealing new facts, and so on, it makes us see what problems really are most vital, and thus brings us nearer to actual solutions. As in the example cited, the individualist and the collectivist are both brought to realize that they must determine what kinds of individual variation and of social regulation they consider advisable, and under what conditions.

A fourth result of reflection in ethics is to make our conduct more fully our own, more voluntary and less of a blind obedience to custom. It seems more human to know why one is doing what he is doing. When asked what good his philosophy did him, Aristotle is reported to have said that because of it he did voluntarily what other men do only for fear of the law. Socrates, if asked the same question, might have answered that, because of it he did what other men, for fear of the law, dared not do.

Reflection on morals may never lead us to a general agreement on fundamental standards. It may be doubted whether such agreement, if it could be reached, would really be desirable. But reflection can at least make us cognizant of ideals different from our own, and this will lead us in some cases to assimilate the values of other positions, thus producing a greater agreement among men than would otherwise exist. But even where this is not the case, and wide differences in desire continue to exist, nevertheless, the very attempt to understand desires different from one's own often provides a basis for better coöperation in matters not affected by the difference, and thus for living together with more profit and understanding and happiness.

Taking all these factors into consideration, we arrive at a test of good reflective thinking in ethics. From blind adherence to a vaguely understood principle, it should bring us to the voluntary adoption of a clearer standard, more intelligible to ourselves and to others, including those who disagree; a standard based upon a consideration of more facts, and one which leads us more directly to deal with the real problems confronting us.

Section 4.   The Evaluation of Character

Thus far we have considered only reflection upon standards of conduct. Every one is familiar from daily experience with the distinction between character and conduct, between what a man does and what he is, though there is no general agreement as to the exact relation between the two. Every one also agrees that we should judge a man's character from a fair sampling of his conduct, but people differ in their ideas as to what such a fair sampling would be. Some think that we should give chief weight, if not exclusive weight, to his motives, to what he wants to accomplish, and the spirit with which he attempts it, since what he actually does accomplish depends so much on circumstances outside of his control. "There is nothing absolutely good in the world," writes Kant, "save a good will." On the other hand, it is urged that efficiency and capacity are virtues which must be counted in estimating character, so that it is not only a man's motives, but also his success, which must be measured.

Without undertaking to settle these disputes, we may distinguish three different kinds of character evaluation, which are supplementary rather than mutually exclusive. Each is designed to serve a different purpose, and the results of all three would have to be considered in forming a total estimate of any one's entire character. In the first place, there is the judging of a person's spirit, his motives and intentions, his sensitivity, the fineness of his feelings, and so on. These things are revealed in considerable measure through a person's outward acts, but never entirely so. We say we know a person well or intimately when we are able to sense these inward factors immediately in a rather subtle, intuitive fashion. Of very different sort is the appraisal of a person's fitness to perform certain specific functions. Here objective measurement is often possible if we can define the function exactly enough and devise a test that gauges just those qualities demanded by this function. The tests devised during the World War to measure potential aviators were tests of this kind. Finally, there is a kind of character evaluation which attempts to estimate the whole person taking into consideration all factors. This is of all kinds the most difficult, for the thing to be measured is very complex, containing factors incommensurable with each other, and the standard by which we measure, our conception of what the person ought to be, is apt to be either very arbitrary or else indefinite and vague.

All manner of difficult problems arise out of this attempt to evaluate human character. To what common standards should every person in a given group be held, and in what respects is the ideal self, if there be such a thing, unique for every individual? Furthermore, suppose that some individuals are vile and evil in our eyes, entirely unsatisfactory when measured by our notions of human excellence, do we not, in spite of this, recognize some worth in them by virtue of their very humanity? What kind of worth is this?

These are some of the more ultimate problems in ethical philosophy which cannot be treated here.

Section 5. The Practical Aim of Ethics

Reflection in ethics is intended to secure, not merely the knowledge of what is good, but rather the increased practice of it, the actual living well. In this endeavor the clarification and improvement of ideals, which we have been discussing in this chapter, is only one factor. What people do badly they do badly not only because their standards are poor, but perhaps even more frequently because they do not know how to live up to their standards. To know wherein efficiency and kindness consist does not prevent us from becoming tired and irritable.

Persistent failure to achieve a standard may raise two questions. Is the standard a good one? How might one realize it? These two questions are not unrelated. Some people hold that standards are proved bad if the conditions for their realization cannot be devised. The really good must be an actually attainable good. Not so, say others. If an end, e.g., immortality, is good, it is no less good for being perhaps impossible.

However wide and full of consequences this disagreement on the nature of standards may be, both disputants are likely to agree that human morality has suffered from an excess of condemnations and approvals, coupled with a lack of practical invention. It is much easier to blame a person for falling short of a certain standard than to suggest how he might have attained it. And the actual attaining may be harder still. If ethics is taken seriously as concerned with the actual improvement of life, it will be no isolated inquiry into standards merely, but reflection will pass from it into other departments of knowledge, into psychology, and politics, and economics, and the natural sciences, gathering from the whole realm of man's experience the materials for his happiness.

QUESTIONS AND EXERCISES

1. In what way does the training in morals provided for the young differ from the corresponding education in science or literature? What consequences result from this difference?

2. The moral life, on any view, involves self-denial. What is the justification alleged for this self-denial (a) by the individualist, (b) by the collectivist?

3. The individualist contends that constraint causes loss of individuality. (a) If this is understood to mean that those who are responsive to the control of tradition tend to be cast in a stereotyped mold — do you think that the facts bear out the statement? (b) Do the "conventions" in auction bridge diminish or increase the freedom of the player who observes them?

4. Under what circumstances is "the man versus the state" a real issue?

5. In the course of the argument in the foregoing chapter, the transition has been given from an extréme individualistic to an extreme collectivistic position, and thence to one intended as a compromise between the two. In the course of the argument, how have the following terms altered in meaning: (a) the individual, (b) the state or society, (c) the other members of society, (d) freedom?

6. What is meant by an ideal or ultimate standard of conduct? Describe three such ideals which are held to-day.

7. Show how each of these ideals would affect the solution of some specific moral problem.

8. What are the uses and limitations of reflection in evaluation? Illustrate by reference to the problem discussed above.

9. How is the evaluation of conduct related to the evaluation of character?
10. Give an example of failure to solve a moral problem due to inadequate ideals, and one where it is due to failure to live up to an ideal. How might each kind of deficiency be corrected?
11. How can conflicts between people as to ultimate ideals be resolved?

BIBLIOGRAPHY

F. Adler: *An Ethical Philosophy of Life.* New York: Appleton, 1918.

Aristotle: *Ethics.* Welldon translation. Macmillan Co.

E. Barker: *Political Thought from Spencer to Today.* New York: Henry Holt & Co., 1915.

B. Bosanquet: *The Philosophical Theory of the State,* 2d ed. London: Macmillan and Co., 1910.

F. H. Bradley: *Ethical Studies* (chapter on "My Station and its Duties"). London: King and Co., 1876.

Lord Hugh Cecil: *Liberty and Authority.* London: Edward Arnold, 1910.

Dewey and Tufts: *Ethics.* New York: Henry Holt & Co., 1908.

J. Dewey: *Human Nature and Conduct.* Henry Holt & Co., 1922.

G. L. Dickinson: *Justice and Liberty.* London: J. M. Paul & Co., 1919.

W. Fite: *Individualism.* New York: Longmans, Green & Co., 1916.

L. T. Hobhouse: *The Metaphysical Theory of the State.* London: George Allen and Unwin Ltd., 1918.

J. S. Mill: *On Liberty.* London: Longmans, 1871. Also in "Everyman's Library."

Utilitarianism. Everyman's Library.

H. Rashdall: *Ethics.* The People's Books. New York: Dodge & Co.

J. Royce: *Philosophy of Loyalty.* Macmillan Co., 1908.

B. Russell: *Why Men Fight.* New York: The Century Co., 1917.

Political Ideals. New York: The Century Co., 1917.

H. Spencer: *The Man versus the State.* London: Watts and Co.,1909.

J. F. Stephen: *Liberty, Equality, Fraternity.* New York: Holt and Williams, 1873.

CHAPTER XIII

SUMMARY

Section 1. The Modern Consciousness of Science

MOST of us who live in the civilized nations of to-day know that there is such a thing as science. We are very conscious, indeed, of its great practical achievements in the cure of disease, and in creating those instruments of commerce and industry which chiefly distinguish modern life from the life of earlier times. It is not only the fruits of science, however, of which we are aware, but also, in some degree, of the knowledge underlying these fruits. We are conscious of possessing much information, and a power of acquiring more, that was unknown to other ages. These possessions are an occasion of no small pride to us.

A distinction between ignorance and knowledge, the same pride in learning, appears in the literature of all times and peoples. But it may be doubted whether any people, save perhaps the ancient Greeks, were as conscious of the possession of science as we are to-day. This does not mean, however, that we understand the nature of our possession, what knowledge is, how best to acquire and to test it. Every schoolboy knows that the earth goes round the sun, and he looks upon the Ptolemaic theory as superstition; but how many of our adult men and women could give adequate reasons for believing the Copernican hypothesis?

The purpose of this book is to help in adding another dimension to our consciousness of science, namely, an understanding of its processes. If this purpose could be accomplished, we should be much enriched spiritually. We should see man and the world in a clearer, fuller light. We should also be more critical of whatever is reported to us, and better prepared to add to our fund of tested knowledge.

Section 2.   How are Beliefs to be Tested?

In the first chapter of this *Introduction to Reflective Thinking* we distinguished such thinking from several other types. We contrasted it with the random flow of ideas through the mind, with the thinking involved in imaginative constructions that are not intended for belief, and with the uncritical acceptance of beliefs. By means of these contrasts certain characteristics of reflective thinking became manifest, and we realized that we must look for these characteristics if we would test whether any act of thought was reflective or not.

But, furthermore, it appeared that within the limits of reflective thinking we might also distinguish a better and a worse. Though the whole enterprise of science is reflective, we can recognize a progress in it. Ptolemy's hypothesis was certainly a product of reflective thinking. Yet that of Copernicus was better. Thus it seemed as if we could get further light upon the tests of thought by considering some instances in which old beliefs had given place to new considered better.

Our method may be clarified by using an analogy. Suppose our problem were to find the best of airplane motors. We might begin by eliminating from consideration such motors as were obviously unadapted for aerial navigation. The remaining motors would then be carefully compared in such respects as weight and speed and power. The one selected as the best, by means of these comparisons, might be surpassed at any later time by one still better.

Just so, in testing thought, we can begin by separating that which is obviously uncritical and unreflective from that which is not. Then the remaining beliefs, for which there seems to be some critical, reflective foundation, must be compared with each other, and tested. The belief thus selected as the best is not necessarily the very best possible belief on the subject, but simply the best we have. Sometimes we must make use of hypotheses for which there is no great evidence, simply because no one has suggested anything better.

Some people are intellectually demoralized by the spectacle of scientific progress. If beliefs, apparently well founded, give place to new, is there anything certain? Perhaps not; but is that an adequate reason for abandoning the best tests we have to distinguish between better and worse beliefs? It is not enough for the critic of reflective thinking to show that no certainties are established thereby; he must suggest a better methodology. The fact that serious questions can be raised against the proof of every statement does not mean that every statement is of equal value. Of course, the thoroughgoing philosophic skeptic will reply that to challenge him for a better methodology is to beg the question. How can one speak of a better when none are any good? Why seek a better lifeboat to drown in? The only answer to this position seems to be to show the skeptic that in simple, practical affairs he acts upon a distinction between better and worse thinking, which he disavows in argument. If reason and experience are useful in choosing a cigar, perhaps we can trust them in choosing a moral ideal.

Section 3.   The Tests of Thought

The real question is not whether reflection has any value, it is the question of how it can be made most valuable, and this is a question concerning the concrete tests to which it can be put in specific situations. In comparing airplane motors, for instance, to determine which is best, we must know what features to look for. Our conclusions may be wrong, not only because of error in applying some test, but also because of failure to apply all relevant tests.   There may be some quality essential to a good motor of which we are not aware.

Likewise in comparing beliefs we must endeavor to test all qualities with respect to which one belief may be said to be better than another.   Now there has never been perfect agreement as to just what qualities are to be included in this category.   Most people will agree that clarity and intelligibility are desirable qualities in thought, and that in testing our beliefs we should determine whether they possess these qualities.   On the other hand, there is great disagreement as to whether such a quality as personal preference for a belief should be considered in attempting to measure its value, apart from the reasons for which it is preferred.   In a field like astronomy the power of certain ideas to enlist personal affections of this sort would seem irrelevant to most of us.   But would it in the field of ethics?

Some philosophers, like Aristotle, have given systematic accounts of tests which may be applied to determine the validity of beliefs.   These accounts constitute that branch of philosophy which is usually called logic.   By some, logic is regarded as a completed science; that is, they believe all the tests of thought have been discovered. We shall not inquire into this question, but shall content ourselves with recalling those important tests upon which nearly all logicians are agreed, and which are amply illustrated in the examples of reflective thinking discussed in this book. They are as follows:

1. *Clarity.* A good belief is unambiguous. We know unmistakably what it means.
2. *Consistency with the facts.* A good belief is founded on extensive and accurate observation. It is not contradicted by experience.
3. *Consistency with other beliefs.* There is a presumption against a belief that conflicts with other beliefs well certified by experience. Sometimes, however, it is the latter beliefs rather than the former that need to be revised.
4. *Utility.* A good belief is often distinguished by its usefulness in suggesting further good beliefs.
5. *Simplicity.* Other things being equal, that belief is best which makes fewest assumptions.

Section 4. The Influence of Subject-Matter upon the Tests of Thought

The use of the above-mentioned tests of thought is not confined to any particular subject-matter; we can test reflection in any field by these criteria. But the meaning of these criteria is not exactly the same in every field, it varies with the nature of the subject-matter. For example, we may speak both of an astronomical law and of a child labor law as being in agreement or in consonance with the facts of experience, but not the same kind of agreement will be meant. In astronomy we mean that the law correctly describes a relation obtaining between certain phenomena; in legislation we mean that considering the facts of the situation the law is likely to achieve the desired result.

We cannot understand what the criteria of good reflective thinking really mean unless we consider them in connection with the subject-matter in which they are employed. Also, it appears that the relative importance of these criteria is different in different fields. In a mathematical system the consistency of one belief with another is more important than in a penal code.

Clarity, unambiguity, is a quality to be desired of thought in all fields, and its meaning also is the same in all. Whatever the content of a statement may be, whether it be mathematical, historical, or juridical, we want that content to be understood exactly as we mean it. This is essential. One reason why mathematics is such an important and universal instrument of thought is because of this universal importance of clarity. To express an idea in mathematical terms is the most exact and unambiguous way of expressing it. If we say that A is fairly good in arithmetic, no one knows what is meant, except in a very vague way. But if we can say that A's rating on a standardized arithmetical test is 79, we get much more definite information.

Consistency with the facts is also essential to reflective thinking in all fields — with possibly one exception, in the case of systems designed to develop the implications of definitions rather than to describe facts. We may construct a system of propositions, each consistent with the others, but having no essential relation to observed facts. Mathematics is regarded by many as a creation of this kind. Its astounding usefulness, its almost universal applicability, is not intrinsic to it, but accidental. "If mathematics has been the beacon light of the sciences, it is not the fault of mathematicians," says one of them. The mathematician is concerned to work out the relationships between certain ideal entities that happen to interest him. If these relationships are found to correspond to relationships existing outside the purely mathematical realm, in the realm of physical objects, for example, the findings of the mathematician can be carried over into that field, but the correspondence which makes this possible was not deliberately sought by him.

There are some dissenters from this view of mathematics. They fall into two classes. First, those who insist that the mathematician does keep one eye on the physical world, and that his definitions, axioms, and postulates are intentionally relevant to what he sees there. A second group holds that, even if the mathematician keeps both eyes shut to the physical world, he is nevertheless compelled by the inner nature of his being to think in terms appropriate to that world. A case can, therefore, be made on either of these grounds for believing that mathematics is really no exception to the general rule that reflective thinking may be tested by its consistency with fact.

Certainly this is *the* test, if any is, in all other fields. But by consistency with fact we do not always mean the same thing. If a belief purports to describe a situation, we say it is consistent with the facts if no significant element in that situation is overlooked or wrongly described. On the other hand, if a belief is intended to explain a situation — as, for example, the molecular theory is intended to explain heat and certain other phenomena — then we mean by consistency with fact a very different thing. We mean that the belief seizes upon a certain fact that accounts for the phenomena to be explained, makes their behavior intelligible upon a single principle, makes them predictable, and sometimes controllable. Again consistency with fact has a third meaning when used of a belief that is intended neither to describe, nor to explain, but rather to guide conduct. A labor law or a practical idea may be said to be in agreement with facts if it accurately expresses existent desires and proves efficacious in their realization. Thus, the meaning of this important test, consistency with the facts, depends on whether we are testing a description, an explanation, or a rule of action.

Consistency with other beliefs also has various meanings. It may mean a relation of implication, such that one belief cannot be true without another's being true. In some instances, this kind of consistency is demanded. For example, A and B cannot be brothers unless they are children of the same parents. A second kind of consistency between beliefs may be described as compatibility without implication. As far as we know, the atomic theory of matter implies neither the truth nor the falsity of the theory of evolution. Each may be held without the other, and both may be held together; the evidence for each is different without being conflicting. Some philosophers hold that, if our knowledge of the universe could be made complete, all true propositions would be shown to imply each other. Whatever position we may take on this question, most of us will probably agree at least that true propositions will not contradict each other.

We can tell by an analysis of their meaning whether propositions imply each other or contradict each other. Logicians have devised ingenious tables showing how one statement qualifies others. But implication and compatibility are not the only senses in which we speak of consistency between beliefs. Sometimes we mean not that one belief implies another, or that it is merely compatible with another, but rather that one belief increases the probability that another belief is true. Thus, for example, the belief that the earth is much more than six thousand years old does not imply the theory of evolution. On the other hand, it is something more than compatible with that theory; it increases the value of the evidence for it by making the explanations of evolution more feasible.

Finally, there is a sense in which consistency between beliefs means only that it is psychologically possible for the same person to hold the various beliefs in question. For instance, it is possible for the same person to believe that clemency is good, and yet also bad, at least sometimes. Of course, there may be no logical conflict between these two views, since the instances in which clemency is believed to be good may be a different set from those in which it is regarded bad. But if the individual can give no criterion for distinguishing clearly these two sets of instances, he is obliged to carry two apparently conflicting beliefs. Furthermore, the conflict is intensified if, as sometimes happens, he regards clemency as both good and bad in the same instance, but is unable to decide whether the respects in which it is good outweigh those in which it is bad, or *vice versa*. Some people would say that the psychological possibility of holding two beliefs is not at all what is meant when we use the consistency of beliefs with each other as a test of their validity. If logical compatibility does not obtain between the beliefs, the fact that they could be held by one person would indicate that he had a poor mind, or that he had not solved his problem, rather than that the beliefs are both valid. So says one group. Others, however, think that in certain fields equally valid judgments may conflict. We may condemn and praise a piece of music for being sentimental. In cases like this the only kind of consistency which can be demanded between several judgments is the psychological possibility of holding them all. It is probably true, however, that psychological consistency of this kind is more frequently abused to the detriment of science, than wisely used to its benefit.

The kind of consistency which is appropriate between beliefs depends upon the nature of the subject-matter and the problem. Implication, the strictest form of consistency, plays most part in mathematical systems, but it appears in all fields. In the natural sciences we have a network of beliefs which are all compatible with each other, as far as we know, and which in many cases lend support to each other. Thus the more general hypotheses, like the theory of evolution, are supported by evidence accumulated from many diverse fields, and giving rise to a group of beliefs pointing in the direction of evolution. In jurisprudence, in morals, in æsthetics, in all fields involving evaluation, we have these three types of consistency among the most tested beliefs. But in these fields we also admit as valid some judgments which may seem inconsistent with others: that is, the only kind of consistency we require of them is that we should be psychologically able to accept them along with the conflicting judgments. The reason for this is that in these fields the primary demand which we make of our beliefs is that they be consistent with our desires, and our desires are proverbially inconsistent and conflicting with each other.

By the *utility* of a belief is meant the opportunity

which it affords of predicting further facts, either because they are actually implied in it, or because they are made probable by it, or simply because they are suggested by it. In this connection we should remember that a belief need not be well substantiated itself in order to suggest what may prove to be positive facts or good hypotheses. False beliefs have often been useful in stimulating scientific imagination. The mechanism of suggestion (if there is such a mechanism) is still the most mysterious and least understood of all things. Often we cannot produce the most appropriate ideas at will, and the order in which we do think seems to have no very discernible pattern. This accounts in part for the large give-and-take between all fields of knowledge. An idea developed in connection with one subject-matter may strike in and prove useful almost anywhere else. The interdependence of sciences has been abundantly illustrated by even the few problems discussed in this book.

Simplicity as a test of belief is frequently misunderstood. Ease or facility in using the belief is not what is meant. A "simpler" hypothesis may involve more difficult mathematical calculations than one more "complex." Neither do we mean by simplicity that the belief can be easily understood. The world described by modern science is far more difficult to understand than the world pictured in popular superstition. By simplicity is meant making few assumptions, taking few things for granted. Other things being equal, such as consistency with observed facts, etc., that belief is best which requires us to make the fewest suppositions.

This principle of parsimony, as it is called, used to be expressed as late as Newton's time by saying that "nature always takes the simplest course," or words to that effect. Nowadays philosophers usually prefer to regard parsimony as a principle of science rather than of nature. For is it not possible that our best accounts of the universe are simplifications of what actually takes place there? Might not nature take a very complicated course to produce phenomena which we interpret on the basis of a few meager ideas — especially since our observations may omit very much?

Section 5. Some Ultimate Problems Concerning Knowledge

Ultimate questions of this sort keep coming up at frequent points in our study of reflective thinking. A list of such questions, raised by the material in this book, would include the following:

1. What justification have we for basing general laws on the observation of particular instances? (See Chapter IV, p. 94.)
2. What is the relation between mathematical truths and objects observed with the aid of the senses? (See Chapter V, p. 112.)
3. Is the principle of parsimony simply a convenience to man, or is it a law of nature? (See Chapter III, p. 53.)
4. In what respects do the methods of evaluation resemble those of the natural sciences, and in what respects are they different? (See Chapter IX, pp. 230–237.)
5. What sanction have the tests which we apply to reflective thinking? Are all the tests known? What are they? (See Chapter XIII, pp. 332–334.)
6. Some sense-images are discovered to be illusory. Does this fact cast doubt upon the validity of all sense-data?[1]

[1] This problem has not been explicitly raised in any of our chapters, but it belongs to this group of ultimate questions. See Descartes, *Meditations*, pp. 147–49.

Questions like these as to the nature of knowledge it-self, its objects, its extent, and validity, have perplexed mankind for ages without ever having been answered to the satisfaction of every one.   Men who agree in using the reflective methods studied in this book do not agree in their answers to such ultimate questions concerning these methods.   Philosophy on its methodological side, in logic and epistemology, is concerned with these questions.

The praise of philosophy, as a necessary basis for reflective thinking, is a theme on which philosophers like to end their books.   But Plato admonishes us of a better way.   In his *Republic* he describes the philos-opher dazzled by a splendid vision of the highest knowl-edge.   Yet afterward he is reminded of the actual state of ignorance among mankind.   How weak and power-less every mere account of science seems in overcoming the tremendous difficulties that stand in the way of widespread and thorough reflective thinking!   Can talk convey an adequate impression to the average man of what it means really to test a single dubious fact?   Can the best of lectures furnish compasses to guide us through the clouds of opinions by which we are so thickly enveloped in these days?   No, practice in abun-dance must be added.   "It is only by doing just acts that we become just," says Aristotle, and likewise only by practice in reflection can we become reflective.

INDEX

Accomplishment, chart showing range of, 256.

Adams, computations in discovery of Neptune, 59.

Almagest, explanations of, 40–42.

Analogy, explanation by, 119–123.

Anatomy, comparative, facts of intelligible under evolutionary theory, 170.

Anthropocentism, definition of, 176.

Anthropomorphism, effect of on biological belief, 175.

A priori reasoning, in support of traditional view of Old Testament, 205–209.

Aristotle, solar theory compared with Ptolemy's, 43, 44; possible uses of term "cause," 88, 89; effect of his ethical physics, 125; disregard of scientific analogy, 208; on value of philosophy, 324; on becoming just, 342.

Astronomy, development of hypotheses in, 35–61; first of the natural sciences, 36; observed facts of, 36–40; explanation in, 121.

Authoritarian and scientific explanations, conflict of, 45, 46.

Authority, improper use in determining opinion, 46; as used in traditional view of Old Testament, 203–205; reinforcement by associated emotions, 204; in scientific inquiry, 204, 205; Saint Jerome's reference in Vulgate, 205.

Autocracy, arguments for, 227.

Axioms, use in proof for Pythagorean theorem, 111; different sets of, 111, 112; regarded as conventional assumptions, 112; of Euclidean geometry as *abstractions from experience*, 114.

Bacon, on the method of investigation, 76; *Advancement of Learning*, quotation from, 267.

Beliefs, superiority of one over another, 331; how tested, 331–34;

consistency between, 337–339; utility of, 339, 340; simplicity as a test of, 340, 341. *See also* Thought.

Bessel, measurement of star Cygni, 55; relation of his measurements to Copernican theory, 56.

Bible, early division of books of, 190–91; opposition between two views of, 195; value of, 209; a human and divine collaboration, 210; first in spiritual literature of world, 210, 211; Coleridge's test of, 210, 211.

Biblical writings, present acceptance of, 191.

Biological evolution, alleged disproof of divine creation, 138; belief, psychological factors in, 174–177.

Biology, discovery of causal relations in, 63–95.

Blackie, J. S., on the criticism of the *Iliad*, 195.

Blood-tests, as evidence for evolution, 172.

Bradley, discovery of star movements, 56.

Brahe, Tycho, planetary system of, 55.

Brandeis, L., brief in case of Ritchie & Co. *v.* Wayman, 295–296.

Bryce, summary of arguments for democracy, 223–225.

Burns, D., arguments for autocracy, 227.

Cabot, R. C., *Differential Diagnosis*, 20.

Caloric theory, early physicists', 130; effect of thermometer on, 131; dis proof of, 132.

Career, two ways of choosing, 253, 254; information necessary for choice of, 254.

Catastrophic theory, uniformitarianism opposed to, 159, 160; violation of Law of Parsimony, 160; James Hutton's criticism of, 161.

Causal laws, function of, 119.